IMPORTANT PRE-COLUMBIAN AND NATIVE AMERICAN ART

THE HENDERSHOTT COLLECTION – SESSION II

Heritage Signature Auction #643 • September 29, 2006 • New York City

LOT VIEWING IN DALLAS

Heritage Auction Galleries, 3500 Maple Avenue
10th Floor Gallery, Dallas, Texas 75219

Public Viewing
Tuesday, September 12, thru Friday, September 15
9:00 AM – 6:00 PM CT

Opening Reception
Tuesday, September 12, 5:00 – 8:00 PM CT

LOT VIEWING IN NEW YORK CITY

The Fletcher-Sinclair Mansion
(The Ukrainian Institute of America)
2 East 79th Street, New York 10021

Public Viewing
Tuesday, September 26, 2:00 – 8:00 PM ET
Wednesday, September 27, thru Thursday, September 28
9:00 AM – 6:00 PM ET or by appointment

FAX BIDDING

Deadline, Thursday, September 28, by 6:00 PM ET
Fax: 214-443-8425

INTERNET BIDDING

HA.com/FineArt • Bid@HA.com
Bidding closes Thursday, September 28, at 10:00 PM ET

LIVE TELEPHONE BIDDING

Customer Service: 866-835-3243
Must be arranged on or before Thursday, September 28, by 5:00 PM ET

LIVE AUCTION SESSIONS IN NEW YORK CITY

The Fletcher-Sinclair Mansion
(The Ukrainian Institute of America)
2 East 79th Street, New York 10021

Session I
Pre-Columbian Art
Friday, September 29, at 10:00 AM ET
Lots 47001 – 47259

Session II
Native American Art
Friday, September 29, at 2:00 PM ET
Lots 48001 – 48234

Lots are sold at an approximate rate of 75 lots per hour.

View lots online at HA.com/FineArt

For Terms and Conditions of auction, see pp.238-239.

For explanation of Bidding Methods, see pp.240-241.

AUCTIONEERS

Kathleen Guzman	NY Day license #0762165
Samuel W. Foose	NY Day license #0952360
	NY Night license #0952361

BUYER'S PREMIUM

19.5%

AUCTION RESULTS

Immediately available at HA.com/FineArt

LOT PICK-UP

By appointment. Call customer service at 866-835-3243

D1501151

HERITAGE
Auction Galleries

Direct Customer Service Line: Toll-free 866-835-3243 (24-hour VM)
3500 Maple Avenue, 17th Floor, Dallas, Texas 75219-3941
214-528-3500 • 800-872-6467 • 214-443-8425 (fax)

THIS AUCTION IS CATALOGUED AND PRESENTED BY HERITAGE AUCTIONS, INC.

Catalogued by: Richard Pohrt, Jr.

Edited by: John Lunsford, Mary Brinker, and Courtney E. Kennedy

Production and Design by: Mandy Bottoms, Cindy Brenner, Carlos Cardoza, Keith Craker, Lisa Fox, Cathy Hadd, Mary Hermann, Matt Pegues, Michael Puttonen, Marsha Taylor, and Carl Watson

Catalogue and Internet Imaging by: Terry Thibeau, Ray Proska, Steve Robinson, John Noeding, Matt Roppolo, Kim Patterson, Haley Hagen, Nina Castro, Tony Webb, Butch Ziaks, Bea Faustino, Shaun Zokaie, Chandler Thompson, Lucas Garritson, Colette Warren, and Lori McKay

Special thanks to Mary Brinker, Caitlin Owen, Emily Hoyle, and Erin Emerson for their assistance in the organization of this volume.

HERITAGE
Auction Galleries

World Headquarters
3500 Maple Avenue, 17th Floor
Dallas, Texas 75219-3941
800-872-6467

HA.com/FineArt

Edmund P. Pillsbury, Ph.D.
Director of Fine & Decorative Arts
Ext. 533 • EPP@HA.com

Norma Gonzalez, Vice President Operations
Ext. 242 • Norma@HA.com

UNITED STATES COINS

HA.com/Coins
U.S. Coins

Leo Frese, Ext. 294
Leo@HA.com

Charles Clifford, Ext. 477
CharlesC@HA.com

Sam Foose, Ext. 227
SamF@HA.com

Jim Jelinski, Ext. 257
JimJ@HA.com

David Lewis, Ext. 520
DLewis@HA.com

David Lisot, Ext. 303
DavidL@HA.com

Bob Marino, Ext. 374
BobMarino@HA.com

David Mayfield, Ext. 277
DavidM@HA.com

Matt Orsini, Ext. 526
MattO@HA.com

Bob Phillips, Ext. 588
BobP@HA.com

Mike Sadler, Ext. 332
MikeS@HA.com

UNITED STATES COINS PRIVATE TREATY SALES

HA.com/Coins

Todd Imhof, Ext. 313
Todd@HA.com

CURRENCY

HA.com/Currency
Paper Money

Len Glazer, Ext. 390
Len@HA.com

Allen Mincho, Ext. 327
Allen@HA.com

Dustin Johnston, Ext. 302
Dustin@HA.com

Jim Fitzgerald, Ext. 348
JimF@HA.com

Michael Moczalla, Ext. 481
MichaelM@HA.com

WORLD COINS

HA.com/Coins
World Coins & Currencies

Warren Tucker, Ext. 287
WTucker@HA.com

Scott Cordry, Ext. 369
ScottC@HA.com

Harvey Gamer, Ext. 676
HarveyG@HA.com

COMICS

HA.com/Comics
Comics, Original Comic Art and Related Memorabilia

Ed Jaster, Ext. 288
EdJ@HA.com

Lon Allen, Ext. 261
LonA@HA.com

MUSIC & ENTERTAINMENT MEMORABILIA

HA.com/Entertainment
Stage-Worn Costumes, Records, Signed Photos & Memorabilia

Doug Norwine, Ext. 452
DougN@HA.com

John Hickey, Ext. 264
JohnH@HA.com

POLITICAL MEMORABILIA & AMERICANA

HA.com/Americana
Historical & Pop Culture Americana, Vintage Toys, Presidential & Political Memorabilia, Buttons & Medals, Books & Manuscripts, First Editions and Collectible Autographs

Tom Slater, Ext. 441
TomS@HA.com

Marsha Dixey, Ext. 455
MarshaD@HA.com

John Hickey, Ext. 264
JohnH@HA.com

SPORTS COLLECTIBLES

HA.com/Sports
Sports Cards, Artifacts, Game-Used Jerseys & Equipment

Chris Ivy, Ext. 319
CIvy@HA.com

Stephen Carlisle, Ext. 292
StephenC@HA.com

Jonathan Scheier, Ext. 314
JonathanS@HA.com

Mark Jordan, Ext. 187
MarkJ@HA.com

Mike Gutierrez, Ext. 183
MikeG@HA.com

VINTAGE MOVIE POSTERS

HA.com/MoviePosters
Posters, Lobby Cards, and Hollywood Ephemera

Grey Smith, Ext. 367
GreySm@HA.com

FINE ART

HA.com/FineArt
Impressionist, Old Masters and Contemporary Drawings, Paintings, Sculpture and Photography

Edmund P. Pillsbury, Ph.D., Ext. 533
EPP@HA.com

Ed Jaster, Ext. 288
EdJ@HA.com

Lucas Rigby, Ext. 483
LucasR@HA.com

Lindsay Davis, Ext. 542
LindsayD@HA.com

TEXAS ART

HA.com/TexasArt
Early Texas Art, Drawings and Paintings

Larry Boettigheimer, Ext. 523
LarryB@HA.com

ILLUSTRATION ART

HA.com/FineArt
Pinups and Illustration Art

Ed Jaster, Ext. 288
EdJ@HA.com

DECORATIVE ARTS

HA.com/FineArt
Art Glass, European & American Silver, Pottery & Ceramics

Michael Wolf, Ext. 541
MWolf@HA.com

Tim Rigdon, Ext. 119
TimR@HA.com

Christine Carmody, Ext. 689
ChristineC@HA.com

JEWELRY & TIMEPIECES

HA.com/Jewelry
Jewelry & Timepieces

Jill Burgum, Ext. 697
JillB@HA.com

MEDIA RELATIONS

Marketing and Public Relations

Cathy Hadd, Ext 216
Cathy@HA.com

John Petty, Ext 283
JohnP@HA.com

CREDIT DEPARTMENT

Marti Korver, Ext 248
Marti@HA.com

CORPORATE OFFICERS

R. Steven Ivy, Co-Chairman
James L. Halperin, Co-Chairman
Gregory J. Rohan, President
Paul Minshull, Chief Operating Officer

FOR THE EXTENSIONS ABOVE, PLEASE CALL 800-872-6467

FOR TOLL-FREE DIRECT CLIENT SERVICES, CALL 866-835-3243 (24-HOUR VM)

07/18/06

Steve Ivy
CEO
Co-Chairman
of the Board

Jim Halperin
Co-Chairman
of the Board

Greg Rohan
President

Paul Minshull
Chief Operating
Officer

3500 Maple Avenue, 17th Floor, Dallas, Texas 75219-3941
214-528-3500 | 800-872-6467 | 214-443-8425 (fax)

FINE AND DECORATIVE ARTS

Edmund Pillsbury, Ph.D.
Managing Director

John Lunsford
Senior Expert,
Pre-Columbian

Courtney E. Kennedy
Associate Managing
Director

Kathleen Guzman
Fine Art Representative/
Senior Expert

Michael Wolf
Deputy Managing
Director

Tom Slater
Director, Americana

HERITAGE
Auction Galleries

FEW PEOPLE HAVE COLLECTED WITH THE PASSION AND INTELLECTUAL CURIOSITY of Gary Hendershott, whose important holdings of ancient and Native American art Heritage Auction Galleries is honored to have the opportunity to record for posterity in these fully-illustrated volumes of critical text.

Mr. Hendershott, like many others, fell in love with things of beauty as a boy, acquiring stamps, coins, arrowheads, and eventually all kinds of art and memorabilia. Through his acquisitions, he developed a lifelong fascination with history – an obsession for knowledge that has never abated. His interest in ritual and ceremony, rulers and warlords, the struggles and feats that have shaped society over time, has been insatiable. As a result, over more than three decades of ceaseless activity he has assembled collections of various kinds ranging from the beginnings of civilization in ancient Greece to the founding of American democracy in the eighteenth and nineteenth centuries.

None of these collecting pursuits has been more heartfelt and personal than his devotion to Pre-Columbian art in general and its later manifestation in Native American culture in particular. The Hendershott Collection possesses an outstanding array of gold artwork, primarily from Costa Rica, Panama, Columbia and Peru, dating from approximately 100 A.D. to 1500 A.D. Also noteworthy are his collections of Maya jades and great Peruvian weavings, which display a stunning range of color and textile techniques and date between 300 B.C. and 1500 A.D. Likewise, the Native American collection, filled with museum-quality objects, reflects the collector's personal tastes and interests. Featuring impressive examples of classic Navajo weavings and chiefs' blankets and a broad selection of Plains Indian works, the collection includes war shirts, war shields, tomahawks and Indian weaponry from the Comanche and Kiowa of the Southern Plains to the Cheyenne and Sioux of the Northern Plains. The highlight of the collection is a complete ledger book filled with thirty spectacular hand-colored drawings by the Sioux artist Walter Bone Shirt, one of the finest surviving examples of Indian painting of the nineteenth century and arguably the best of its kind still in private hands.

First and foremost, we have Gary Hendershott to thank for making his valuable and important collections available to Heritage Auction Galleries for publication and public sale. We must also express our sincere gratitude to those experts who have devoted countless hours to researching and cataloguing the works. In particular, we received invaluable assistance from John Lunsford, Curator Emeritus of the Dallas Museum of Art. Mr. Lunsford oversaw the development of the DMA's pre-eminent holdings of ancient American art over some twenty-eight years and also had a pivotal role in the enrichment of the Kimbell Art Museum's more select holdings in the same field in the 1980s. His wealth of experience and knowledge has shed valuable light upon the identity, function, meaning, and condition of the individual works in the Hendershott holdings of Pre-Columbian art. Dr. Robert Sonin's opinions on the gold works, in particular his views of the works from the Charles Craig estate, have been invaluable, as has the contribution of Stanley Guenter on the inscribed Maya jade pectoral.

In addition, Heritage Auction Galleries has benefited from the expertise of one of the foremost authorities on historic Native American art. Richard Pohrt, Jr., prepared the descriptions and analyses of the Native American artifacts belonging to Mr. Hendershott, and his writing will ensure the importance of this catalog for future generations of curators, collectors and students. In the case of the Bone Shirt ledger album and the buffalo hide robe, we have also benefited from the insights and perspective of Mike Cowdrey. Ted Brasser offered his expertise for the Ojibwa shaman's costume.

Richard Pohrt, Jr.

Heritage Auction Galleries has spared no effort in presenting the Hendershott Collection in the interest of serving a field of art and history about which so much remains to be written and known. As discoveries continue apace, we come to have a fuller understanding of the richness of the indigenous cultures of the Americas.

Ted Pillsbury

Edmund P. Pillsbury, Ph.D.
Chairman and Managing Director of Fine Arts
Heritage Auction Galleries

A NATIVE OF ARKANSAS, GARY HENDERSHOTT gained his love of collecting as most boys did, through the wonderful medium of stamps and coins.

"I started collecting in the 1950s when I was 8 years old," Hendershott said. "I would ride my bicycle to the 5 & Dime store to buy bags of assorted world stamps, plus I enlisted the help of a group of secretaries in downtown Little Rock who would save for me all the interesting stamps that crossed their desks. The weekly rounds I made on my bicycle to pick them up from their offices was a fondly-remembered pilgrimage. The very first coin I ever found was a large Greek silver piece in the alley behind my home. It was after WWII, and we had neighbors from all over Europe. One of them must have dropped this coin, which I still have in my collection."

"I became fascinated with the sense of history that stamps and coins presented to me," Hendershott said, "and that love of history has followed me through the years and through a number of different collections."

"Perhaps even more significantly," Hendershott remembered, "was finding my first arrowhead on our family farm in Arkansas. This was the start of my lifelong fascination with Native American artwork – an interest born, in part, of my own American Indian ancestry."

Years later, at the age of 18, Hendershott climbed the pyramid at Cobá, the tallest Mayan pyramid in existence, and watched the sunrise over the Yucatan and the Caribbean. "It was magnificent," Hendershott remembers, "and that was the beginning of my love affair with Pre-Columbian material."

Following that experience, Hendershott began buying pieces of Pre-Columbian art at auction, building a collection that would be unrivaled in its scope and its depth. "This is an exceptionally pure artform," Hendershott said, "uninfluenced by European trends and styles. The people that made these magnificent pieces made them, and used them, for both daily and ceremonial use. This exquisite art was truly an indispensable part of their lives."

Currently, Gary's collecting passion is material related to Alexander the Great (356 – 323 B.C.). "By the age of 26, Alexander had conquered the entire known world," Hendershott said, "an unparalleled achievement in the annals of human history. He also facilitated the rise of Christianity, which came about through his One World, One Nation vision. I find him to be a fascinating figure, and one that I look forward to learning more about."

When asked why he chose to sell his impressive collection of Native American and Pre-Columbian art, Hendershott replied, "I have gone as far as I can go with this current collection within my means, and it's now time to let someone else take it to the next level. However, as my interests are still fairly broad, I'm also looking to build a comprehensive collection documenting the history of mankind, from 1000 B.C. to the present. I've already got a good start through coins, but now I'll be adding to it with artwork and other fascinating pieces."

"I'm proud to have been the temporary custodian of these great works of art," Hendershott said, "and I'm pleased that the next generation of collectors will cherish them as I have. The collecting world is a wonderful fraternity that I'm thrilled to be a part of, and I look forward to many more exciting adventures brought about by this wonderful hobby in the future."

Pottery and Baskets

48001

CASAS GRANDES POLYCHROME POTTERY JAR

Circa 1200-1450 AD
Height 9¾ in. Diameter 9 in.

This excellent example features a round base, short flaring sides and a tall tapering body with a slightly raised rim. The jar is painted on each side with a wide diamond shaped form composed of fine parallel lines framing two semi-circular fine lined bands. Triangular forms in red and black, negative spheres, and ticked vertical bands separate the two large diamonds. Casas Grandes was one of the largest prehistoric communities in North America. Casas Grandes (big houses) is located in Chihuahua, Mexico about 100 miles south of the New Mexico border.

Provenance
Bonhams and Butterfields, Sale 7477E, Lot 3308, December 8, 2003.

Estimate: $500-$1,000

48002

CASAS GRANDES POLYCHROME POTTERY JAR

Circa 1200-1450 AD
Height 8 in. Diameter 7¾ in.

This classic jar features a round base, short flaring sides, a tapering body, and slightly flared rim. The vessel is painted with two design bands in red and black against a tan slip. The lower band is decorated in a step pattern and long diagonal lines with fine line painting. The upper band repeats the fine diagonal line pattern.

Provenance
Bonhams and Butterfields, Sale 7437E, Lot 5320, June 9, 2003.

Estimate: $500-$1,000

48003

TWO CASAS GRANDES POLYCHROME EFFIGY JARS

Circa 1200-1450 AD
(A) Height 7¼ in.
Diameter 6½ in.
(B) Height 8⅛ in.
Diameter 6⅛ in.

Each jar has a rounded base, globular body, and an effigy head raised above the rim. Both jars are painted with broad diagonal, vertical, and horizontal lined bands with stepped or serrated elements framed within. One face has pronounced orb eyes and an open mouth while the other has slit eyes and mouth. Each figure has facial paint in geometric patterns.

Writing about a number of human effigy vessels excavated at Casas Grandes, Charles DiPeso states, "The human forms represented in this group were of particular importance as cultural mirrors for not only do they demonstrate the clothing, hairdo, and facial painting styles of the period, but also the gods of their day. Those local Casas Grandes deity designs are particularly exciting because they have been recognized as belonging to the complicated Mixtecan-Puebla god pantheon of Mesoamerica. For this reason, these particular vessels are much prized by anyone who wishes to study the spread of Mesoamerican iconography into the northern frontier."

Provenance
Bonhams and Butterfields, Sale 7437E, Lot 5319, June 9, 2003.

Reference
DiPeso, Charles, "Casas Grandes Effigy Vessels", *American Indian Art Magazine*, Volume 2, Number 4, Autumn, 1977, pp. 32-37.

Estimate: $1,000-$1,500

48004

CASAS GRANDES POLYCHROME POTTERY JAR

Circa 1200-1450 AD
Height 8¼ in. Diameter 8½ in.

This classic example features a round base, short flaring sides, a tapering body, and slightly flared rim. The jar is painted with a series of broad diagonal, vertical, and horizontal bands made of several fine lines, some having dotted squares within them. Negative lightning bands within quadrilateral frames, together with black and red triangles, fill the background space.

Provenance
Bonhams and Butterfields, Lot 5320, June 9, 2003.

Estimate: $500-$1,000

48005

TULAROSA BLACK ON WHITE POTTERY JAR

Circa 1100-1250 AD
Height 12¾ in. Diameter 16 in.

This large, classic example is of a globular form with a tall cylindrical neck. The body is painted with a bold design of solid and finely striated spiraling and terraced elements. The neck is decorated with a band of scrolling and double key motifs.

Provenance
Christie's, Sale 1248, Lot 51, June 20, 2003.

Estimate: $4,000-$6,000

48006

SOCORRO BLACK ON WHITE BOWL

Circa 1050-1275 AD
Height 4½ in. Diameter 11¼ in.

This ancient oval bowl is painted on the interior with a matching pair of large, angular, double hook motifs, each outlined with a serrated spine, against a finely painted hatched background.

Provenance
Bonhams and Butterfields, Sale 7477E, Lot 3310, December 8, 2003.

Estimate: $2,000-$3,000

48007

MIMBRES BLACK ON WHITE POTTERY BOWL

Circa 1000-1150 AD
Height 5 in. Diameter 12¼ in.

This classic bowl is painted on the interior with a complex geometric pattern. The various design elements include hatched triangles, hatched stepped triangles, negative lightning bands, and crosshatched tail feather motifs. The bowl has an open ringed center with a kill hole. "About two thirds of all burials during the Classic period included a painted bowl. Usually, but not always, the bowl had a hole punched in its bottom, a feature often colloquially referred to nowadays as a 'kill hole'. Many people have speculated on the meaning of the kill hole, but any interpretation is confounded by the evolution of Mimbres funeral practices over time. Before the Classic period, bowls (without kill holes) were usually broken and the pieces scattered in the burial pit. Later, just the hole was made, and the bowl was buried otherwise intact. Breaking the bowl might have been to release the bowl's spirit whereas—drawing on ethnographic analogy—making the hole might have been to let the spirit of the deceased pass through the bowl. Possible explanations abound, but we really have no way of knowing what the intent was."

Provenance
Bonhams and Butterfields, Sale 7477E, Lot 3311, December 8, 2003.

Reference
LeBlanc, Steven, *Painted By A Distant Hand*, Peabody Museum Press, Harvard University, 2004, p. 20

Estimate: $2,000-$3,000

48008

MIMBRES BLACK ON WHITE POTTERY BOWL

Circa 900-1000 AD
Height 5¼ in. Diameter 12¾ in.

This classic example is painted with linear designs in black against the white slip. The artist has divided the interior into unequal quadrants, each painted with alternating bands of fine, narrow lines and negative space.

Provenance
Bonhams and Butterfields, Sale 7437E, Lot 5329, June 9, 2003.

Estimate: $1,000-$2,000

48009

SANTO DOMINGO POLYCHROME POTTERY JAR

Circa 1890
Height 17 in. Width 17½ in.

This large storage jar is of classic form with the typical globular shape of 19th century examples. The main body is decorated in a negative use of lozenge forms with interconnected six point stars on the shoulder and a row of scallop designs on the neck. The underbody is red. There are two dramatic fire clouds on the side indicative of the primitive firing technique.

Provenance
Parsons Fine Art, Taos, New Mexico.

Estimate: $8,000-$12,000

48010

SANTO DOMINGO POLYCHROME DOUGH BOWL

Circa 1930
Height 8¾ in. Width 15½ in.

This typical three-color bowl is painted with an exterior design of interconnected six point stars and a red underbody. The interior is painted with a large four-quadrant medallion (this area exhibiting some paint loss).

Provenance
Christie's, sale 1142, Lot 74, January 13, 2003.

Estimate: $6,000-$8,000

48011

SAN ILDEFONSO POLYCHROME POTTERY JAR BY ANA MONTOYA

Circa 1910
Height 9½ in. Width 11 in.

This classic three-color olla features a globular body and a tall neck. It is painted with a frieze of scrolling hooks around the middle along with two friezes above, each of abstract feather forms, all on a cream slip, and a red underbody. Ana Montoya was the sister of Maria Martinez. Ana would work in concert with her husband, Crescencio Martinez. Writing of this artist's work, Jonathan Batkin of the Wheelwright Museum in Santa Fe states, "Anna apparently preferred a red rim after most other San Ildefonso potters had begun painting rims black. Her pots are well made. In fact, in many cases they are as well made as Maria's...I consider Ann's and Crescencio's pots to be every bit as important as Maria's and Julian's..."

Reference
Bernstein, Bruce and Brody, J. J. *Voices In Clay*, Miami University Art Museum, Oxford, Ohio, 2001, cover photo and p. 89.

Provenance
Parsons Fine Art, Taos, New Mexico.

Estimate: $5,000-$7,000

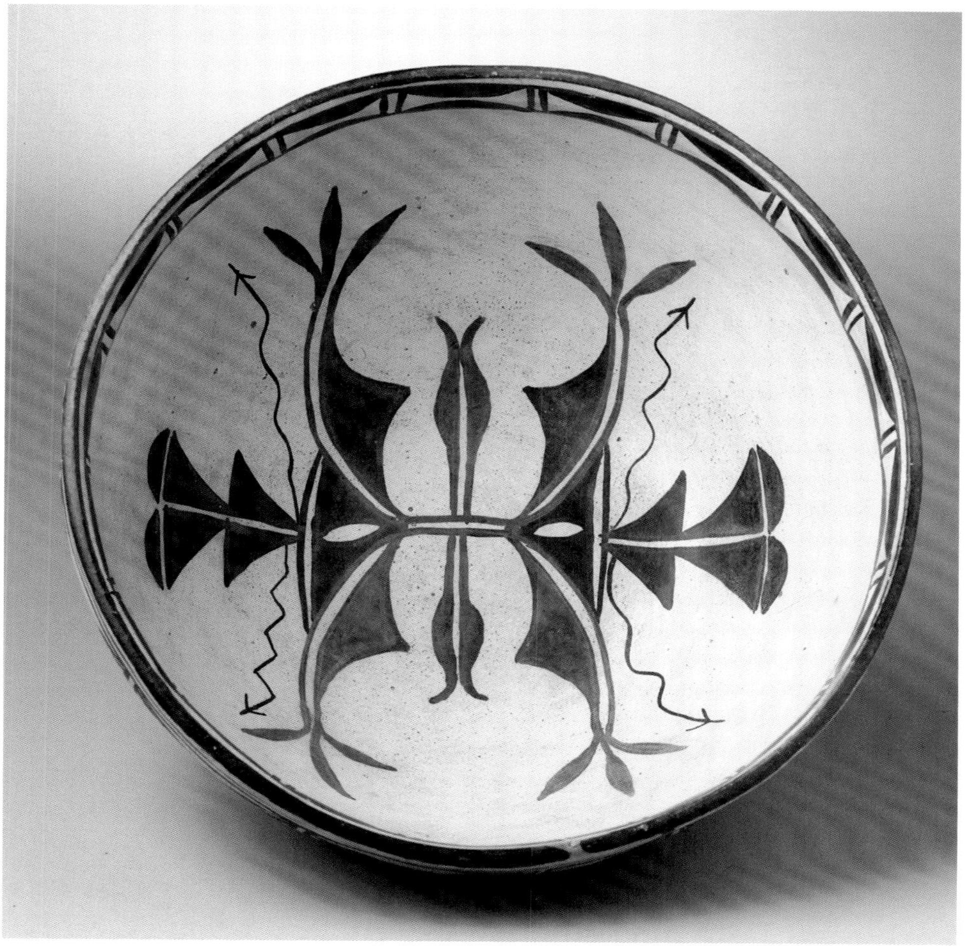

48012

COCHITI POTTERY BOWL

Circa 1940
Height 4½ in. Width 9 in.

This flaring bowl has an interior arrangement of symmetrical stylized plant forms, split feathers, and lightning bands. A frieze of boxed scallops decorates the interior rim. The exterior is painted with a band of split, four leaf blossoms.

Provenance
Bonhams & Butterfields, Sale 7477E, Lot 3334, December 8, 2003.

Estimate: $1,000-$1,500

48013

ZIA POLYCHROME POTTERY JAR

Circa 1930
Height 12 in. Width 18¾ in.

This large three color storage jar is painted with a wide frieze containing three *Zia* style birds separated by a pair of red undulating bands over a cream slip with each bird flanked by stylized bats. There is a red underbody and a scalloped band around the rim.

Provenance
Parsons Fine Art, Taos, New Mexico.

Estimate: $8,000-$12,000

48014

ZIA POLYCHROME POTTERY JAR

Circa 1920
Height 8¼ in. Diameter 8¾ in.

This olla is characterized by a concave base, flaring sides, a hint of a shoulder, and tapering neck. The body is painted in a single design band of angular step devices surmounted with rain clouds and flanked by hatched feather motifs.
The underbody is red with a slip band at the top.

Provenance
Bonhams and Butterfields, Sale 7437E, Lot 5347, June 9, 2003.

Estimate: $1,000-$1,500

48015

***ZIA* POLYCHROME POTTERY VESSEL**

Circa 1930
Height 6½ in. Width 7½ in.

This three-color jar features a tall red neck, handles, and a flat base. The body is painted with classic *Zia* birds, one on each side, and both flanked by foliate sprays. The pot is unsigned but can be accurately attributed to Geronima Medina (see Lot 48016).

Provenance
Bonhams and Butterfields, Sale 7477E, Lot 3337, December 8, 2003.

Estimate: $1,000-$1,500

48016

***ZIA* POLYCHROME POTTERY VESSEL**

Circa 1930
Height 6¾ in. Width 8 in.

This three-color jar is characterized by its tall red neck, handles, and flat base. The body is painted with classic *Zia* birds, one on each side, and both flanked by foliate sprays. A frieze of split triangular devices frames the upper portion just below the neck. Signed on the base "Geronima Medina *Zia* Pueblo".

Provenance
Bonhams and Butterfields, Sale 7477E, Lot 3337, December 8, 2003.

Estimate: $1,000-$1,500

48017

ZIA POLYCHROME POTTERY JAR

Circa 1920
Height 8¾ in. Width 11 in.

The jar is of classic olla form including flaring walls extending upwards from the narrow, concave base, then tapering in at the neck. Three *Zia* style birds, each with different plumage and decorative medallions, alternate with floral sprays against the orange/tan background. The underbody is the typical red.

Provenance
Christie's, Sale 1142, Lot 93, January 13, 2003.

Estimate: $4,000-$6,000

48018

ZIA POLYCHROME POTTERY JAR

Circa 1920
Height 8¼ in. Diameter 10 in.

This classic olla has a concave base, globular body, and tapering neck. It is painted with two *Zia* birds, each within double rainbow bands edged with feather motifs. The birds are separated by large framed diamond elements whose interior is divided into quadrants. There is a narrow scalloped band at the rim and the typical red underbody.

Provenance
Bonhams and Butterfields, Sale 7477E, Lot 3336, December 8, 2003.

Estimate: $2,500-$3,500

48019

ACOMA POLYCHROME POTTERY JAR

Circa 1910
Height 11 in. Diameter 12 in.

This four color olla has a high neck and slight shoulder. It is painted with a series of triangular forms, both hatched and colored, plus foliate decorations, all with a very precise hand.

Provenance
Bonhams & Butterfields, Sale 7437E, Lot 5357, June 9, 2003.

Estimate: $6,000-$8,000

48020

ACOMA POLYCHROME POTTERY JAR

Circa 1930
Height 9½ in. Diameter 11¾ in.

This jar is characterized by its concave base, expansive sides, high rounded shoulder, and short tapering neck. The body is painted with stylized feather motifs, both solid and hatched, across two opposing panels. The two other design panels feature a large framed rectangle containing opposing angular scrolled and step devices. An angular red band with floating black geometric accents decorates the rim.

Provenance
Bonhams and Butterfields, Sale 7477E, Lot 3365, December 8, 2003.

Estimate: $2,000-$3,000

48021

ACOMA POLYCHROME POTTERY JAR

Circa 1910
Height 9 in. Width 12 in.

This classic olla is characterized by its nicely flaring sides and tapering neck. It is painted with a series of hatched and solid, positive and negative, geometric elements. Solid feather motifs and negative lozenge forms are also integrated into the overall design.

Provenance
Christie's, Sale 1142, Lot 90, January 13, 2003.

Estimate: $3,000-$5,000

48022

ACOMA POLYCHROME POTTERY JAR

Circa 1930
Height 9 in. Diameter 11½ in.

This three-color olla features a concave base, flaring sides, a high shoulder, and tapering neck. The body is decorated with a single design band consisting of a series of medallions, each enclosing a six petal flower motif set against a finely painted hatched background, and surrounded by a stepped perimeter. The jar has an orange underbody.

Provenance
Bonhams and Butterfields, Sale 7477E, Lot 3368, December 8, 2003.

Estimate: $2,000-$3,000

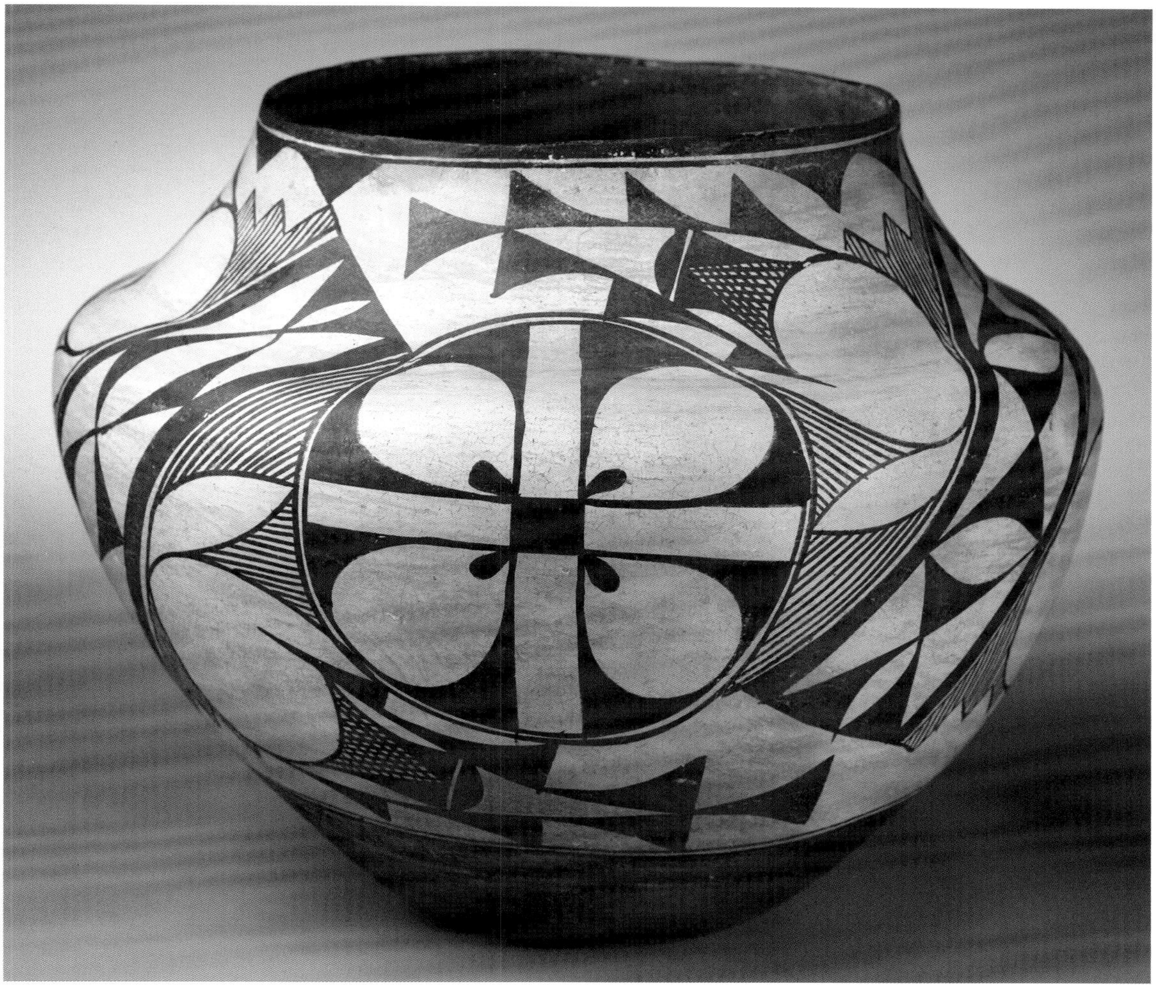

48023

ACOMA POLYCHROME POTTERY JAR

Circa 1920
Height 9¾ in. Diameter 12 in.

This classic olla has a concave base, flaring sides, a narrow shoulder, and tapering neck. The three-color jar is painted with a single design band whose elements include three large medallions, each divided into quadrants and flanked by stylized bird and feather motifs that are solid, hatched, and cross-hatched. The medallions are separated by diagonal bands with negative lozenge motifs.

Provenance
Denver Art Museum.
Christie's, Sale 1332, Lot 108, January 12, 2004.

Estimate: $3,000-$5,000

48024

ACOMA POLYCHROME POTTERY JAR

Circa 1940
Height 8¾ in. Diameter 9½ in.

This olla features a small concave base, flaring sides, high shoulder, and tapering neck. The jar is painted in three distinct design bands. The upper and lower are similarly conceived with elongated geometric forms, solid and hatched, with a central cross and separated by a zigzag line framing solid triangular elements with small circles in their centers. The middle design band is a negative lightning pattern framed in black against the cream slip.

Provenance
Bonhams and Butterfields, Sale 7437E, Lot 5345, June 9, 2003.

Estimate: $1,000-$2,000

48025

ACOMA POLYCHROME POTTERY JAR

Circa 1890
Height 11½ in. Width 12½ in.

This olla is characterized by its graceful flaring walls and tapering neck. It is painted with a series of geometric forms outlined in black, black on white designs within, all floating against a red ground, and with an unusual scalloped red underbody. A note in pencil written on the side of the jar: "Pot of Pueblo Indian, Sept. 16, 1911, Alaska, New Mex."

Provenance
Christie's, Sale 1142, Lot 92, January 13, 2003.

Estimate: $4,000-$6,000

48026

ACOMA POLYCHROME POTTERY JAR

Circa 1920
Height 9¼ in. Diameter 13 in.

This classic olla has a concave base, flaring sides, high shoulder, and tapering neck. The jar is painted with a single design band consisting of large scalloped medallions with negative foliate, lozenge, and triangular motifs flanked by solid designs in red and black and hatched forms in black. Each medallion is separated by a red-bordered diamond form. The jar has a red underbody.

Provenance
Bonhams and Butterfields, Sale 7477E, Lot 3369, December 8, 2003.

Estimate: $2,000-$3,000

48027

ACOMA POLYCHROME POTTERY JAR

Circa 1920
Height 10¼ in. Diameter 11 in.

This classic three-color olla has a concave base, flaring sides, and a tall tapering neck. The body is painted with a single design band consisting of a strong vertical zigzag band in deep red. The intervening space is filled with triangular and split leaf forms in black against the cream slip.

Provenance
Denver Art Museum.
Christie's, Sale 1332, Lot 107, January 12, 2004.

Estimate: $2,000-$3,000

48028

ACOMA POLYCHROME POTTERY JAR

Circa 1930
Height 9¼ in. Diameter 12 in.

The three-color olla is characterized by a concave base, flaring sides, high shoulder, and tapering neck. The jar is painted in a single wide band around the body using various stylized bird and feather elements, both solid and hatched, in red and black against the cream slip.

Provenance
Bonhams and Butterfields, Sale 7477E, Lot 3366, December 8, 2003.

Estimate: $2,000-$3,000

48029

ACOMA POLYCHROME POTTERY JAR

Circa 1930
Height 9¼ in. Diameter 11¾ in.

This typical three-color olla has a concave base, flaring sides, high shoulder, and tapering neck. Two pairs of mirrored thunderbirds are painted in a single band around the jar with solid and hatched elements in black and orange against the cream slip. The thunderbirds are separated by diagonal bands containing negative lozenge forms. The jar has an orange underbody.

Provenance
Bonhams and Butterfields, Sale 7477E, Lot 3366, December 8, 2003.

Estimate: $2,000-$3,000

48030

ZUNI POLYCHROME POTTERY JAR

Circa 1890
Height 12 in. Width 13½ in.

This classic olla is characterized by the graceful shoulder and slight flare at the rim. It is painted red and black over a cream white slip with three large, scalloped rosettes alternating with scrolling rainbird motifs, flanked by crosshatched triangular elements and bisected by a narrow scrolled band. A frieze of hatched and cross-hatched "daggers" encircles the neck.

Provenance
Denver Art Museum.
Christie's, Sale 1132, Lot 117, January 12, 2004.

Estimate: $8,000-$12,000

48031

ZUNI POLYCHROME POTTERY JAR

Circa 1885
Height 9¼ in. Width 12¼ in.

This three-color jar of classic olla form has a strong shoulder, a pronounced flare at the rim, and a noticeable puki line. The body is painted with a repeating pattern of hatched and solid triangular shaped forms in black, bisected by a band of ovals, two feather elements in red and black inside each. Solid and hatched feather forms fill the area between the shoulder and the neck.

Provenance
Christie's, Sale 1142, Lot 104, January 13, 2003.

Estimate: $5,000-$7,000

48032

ZUNI POLYCHROME POTTERY BOWL

Circa 1890
Height 6 in. Width 15 in.

The interior is decorated with three heartline deer, each enclosed by a hooked and feathered arch and standing on the central medallion. A chain of narrow rectangles forms a frieze around the top inside edge. The exterior is painted with a series of hooked devices.

Provenance
Bonhams & Butterfields, Sale 7437E, Lot 5358, June 9, 2003.

Estimate: $5,000-$7,000

48033

HOPI POLYCHROME POTTERY JAR ATTRIBUTED TO NAMPEYO

Circa 1900
Height 4½ in. Width 9½ in.

The jar is characterized by its steeply tapering sides and small rounded shoulder. It is painted with a pair of abstract avian forms, each with a curving scroll beak and splayed feathers between wide framing bands. An eagle tail design was a favorite motif and Nampeyo continually reworked this design concept. "Nampeyo, the famous Hopi-Tewa potter (1860-1942) is known for the grace and beauty of her work…By the turn of the twentieth century, Nampeyo had revitalized Hopi pottery by creating a contemporary style inspired by prehistoric ceramics."[1]

Provenance

Bonhams & Butterfields, Sale 7477E, Lot 3340, December 8, 2003.

"The attribution to Nampeyo has been made by Martha Struever in an expertise gained through years of study and interest in Nampeyo's work and through personal contact with her descendants. In a letter referring to this jar she writes: 'The four color pottery jar can be attributed to Nampeyo based on several identifiable characteristics: the long swooping arcs ending in a simple scroll can be seen in illustrations of Nampeyo's work in *American Indian Art* magazine, Summer 1976, p. 26, figures 2 and 3, and p. 27; the use of the pair of feathers below the upper framing line; the general layout and form with slightly layered out-turned rim are often found in Nampeyo's pottery. An unusual feature of this vessel is the lower framing lines at the shoulder that overlap and do not join as the upper framing line does. Vessels of similar form and composition are exhibited at the Milwaukee Public Museum. (Photo #XE-482-13E, Milwaukee Public Museum.) *Nampeyo and Her Pottery*, Kramer, Barbara, University of New Mexico Press, p. 111.'"

References

[1]Kramer, Barbara, *Nampeyo and Her Pottery*, University of New Mexico Press, Albuquerque, 1996, Dust jacket sleeve.

[2]Bonhams and Butterfields: *Native American, Pre-Columbian and Tribal Art*, San Francisco, 2003, p. 90.

Estimate: $6,000-$8,000

48034

HOPI POLYCHROME POTTERY BOWL

Circa 1920
Height 4 in. Diameter 9 1/2 in.

This bowl is characterized by its rounded base, everted rim, and a pierced suspension knob. The interior is painted with highly stylized bird motifs including curving beaks and red and black feathers, solid and hatched, against the cream slip. A thick black band frames the design just below the rim. The exterior is further decorated with bird designs.

Provenance
Bonhams and Butterfields, Sale 7477E, Lot 3354, December 8, 2003.

Estimate: $2,000-$3,000

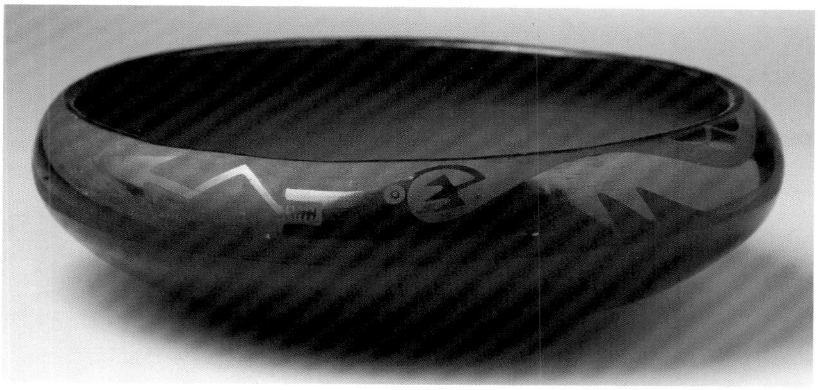

48035

SAN ILDEFONSO BLACKWARE POTTERY BOWL

Circa 1923-1926
Height 2⅜ in. Diameter 7½ in.

This compressed globular bowl is decorated with an undulating avanyu (water serpent) and rain cloud accents on the polished ground against the matte painted surface. The base is signed "Marie." Maria Martinez was the first Pueblo potter to sign her pottery on a regular basis. 1923 is the generally accepted date for this practice to begin. "Marie" was selected instead of "Maria" because it was suggested that Marie was a name more familiar to the non-Indian public.

Provenance
Bonhams and Butterfields, Sale 7437E, Lot 5393, June 9, 2003.

Reference
Spivey, Richard, *Maria*, Northland Publishing, Flagstaff, Arizona, 1994, pp. 63-68.

Estimate: $2,000-$3,000

48036

SAN ILDEFONSO BLACKWARE POTTERY JAR

Circa 1923-1926
Height 6½ in. Diameter 7¼ in.

This black on black jar is characterized by its flat base, flaring sides, and tapering neck. It is painted in matte with a series of trapezoidal forms framing linear bands and inverted stepped triangles against the polished black ground. The base is signed "Marie".

Provenance
Bonhams and Butterfields, Sale 7437E, Lot 5387, June 9, 2003.

Estimate: $1,000-$1,500

48037

SAN ILDEFONSO BLACKWARE POTTERY BOWL

Circa 1943-1956
Height 3¼ in. Diameter 6½ in.

This compressed globular shaped bowl is painted with stylized feather motifs in matte over the highly polished black background. It is signed on the base "Marie and Santana". Following the death of her husband Julian, Maria began working with her daughter-in-law, Santana Martinez. Maria continued to mold the pots while Santana did the painting.

Provenance
Bonhams and Butterfields, Sale 7437E, Lot 5393, June 9, 2003.

Estimate: $1,500-$2,500

48038

SAN ILDEFONSO BLACKWARE POTTERY BOWL

Circa 1943-1956
Height 4 in. Diameter 6 in.

The black on black bowl is of globular shape with a flat base. It is painted in matte with stylized feather and bird head motifs over the highly polished black ground. It is signed on the base "Marie and Santana."

Provenance
Bonhams and Butterfields, Sale 7437E, Lot 5386, June 9, 2003.

Estimate: $1,500-$2,500

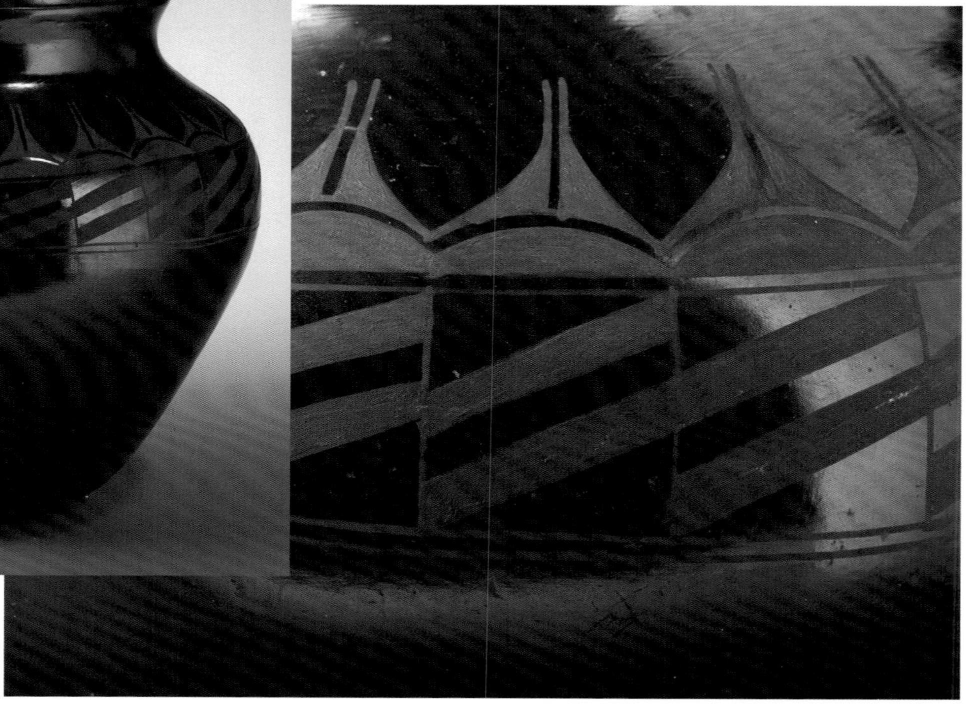

48039

SAN ILDEFONSO BLACKWARE POTTERY OLLA

Height 12½ in. Width 13½ in.

This large, classic jar is decorated with negative feather and cloud forms above a frieze of angled rectangles, all painted in matte over a polished black ground. Unsigned; Collected on San Geronimo Day, 1950, at Taos Pueblo (records of Parsons Fine Art).

Provenance
Parsons Fine Art, Taos, New Mexico.

Estimate: $4,000-$6,000

48040

SAN ILDEFONSO BLACKWARE VASE

Circa 1930
Height 10½ in. Width 7½ in.

This vase is characterized by the flaring sides and tall cylindrical neck. A series of thin lines, two of which are punctuated with small dots, is painted in matte around the shoulder. Above is a frieze of various geometric forms, also painted in matte, against the polished black surface. Signed "Tonita" (Tonita Roybal, 1892-1945). "No other women besides Maria and Tonita seem to achieve the deep lustre of polished jet which characterizes the finish of bowls of their workmanship."

Reference
Bunzel, Ruth, *The Pueblo Potter*, Dover Publications, Inc., New York, 1972, page 67.

Estimate: $3,000-$4,000

48041

TWO SAN JUAN BUFFWARE JARS

Circa 1930
(A) Height 6¼ in. Diameter 8¾ in.
(B) Height 7½ in. Diameter 8 in.

The first example is characterized by a flat base, flaring sides, and a high shoulder tapering to a short neck. The jar is made of micaceous clay decorated with incised linear designs in rectangular, triangular, and chevron patterns. The rim and underbody are polished.

The second example is characterized by a flat base, flaring sides, high shoulder, and a tall neck. This jar is also made of micaceous clay and decorated with incised linear designs in castellated bands around the center and a chevron pattern around the shoulder. The body is lightly polished while both neck and underbody are unpolished.

The incised pottery popular with San Juan artists was based on prehistoric examples excavated at the nearby Otowi ruins. These two examples reflect a contemporary interpretation of the ancient decorative process.

Provenance
Denver Art Museum
Christie's, Sale 1332, Lot 74, January 12, 2004.

Estimate: $1,000-$2,000

48042

SAN ILDEFONSO REDWARE POTTERY JAR

Circa 1990
Height 5 7/8 in. Diameter 7½ in.

This redware jar is characterized by a flat base, short flaring sides, and tapering body. The jar is decorated with a negative feather pattern in the highly polished red against the tan matte painted surfaced. It is signed on the base "Doug & Charlotte Vigil, San Ildefonso Pueblo" (Doug Vigil and Charlotte Vigil, husband and wife, both born in 1954, and relatives of Maria Martinez).

Estimate: $600-$900

48043

PIMA COILED PICTORIAL BASKET

Circa 1920
Height 9½ in. Diameter 15¼ in.

This tightly woven bowl features flaring sides and is decorated with a series of eagles with outspread wings, alternating from top to bottom, circling the basket.

Provenance
William Randolph Hearst Collection.
Bonhams and Butterfields, Sale 13314, Lot 1157, December 5, 2005.
Hudson Trading Co., Oracle, Arizona.

Estimate: $2,500-$3,500

48044

PIMA COILED BOTTLENECK BASKET

Circa 1900
Height 5 in. Diameter 7¾ in.

This finely coiled basket has slightly flaring sides, a high rounded shoulder, and a straight neck flaring at the rim. The basket is decorated with a series of vertical meander lines that mirror each other. The weaver would have to keep the design in her head and any miscalculation would upset the symmetry of the pattern.

Provenance
McCloud Collection
Hudson Trading Co., Oracle Arizona.

Estimate: $4,000-$5,000

48045

PIMA COILED GEOMETRIC TRAY

Circa 1910
Height 1¼ in. Diameter 10 in.

This tightly coiled basket is decorated with concentric rings of stepped triangular forms and stepped rectangles moving out to the rim from the black central start.

Provenance
Hudson Trading Co., Oracle, Arizona.

Estimate: $1,500-$2,500

48046

APACHE COILED PICTORIAL BOWL

Circa 1910
Height 4¾ in. Diameter 17¼ in.

This tightly coiled basket with flaring sides is decorated with Apache Gaan dancers and quadrupeds. The Gaan dancers mask with its elaborated crown is represented by two vertical lines above the figure's head. Those with raised arms are holding Gaan dance wands. The figures are separated by vertical, checkered zigzag bands moving from the central cross to the rim. The basket exhibits a rich honey-colored patina.

Provenance
Terry DeWald, Tucson, Arizona.

Estimate: $4,000-$6,000

48047

APACHE POLYCHROME PICTORIAL BOWL

Circa 1910
Height 4 in. Diameter 15¾ in.

This tightly coiled basket is decorated with a series of human figures and small quadrupeds in both black (devil's claw) and red (yucca root). The figures are posed standing upon a central castellated band. A pattern of small-checkered squares decorates the rim and a double outlined cross fills the bottom center.

Provenance
Philip Garaway, Venice, California.

Estimate: $4,000-$6,000

48048

APACHE COILED PICTORIAL BOWL

Circa 1900
Height 3½ in. Diameter 14⅜ in.

This tightly coiled basket has wide flaring sides and is decorated with human figures and crosses. A vertical four-line step pattern frames the figural elements. The willow background has developed a rich brown patina.

Provenance
Hudson Trading Co., Oracle, Arizona.

Estimate: $2,000-$3,000

48049

APACHE COILED PICTORIAL BOWL

Circa 1910
Height 3½ in. Diameter 17⅜ in.

This coiled basket with flaring sides features a central eight point star design. Human figures and quadrupeds of varying size are arranged around the sides. Four inverted triangular elements along the rim frame crosses and figures on horseback.

Provenance
Philip Garaway, Venice, California.

Estimate: $3,500-$4,500

48050

APACHE COILED PICTORIAL BOWL

Circa 1910
Height 5 in. Diameter 17¼ in.

This tightly coiled basket with flaring sides is characterized by a central eight-point starburst motif, a checkered zigzag band circling above, four vertical checkered bands, and a group of human figures and quadrupeds variously placed around the sides.

Provenance
David Stock, Scottsdale, Arizona.

Estimate: $4,000-$6,000

48051

APACHE COILED PICTORIAL BASKET

Circa 1910
Height 15½ in. Diameter 13 in.

This olla features a barrel shaped body, a tapering neck, and flaring rim. It is decorated overall in a checkered diamond lattice pattern with human figures and horses (man and horse together in some cases) filling the open spaces. The horses turn their heads to the rear along the bottom row.

Provenance
Bonhams and Butterfields, Sale 7477E, Lot 3195, December 8, 2003.

Estimate: $4,000-$6,000

48052

APACHE COILED PICTORIAL BASKET

Circa 1920
Height 16 in. Diameter 12½ in.

This basket is characterized by its barrel shaped body with slightly flaring sides, rounded shoulder, tall neck, and a flaring rim. The olla is worked overall with a diamond lattice pattern with chickens, crosses, and geometric forms placed within each diamond.

Provenance
Bonhams and Butterfields, Sale 7477E, Lot 3193, December 8, 2003.

Estimate: $3,000-$5,000

48053

APACHE COILED PICTORIAL BASKET

Circa 1920
Height 16⅜ in. Diameter 14¼ in.

This large, tightly coiled olla has a barrel shaped body, rounded shoulder, and flaring neck. The basket is decorated with a variety of geometric devices including squares within squares, checkered diamonds, and diamonds with interior crosses. In addition, there are human figures and quadrupeds (likely horses and dogs) scattered throughout.

Provenance
Hudson Trading Co., Oracle, Arizona.

Estimate: $6,000-$9,000

48054

APACHE COILED GEOMETRIC BASKET

Circa 1915
Height 13⅝ in. Diameter 10¾ in.

This basket has a flat base, flaring sides, a rounded shoulder, and a straight neck. It is decorated with five undulating bands that move horizontally around the olla.

Provenance
Bonhams and Butterfields, Sale 7477E, Lot 3194, December 8, 2003.

Estimate: $1,500-$2,500

48055

APACHE COILED PICTORIAL BASKET

Circa 1910
Height 11 in. Diameter 9¼ in.

This well made basket features a series of human figures standing next to complex vertical and horizontal line forms. Checkered vertical design bands frame the humans from base to rim. The rim is decorated with upright and inverted triangles. The willow background has taken on a soft, mellow patina.

Provenance
Hudson Trading Co., Oracle, Arizona.

Estimate: $3,000-$4,000

48056

CALIFORNIA MISSION POLYCHROME TRAY

Circa 1910
Diameter 11 5/8 in.

This coiled tray is decorated with a rattlesnake design curling around the center. The rattlesnake is flanked by a group of small crosses on both sides of its body and short striped bands towards the outer rim. The realistic depiction of rattlesnakes was common on Mission baskets. Donna Largo, a contemporary Cahuilla weaver comments, "My grandmother told me a story about the rattlesnake and how it got into the basket. She said that the women would all sit on the ground making baskets and a rattlesnake kept coming toward one lady. And she'd chase him away and chase him away. And he kept coming back. And finally she told the rattlesnake, 'If you don't go away, I'm going to put you in my basket.' Well, he wouldn't go away, so that's how we got rattlesnakes in our baskets."

Reference
Bibby, Brian, *The Fine Art of California Indian Basketry*, Crocker Art Museum, Sacramento, 1996, p. 92.

Estimate: $3,000-$4,000

48057

POMO COILED TREASURE BASKET

Circa 1910
Height 2¾ in. Length 8½ in. Width 4¾ in.

The coiled boat shaped basket is decorated overall with a repetitive step pattern. In addition, the rim is decorated with clamshell disc beads and quail topknot feathers. Pendants of shell disc beads and abalone shell hang from the rim at various points. The boat shape is common amongst the Pomo but rarely seen elsewhere. These bowls could be used to hold personal treasures, given as a gift on important occasions, or used as payment. Larger examples were used to hold ceremonial objects. The Pomo basket weavers are renowned for their skills and this well shaped and balanced example is a testament to their abilities.

Provenance
Natalie Linn, Portland, Oregon.

Reference
Barrett, Samuel, *Pomo Indian Basketry*, University of California, Berkeley, 1996, pp. 164 and 165.

Estimate: $2,000-$3,000

48058

POMO COILED GIFT BASKET

Circa 1900
Height 3 in. Diameter 7 in.

This tightly coiled round basket is decorated with stepped triangles whose arrangement is organized both diagonally and horizontally around the body. This design motif was generally referred to as an "arrowhead" by Pomo basket weavers. The rim is decorated in four places with clamshell disc beads and quail topknot feathers. Red woodpecker crest feathers decorate the basket overall.

Provenance
Merrill Domas, Old Chatham, New York.

Estimate: $4,500-$5,500

48059

POMO COILED GIFT BASKET

Circa 1900
Height 2¾ in. Diameter 6 in.

This small, tightly coiled, round basket is decorated with a pattern of stepped triangles staggered from base to rim and back. These finely made gift baskets were in great demand by collectors during the height of their popularity (1890-1915). Many collectors sought baskets that demonstrated the weavers artistic sensibilities rather than traditional utilitarian examples.

Provenance
Merrill Domas, Old Chatham, New York.

Estimate: $1,500-$2,500

48060

MIWOK-PAIUTE COILED BASKET

Circa 1910
Height 5 1/8 in. Diameter 10 in.

This well made bowl is decorated with a variety of complex geometric forms in red (redbud) and black (bracken fern) floating against the tan (sedge root) background. Design elements include diamonds, four point stars, and four large six point forms with serrated edges. During the early years of the 20th century, Miwok and Paiute weavers found a ready outlet for their baskets at nearby Yosemite National Park. "The Indian Field Days, a rodeo and fair held annually in Yosemite Valley between 1916 and 1929, further impressed upon weavers the salability of new-style baskets. Sponsored by the National Park Service and several park concessionaires, the purpose of the Field Days was 'to revive and maintain interest of Indians in their own games and industries, particularly basket and bead work'." Basket competitions were held and prizes awarded. This stimulated keen competition which led to design innovations and baskets of spectacular scale and quality.

Provenance
Russell Kloer, Sonoma, California.

Reference
Bates, Craig and Lee, Martha J., *Tradition and Innovation*, Yosemite Association, Yosemite National Park, California, 1990, p. 91.

Estimate: $2,500-$3,500

48061

YOKUTS COILED PICTORIAL BASKET

Circa 1920
Height 7½ in. Diameter 15½ in.

This basket is decorated with human figures and geometric forms including seven women, seven small crosses, seven complex large crosses, seven solid black rectangular forms, and seven stepped triangles with open bases. An accompanying letter states the basket was originally purchased from the Grace Nicholson collection in Pasadena, California. (Grace Nicholson, 1877-1948, a renowned collector and dealer, first opened her curio shop in Pasadena in 1902. She is well known for her patronage and documentation of the work of Elizabeth Hickox, the famous Karuk basket weaver. Baskets supplied by Nicholson are well represented in a number of public institutions.) In the same letter, Marion Burns, a previous owner, states that the basket may have been woven by Aida Icho. (For information on this basket maker see: Latta, Frank, *Handbook of Yokuts Indians*, Bear State Books, Santa Cruz, California, 1977).

Provenance
Merrill Domas, Old Chatham, New York.

Estimate: $6,000-$9,000

48062

YOKUTS COOKING BASKET

Circa 1910
Height 10¼ in. Diameter 22 in.

This large coiled cooking bowl is decorated with two design bands using the rattlesnake motif. The design elements consist of hourglass forms in black (bracken fern root) and diamonds in red (redbud shoots). The rattlesnake design was highly popular with Yokuts artists and it is a common motif. The Yokuts used large, finely coiled baskets for making acorn soup, a dietary staple. The cooking was done using the stone boiling method in which two or three fire heated stones are set in a basket containing leached acorn dough in water. The red-hot stones are moved around so that the basket is not seriously scorched or burned.

Provenance
Hudson Trading Co., Oracle, Arizona.

Reference
Bibby, Brian, *The Fine Art of California Indian Basketry*, Crocker Art Museum, Sacramento, 1996, p. 55.

Estimate: $6,000-$8,000

48063

YOKUTS COILED PICTORIAL BASKET

Circa 1910
Height 5 3/8 in. Diameter 10 3/4 in.

This deep bowl with curved, flaring sides features nine human figures holding hands around the basket. A negative zigzag band is worked around the rim of the bowl.

Provenance
Bonhams and Butterfields, Sale 7477E, Lot 3206, December 8, 2003.

Estimate: $3,000-$4,000

48064

WESTERN MONO COILED COOKING BASKET

Circa 1900
Height 8¾ in. Diameter 16¾ in.

This deep bowl with wide flaring sides is decorated with a horizontal zigzag pattern interrupted by vertical zigzag bands. A narrow band of small rectangles decorates the rim. "Large bowls were used for feasts. Often acorn soup would be cooked in smaller baskets and then served in a larger bowl. Western Mono and Yokuts weaving is quite similar. There are some differences in the design used, and the Western Mono will often break the horizontal banding with vertical lines of designs. In addition, while Yokuts weavers will invariably weave a bowl on the inside face and to the right, Western Mono weavers will work on either face and in either direction."

Provenance
Bonhams and Butterfields, Sale 7477E, Lot 3190, December 8, 2003.

Reference
Bernstein, Bruce, *Native American Basketry: The Hartman Collection*, The Albrecht-Kemper Museum of Art, St. Joseph, Missouri, 1996, p. 32.

Estimate: $2,500-$3,500

48065

PANAMINT POLYCHROME PICTORIAL BASKET

Circa 1930
Height 5 in. Diameter 7 in.

This fine and tightly woven coiled pictorial basket is decorated with large butterflies, bees, and birds perched on trees. "One aspect of coiled Panamint Shoshone basketry is its great diversity in form and design. Dramatic historical changes in the northern Mojave Desert, which began in the latter half of the 19th century with the arrival of miners, settlers, and eventually tourists, encouraged the creation of a new basket style, which more closely reflected the taste of the new Californians. The gradual transformation of basketry with geometric design made for the Indian's own use, to eventually small, colorful vessels with bird and butterfly illustrations made for the tourist trade was inevitable, because, as society changes, so will its art form."

Provenance
Sandra Horn, Mill Valley, California.

Reference
Slater, Eva, *Panamint Shoshone Basketry*, Sagebrush Press, Morongo Valley, California, 2000, p. 27.

Estimate: $12,000-$16,000

48066

PANAMINT PICTORIAL BASKET BY MARY WRINKLE

Circa 1935
Height 4½ in. Diameter 7¾ in.

This tightly coiled polychrome bowl is decorated with a series of four birds (likely a Scott's oriole), each perched on a flowering branch, alternating with stepped diamond motifs and eight point stars. "It was not by accident that the colorful bird baskets created by Mary Wrinkle originated in Darwin (California). Unlike other Panamint Shoshone settlements in the desert valleys, the sandy hills around Darwin (elev. 4,730 ft.) provided the altitude for yucca to grow. These trees provided the basket maker not only the red sewing material obtained from the root, but additionally the yucca offered nesting places and perches for the woodpecker with pink quill, the black and yellow Scott oriole, and owl among others, the very subject matter for Mary Wrinkle's delightful bird-baskets of the 1930's. Always in the form of a small rounded bowl, Mary Wrinkle's colorful 'for sale' baskets became very popular with collectors. Other basket makers, even as far away as Death Valley and beyond into Chemehuevi territory adopted the use of pink quill as sewing material and for the creation of similar bird designs. Mary Wrinkle's charming illustrations of nature, however, had few equals."

Provenance
Hudson Trading Co., Oracle, Arizona.

Reference
Slater, Eva, *Panamint Shoshone Basketry*, Sagebrush Press, Morongo Valley, California, 2000, pp. 43-48.

Estimate: $8,000-$12,000

48067

PANAMINT POLYCHROME COOKING BASKET

Circa 1900
Height 7¼ in. Diameter 17¼ in.

This finely coiled polychrome bowl has an elaborate vertical design scheme consisting of inverted triangles in black (devil's claw) against a red (yucca root) background. The vertical bands are bordered with rows of right triangles with hooked diagonal lines coming off one angle. (This accent is often referred to as quail plumes or quail topknot feathers.) It is unlikely that this basket was ever used for mixing or cooking food. The sophisticated design and fine condition indicate it was made for sale. (For a similar example see: Bibby, Brian, *The Fine Art of California Indian Basketry*, Crocker Art Museum, Sacramento, 1996, p. 56.)

Estimate: $12,000-$16,000

48068

PANAMINT COILED BASKETRY BOWL

Circa 1920
Height 5¾ in. Diameter 14 in.

This fine, tightly coiled bowl features a small flat base and flaring sides. The body is decorated overall with a stylized butterfly pattern represented by hourglass forms within rectangular black (devils claw) panels. The artist has arranged the individual butterfly elements in a combination of parallel and staggered bands. The visual effect is a sense of motion, suggesting butterflies in flight.

Estimate: $4,000-$6,000

48069

POMO COILED BASKETRY BOWL

Circa 1900
Height 4 in. Diameter 13¼ in.

This coiled bowl features a flat base and wide flaring sides. The rim is fully decorated with clamshell disc beads. Short string fringes of glass beads with abalone shell pendants hang from the rim at various places. This treatment is repeated at scattered points throughout the basket.

Provenance
Pook A Moon Gallery.

Estimate: $3,000-$4,000

48070

KAWAIISU COILED BOTTLENECK BASKET

Circa 1900
Height 5½ in. Diameter 7½ in.

This tightly coiled jar has flaring sides, a rounded shoulder, and a short, slightly flared neck. The body is decorated with two similar but staggered meander lines and the shoulder with a fret pattern. The designs are done in red (Joshua tree root) against the tan (split willow shoots) background. The neck is decorated with a series of black (devils claw) vertical lines arranged in groups of three.

Provenance
Hudson Trading Co., Oracle, Arizona.

Estimate: $3,500-$4,500

48071

HUPA TWINED STORAGE BASKET

Circa 1920
Height 8½ in. Diameter 11 in.

This finely constructed, twined storage basket is decorated with two horizontal bands of large diamonds in black (maidenhair fern) around the central body and a similar band of smaller diamonds circling the rim.

Estimate: $2,000-$3,000

48072

HUPA TWINED OPENWORK BASKET

Circa 1920
Height 10½ in. Diameter 10¾ in.

The basket is decorated around the central body with a series of eight point "stars" in black (maidenhair fern). The "stars" are composed of isosceles triangles with a striated diamond center. A frieze of triangles in brown (spruce root) circles the base and rim. Two sections have been left open with the hazel stick warps crossing over each other and then continuing to provide a foundation for the twined weft beargrass.

Provenance
Transitional Arts, Prescott, Arizona.

Estimate: $1,000-$1,500

48073

WASCO SALLY BAG

Circa 1890
Height 7½ in. Diameter 5½ in.

This twined cylindrical basket is decorated with paired human figures and birds with outstretched wings. "Small cylindrical pouches such as this one were woven in part to serve as receptacles for the ritual harvests of a large variety of native roots, including cous, camas, bitterroot and others." Typical images on these firm but flexible baskets include animals, birds, and human figures. Sally bags with skeletal human figures are the best-known examples of this distinctive basketry form.

Provenance
Merrill Domas, Old Chatham, New York.

Reference
Vincent, Brydon, and Coe (Eds.), *Art of the North American Indian: The Thaw Collection*, New York State Historical Association, Fenimore Art Museum, Cooperstown, 2000, p. 303.

Estimate: $3,000-$4,000

48074

SKOKOMISH TWINED STORAGE BASKET

Circa 1910
Height 13¾ in. Diameter 17 in.

This large storage basket is a classic example of the technical and artistic features common to Skokomish baskets. They preferred plain twinning and large cylindrical forms. The layout usually followed a pattern of vertical geometric design zones and a narrow rim band. This example has a complex design of paired rectangles within rectangles. These vertically stacked elements have been described as "boxes" or "fishnets" by the weavers. Small quadrupeds circle the rim. "The downward-angled tails indicate wolves in the Skokomish and other Salish traditions."

Provenance
Sandra Horn, Mill Valley, California.

Reference
Vincent, Brydon, and Coe (Eds.), *Art of the North American Indian: The Thaw Collection*, New York State Historical Association, Fenimore Art Museum, Cooperstown, 2000, p. 312.

Estimate: $6,000-$8,000

Weavings

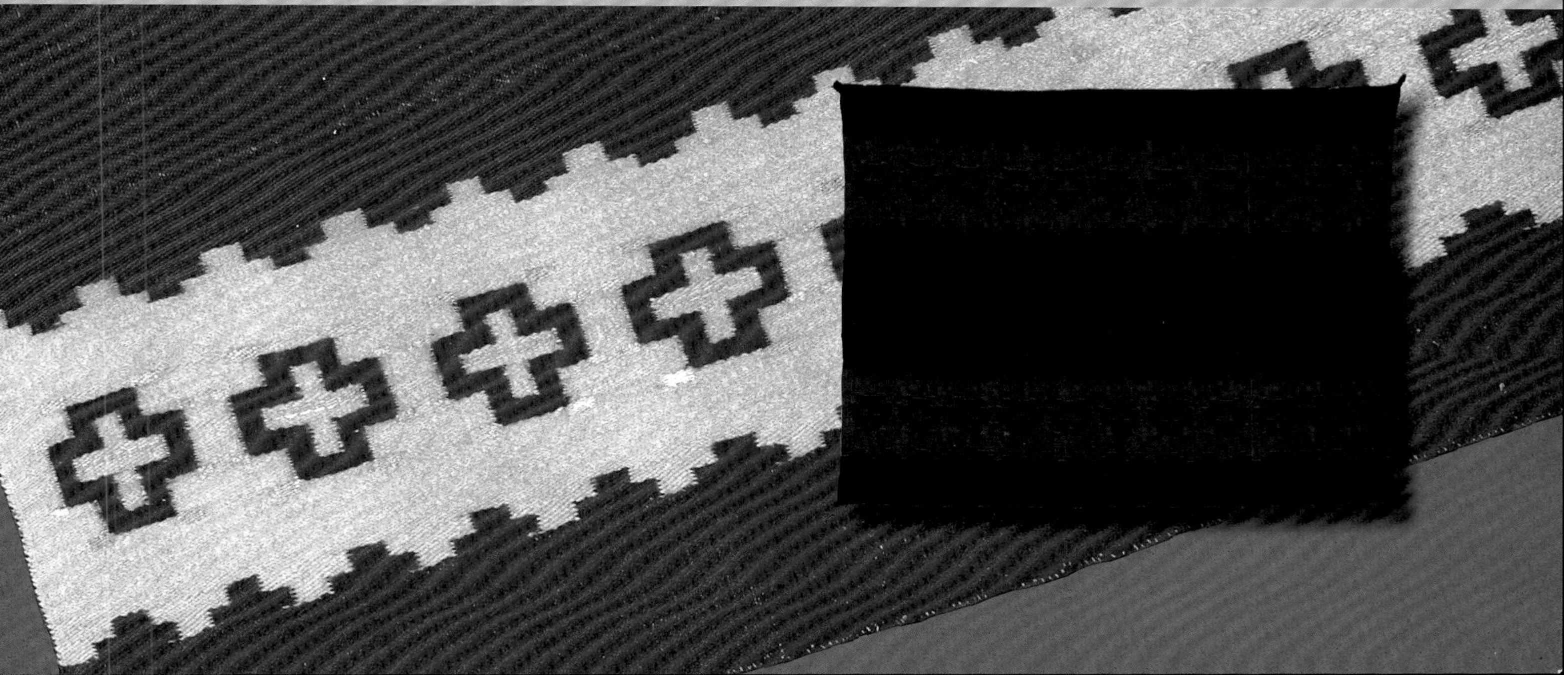

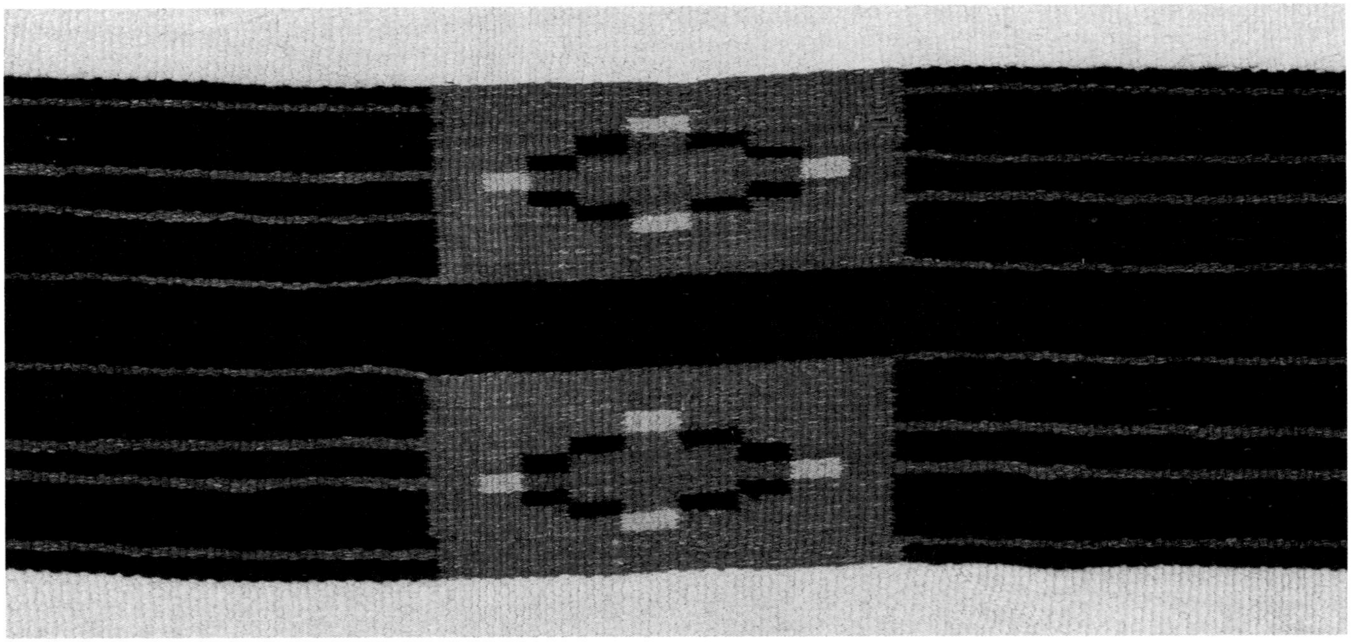

48075

CLASSIC NAVAJO SECOND PHASE CHIEF'S BLANKET COLLECTED FROM THE UTES IN COLORADO

Circa 1865
Length 60 in. Width 67 in.

Second phase pattern blankets differ from the simple banded first phase examples by the addition of rectangles that break up the banded layout. This example forms a classic twelve spot pattern. There are two central red and blue bands, each band enclosing three red rectangles, a stepped diamond outline within. This pattern is repeated in single bands at each end. The background is formed by alternating bands in white and brown. The red yarns in this weaving are all single-ply raveled bayeta, cochineal-dyed (Dye testing was provided by David Wenger, Ph.D.). The blue is handspun wool dyed with indigo, together with vegetal-dyed green and yellow handspun. The brown and white are natural, undyed handspun wool.

Provenance
Descended through the family of General Francis Henry French. General French collected this blanket while stationed in Colorado. General French wrote about his efforts to acquire a Navajo weaving in a letter dated September 22, 1880 from "In camp near Los Pinos Agency, Colorado." French writes that he is "going up to the Agency, Saturday, to see the rations issued to the Indians which is a regular weekly affair. I want to buy a blanket from the Indians also...I had a queer experience with two of them in trying to buy a blanket. I offered one man $5 for a blanket, but he said $8 after a great deal of talking. I agreed to pay $8, and started to get some change from the store, when he wanted $10. In spite of his offer, nothing less than $10 would satisfy him. Seeing I wouldn't take the blanket, another young buck agreed to sell me one for $10 and I drew out the amount immediately so that he should not have a chance to change, but before I could pay, he wanted $5 more, and I would not take the blanket. The only way is to have plentyof silver pieces in your pocket, and when you want to buy anything just show the amount you will pay." General French was finally successful in acquiring a Navajo weaving and this fine example is a testament to his efforts. The Utes were tough negotiators and obviously reluctant to give up their prized Chief's blankets.

General French attended West Point, graduating in 1879. He was commissioned as a Second Lieutenant in the 19th Infantry and assigned frontier duty at Fort Garland, Colorado. His posting was in response to the Meeker massacre of September 30, 1879, as the United States military beefed up its presence throughout Colorado. (Indian Agent Nathan Meeker, together with seven other agency employees and two civilian freighters carrying flour to the agency were all killed that day. An army column on its way to the White River Agency and led by Major Thomas Thornburgh came under attack by the hostile Utes. Major Thornburgh also perished in the fight.) French was promoted to the grade of First Lieutenant in 1888. During the 1890s he served at Fort Clark, Texas.

After the 1890s and during the next 21 years of military service, General French returned several times to the West in various capacities, including Inspector General of the Southwest Division. General Francis French's long and important military career resulted in his final promotion to Major-General. He served in the Philippine Islands, the Hawaiian Islands and was assigned to the War Department in Washington, D.C. and served in Europe during World War I. This lot is accompanied by General French's military records from the National Archives as well as copies of his letters from Colorado (1879-1880) which offer a firsthand account of his life amongst the Ute and Cheyenne Indians.

Christie's, Sale 8383, Lot 68, May 17, 2000.

Estimate: $60,000-$80,000

48076

CLASSIC NAVAJO MOKI STYLE MAN'S SERAPE FROM THE FRED HARVEY COLLECTION

Circa 1870
Length 73½ in. Width 53 in.

This striking wearing blanket features a unique pattern composed of full and halved serrated diamonds, each enclosing a colorful checkerboard design, and overlaying the fine Moki striped ground. The design is accented by two narrow strips of elongated parallelograms across the center and narrow white end bands. "While almost all classic and late classic Moki serapes are divided into horizontal zones, this Moki conforms to the classic format at work in Navajo bayeta serapes and poncho serapes: there is an overall design built around a central diamond, and each design element connects and extends the elements adjacent to it. The presence of checkered design motifs within the serrated diamonds is unique to this example, and echoes the plaid designs at work in historic Hopi bachelor blankets and prehistoric Anasazi ceramic ware."[1]

The yarns in this weaving are as follows: The dark reds are raveled bayeta, dyed with a combination of both lac and cochineal, measuring 5% lac and 95% cochineal (Dye analysis was provided by David Wenger, Ph.D.); the pinks are the same raveled bayeta recarded and respun with white to make pink; the blues are handspun dyed with indigo; the whites and browns are undyed handspun; and the green is handspun dyed with combinations of indigo and vegetal dyes.

"Moki, or Moqui, is a term the Spanish used to identify Hopi Indians, and both the Hopi and the Zuni also wove this style of blanket."[2] Moki style blankets are well illustrated in the literature. Thirty examples are illustrated by Nancy Blomberg in *Navajo Textiles: The William Randolph Hearst Collection*.(pp. 147-180) Tucson: University of Arizona Press, 1988, pp. 147-180. The author states: "First proposed by Mera in 1948, the term banded background is obviously descriptive of the somber blue and brown/black narrow striped ground common to each of these textiles. Despite the sameness of the ground, however, each piece can be unique, with significant variation appearing in the grouping of the stripes and the colorful designs superimposed upon them."[3]

Also, see: Whitaker, Kathleen. *Southwest Textiles: Weavings of the Navajo and Pueblo*. Seattle: University of Washington Press, 2002, pp. 134-151 for twelve examples; and Wheat, Joe Ben and Hedlund, Ann Lane (Ed.). *Blanket Weaving in the Southwest*. Tucson: University of Arizona Press, 2003, pp. 302-308 for seven examples.

Provenance

This serape was purchased by the Fred Harvey Company of Albuquerque, New Mexico, on November 22, 1902, from the Withs Collection and was assigned the inventory code "H9085 89324 DAXSS" and the description "Old Native Wool some bayeta Moki Pattern with squares Blue Red Green White". (See: Harvey Company ledgers housed at the Heard Museum, Phoenix, and the Museum of International Folk Art, Santa Fe.)

This serape is listed in a J.F. Huckel Collection inventory from 1933 as item number 3 of thirty pieces and described: "Very rare Hopi blanket. Ground of black and blue stripes with red Bayetta figures throughout; diamond design through center; half diamonds on the sides. Diamonds filled with checker designs in green, blue, pink and red." It was assigned the "highest" monetary value in Huckel's collection at that time of $1,500.00. The serape was consigned to the Harvey Company by Huckel's heirs for resale sometime between September, 1937, and July, 1939. It was assigned the new inventory code of 1209 B530615 and the description, "Huckel Coll #3 Old Hopi". (Again, reference the Harvey Company ledgers.)

The blanket was sold by the Harvey Company on April 7, 1940, to a family in Santa Barbara, California.

Sotheby's, Sale 7137, Lot 337, May 19, 1998.

References

[1]Joshua Baer, private correspondence, February 16, 1998.

[2]Whitaker, Kathleen. *Southwest Textiles Weavings of the Navajo and Pueblo*. Seattle: University of Washington Press, 2002, p. 134.

[3]Blomberg, Nancy. *Navajo Textiles: The William Randolph Hearst Collection*. Tucson: University of Arizona Press, 1988, pp. 147-180.

Estimate: $80,000-$120,000

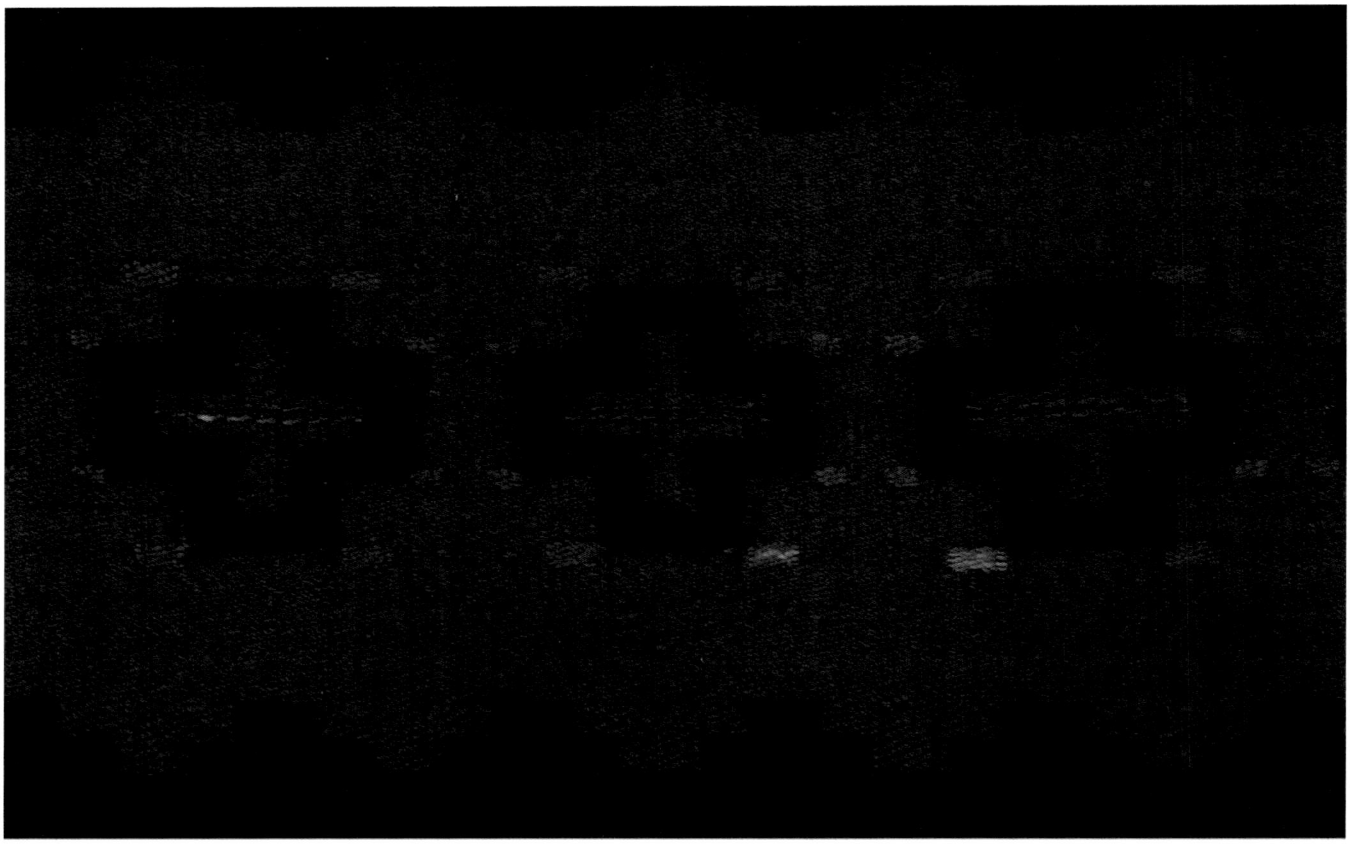

48077

CLASSIC NAVAJO WOMAN'S MANTA

Circa 1870
Length 41 in. Width 53½ in.

The design layout on this attractive manta features two bands of spider woman crosses set against the red background, a brown center, and indigo blue end zones. The indigo-dyed blue ends are done in a diamond twill weave while the rest is done in diagonal twill. "Predominant in Pueblo textiles from the days of the Anasazi through recent times, the various twill weave techniques were rarely used by Navajo weavers after 1800 but made a brief resurgence in popularity in the 1870s, particularly in the weaving of saddle throws and women's mantas. Twill weaves are considered to be sturdier than tapestry weaves... The twill weave mantas of the 1870s appear to be a revival of the earlier Pueblo style."

The materials in this classic weaving include cochineal-dyed red bayeta, indigo-dyed handspun in both light and dark blue, and natural brown handspun.

Provenance
David Cook, Fine American Art, Denver, Colorado.

Reference
Kaufman, Alice and Selser, Chris. *The Navajo Weaving Tradition: 1650 to the Present.* E.P. Dutton, Inc., New York, 1985, p. 138.

Estimate: $20,000-$30,000

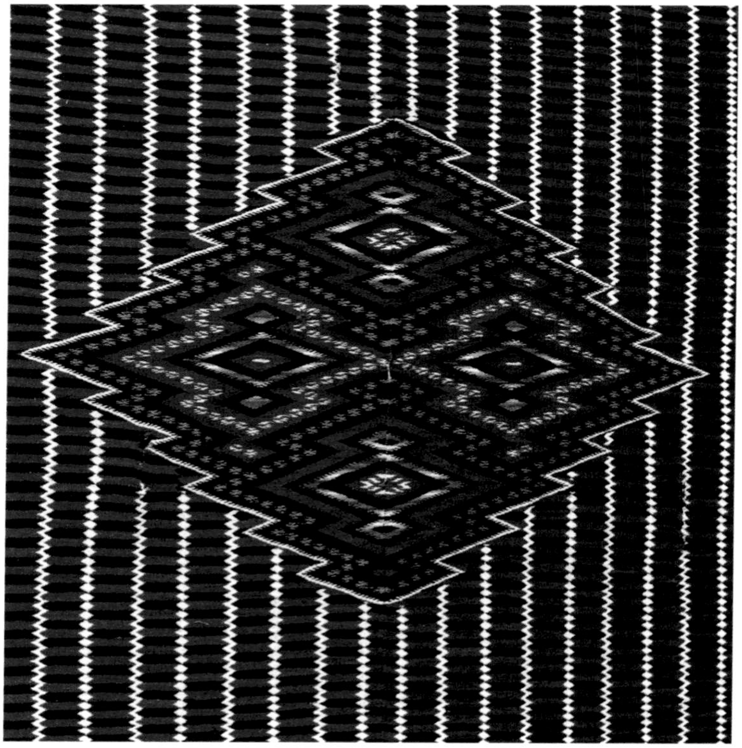

48078

SALTILLO SERAPE

Circa 1870
Length 78 in. Width 44½ in.

This wool blanket is finely woven in two sections, then sewn up the center. The design is a typical four diamond aggregate center with serrated edges. The background is a vertical mosaic field consisting of black and indigo blue bands, each row bordered with either a zigzag line in white or a row of diamonds in white. The weaving has a finely detailed border and banded end panels in indigo blue, black, red, and white.

Provenance
Butterfields, Sale 7307E, Lot 5388, March 25, 2002.

Estimate: $1,500-$2,500

48079

SALTILLO SERAPE

Circa 1870
Length 81½ in. Width 43½ in.

This wool blanket is finely woven in two sections, then sewn up in the center. The design is a typical four diamond aggregate center with serrated edges. The background is a vertical mosaic field of parallelograms framed by white zigzag bands with the resultant eye dazzler effect. The weaving has a finely detailed border and banded end panels in red, blue, green, white, yellow, pink, and black.

Provenance
Christie's, Sale 8317, Lot 369, December 1, 1999.

Estimate: $1,500-$2,500

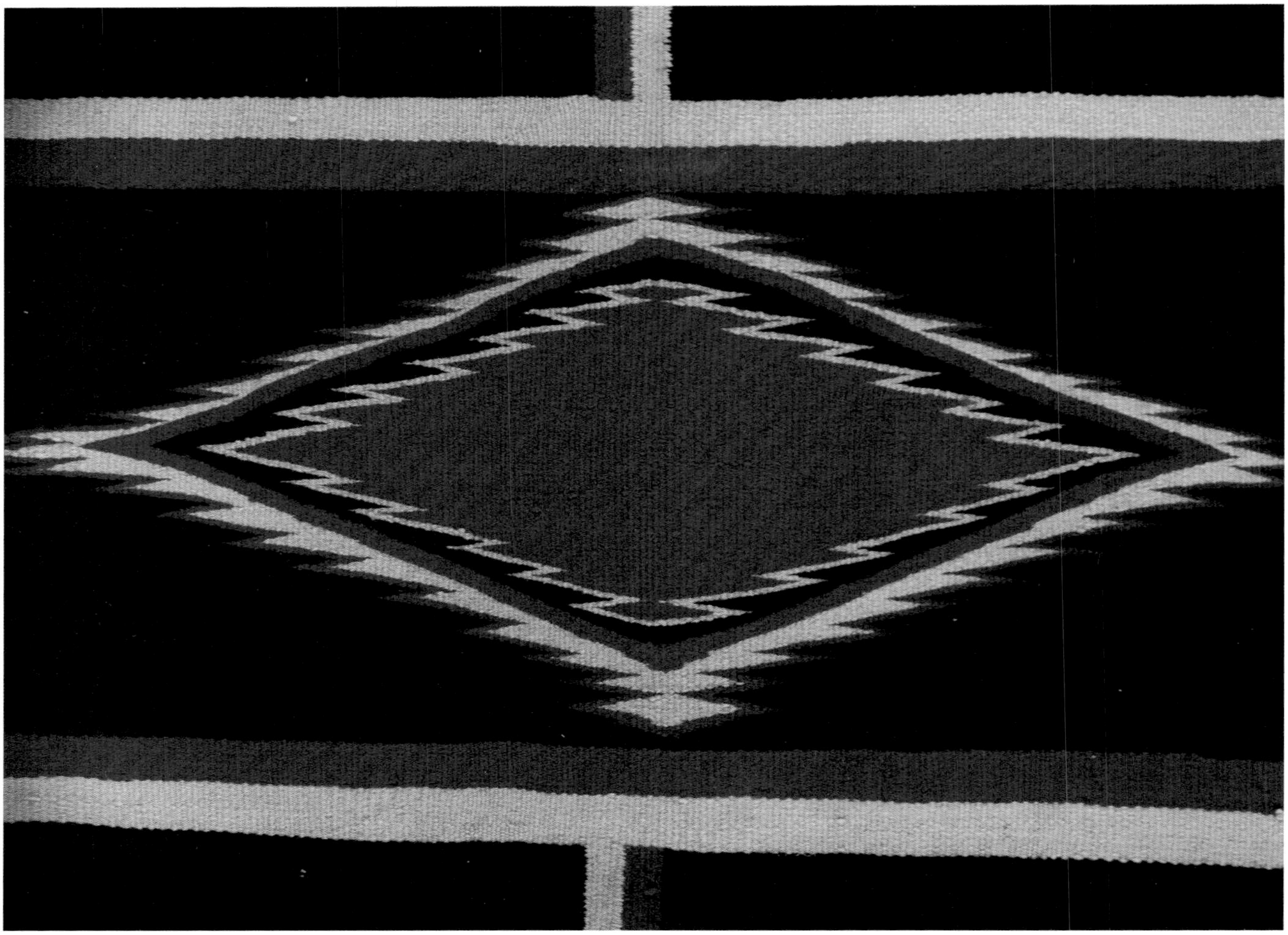

48080

NAVAJO GERMANTOWN MOKI BLANKET

Circa 1890
Length 87 in. Width 60 in.

This large, tightly woven Hubbell revival blanket is done in four-ply, aniline-dyed, Germantown yarns. The design features are laid out in a serape pattern with the central and end bands decorated with serrated diamonds in red and white against the black and blue Moki stripe background. The remaining field is crossed with plain and tracked lines in red and white over the Moki stripes.

Two Moki style blankets with this identical pattern are in the collections of the Southwest Museum in Los Angeles. "It is believed this pattern originated with a weaver either employed by or living near Hubbell Trading Post at the turn of the twentieth century. Although not traced to the Hubbell rug study, it is believed blankets with this pattern were regularly sold to tourists."

Provenance
Sotheby's, Sale 7137, Lot 348, May 19, 1998.

Reference
Whitaker, Kathleen. *Southwest Textiles: Weavings of the Navajo and Pueblo*. Seattle: University of Washington Press, 2002, pp. 140-141

Estimate: $15,000-$20,000

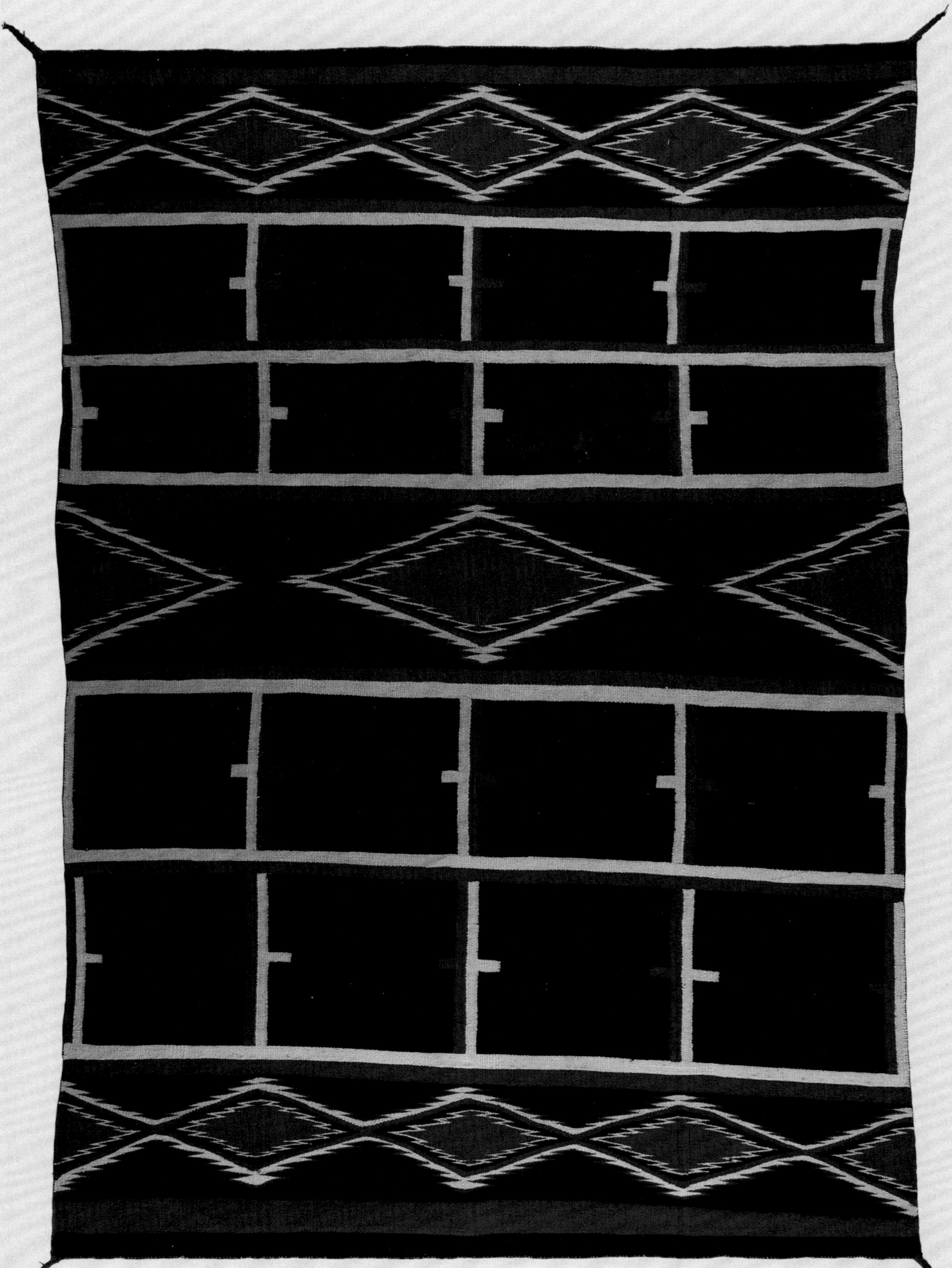

48081

NAVAJO YEI RUG

Circa 1930
Length 56½ in. Width 80 in.

This pictorial weaving features a central cornstalk motif flanked by four Yei figures holding feathers in each hand and wearing necklaces, earrings, and concho belts. "The Ye'ii tapestry is popular among tourists because of its symbolic content. While not sacred in themselves, and not used by the Navajo in rituals, such tapestries are copies of figures seen in Navajo sand paintings. The latter are compositions drawn by medicine men with colored sand and other dry materials, which are used when curing the sick. The sand paintings must be destroyed the same day, which is why some weavers are sensitive about re-creating their images."

Reference
Whitaker, Kathleen. *Southwest Textiles: Weavings of the Navajo and Pueblo.* Seattle: University of Washington Press, 2002, p. 271.

Estimate: $3,000-$5,000

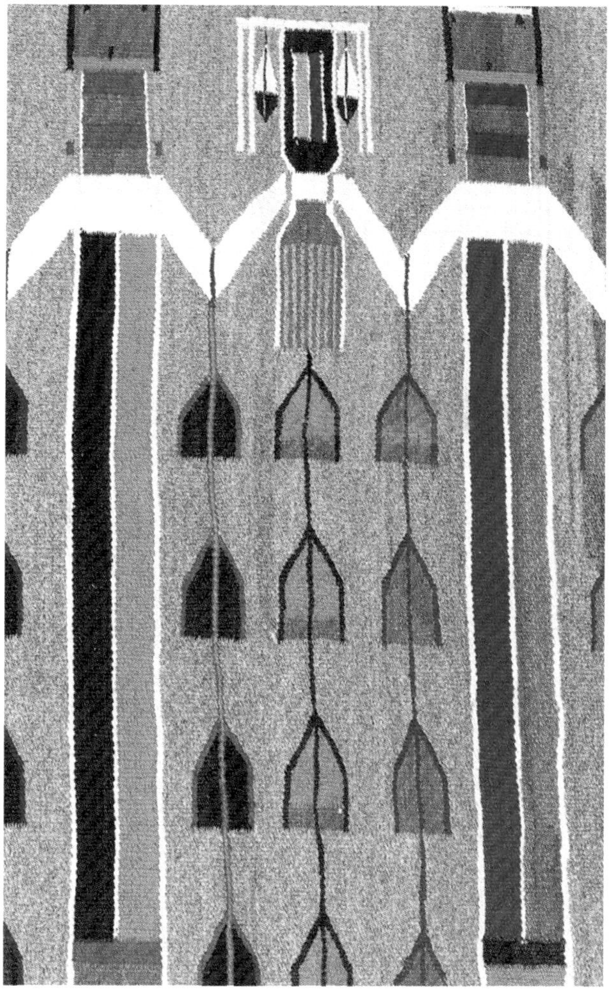

48082

NAVAJO YEI RUG

Circa 1930
Length 64 in. Width 84 in.

This pictorial weaving features five elongated Yei figures with upraised and linking arms. Feathered bands are tied to their hands and arms. The Yei figures are wearing kilts and earrings. The entire composition is enclosed within a red and dark brown border. The rug is woven in red, white, orange, black, and brown, all against a gray background, using both natural and aniline dyed wool.

Provenance
Christie's, Sale 8383, Lot 60, May 17, 2000.

Estimate: $3,000-$5,000

48083

NAVAJO RUG – TEEC NOS POS

Circa 1940
Length 106 in. Width 62 in.

This classic example of the well-known regional style is finely woven in natural and aniline-dyed wool. The weaving is characterized by a complex design of arrow and feather motifs, step patterns, triangles, etc. all outlined with a distinct color and set against the gray background.

Provenance
Bonhams and Butterfields, Sale 7477E, Lot 3393, December 8, 2003.

Estimate: $10,000-$15,000

48084

NAVAJO THIRD PHASE CHIEF'S PATTERN RUG

Circa 1920
Length 51 in. Width 74 in.

The design pattern on this rug is a variant of the classic third phase chief's blanket. It is woven in both natural and aniline dyed wool. The rug is characterized by three horizontal bands of diamond elements, the large diamonds filled in with smaller stepped diamonds and crosses, done in navy blue, green, red, and orange, and alternating with plain bands of white and brown homespun yarn. This style of regional weaving is known as a Red Mesa Outline in reference to the location and the treatment of design elements.

Provenance
Collected by a teacher at the He Dog School on the Rosebud Indian Reservation, South Dakota during the 1920s.
Larry Ness, Yankton, South Dakota.

Estimate: $3,000-$4,000

48085

NAVAJO PICTORIAL RUG FROM THE LUKACHUKAI REGION

Length 100 in. Width 60 in.

This charming rug is woven in varying colors and shades of natural and aniline dyed wool with a depiction of the landscape on the Navajo Reservation. Pictorial elements include hogans, weavings in progress on their looms, a corral and water tank, sheep and cattle, jack rabbits and birds, a highway with pickup trucks, and a mountain backdrop. This rug was woven by Ruth Tsosie in 1973. It comes with a second place ribbon from the "Annual Southwestern Indian Arts Festival, 1973".

Provenance
Christie's, Sale 1332, Lot 21, January 12, 2004.

Estimate: $2,000-$3,000

Plains

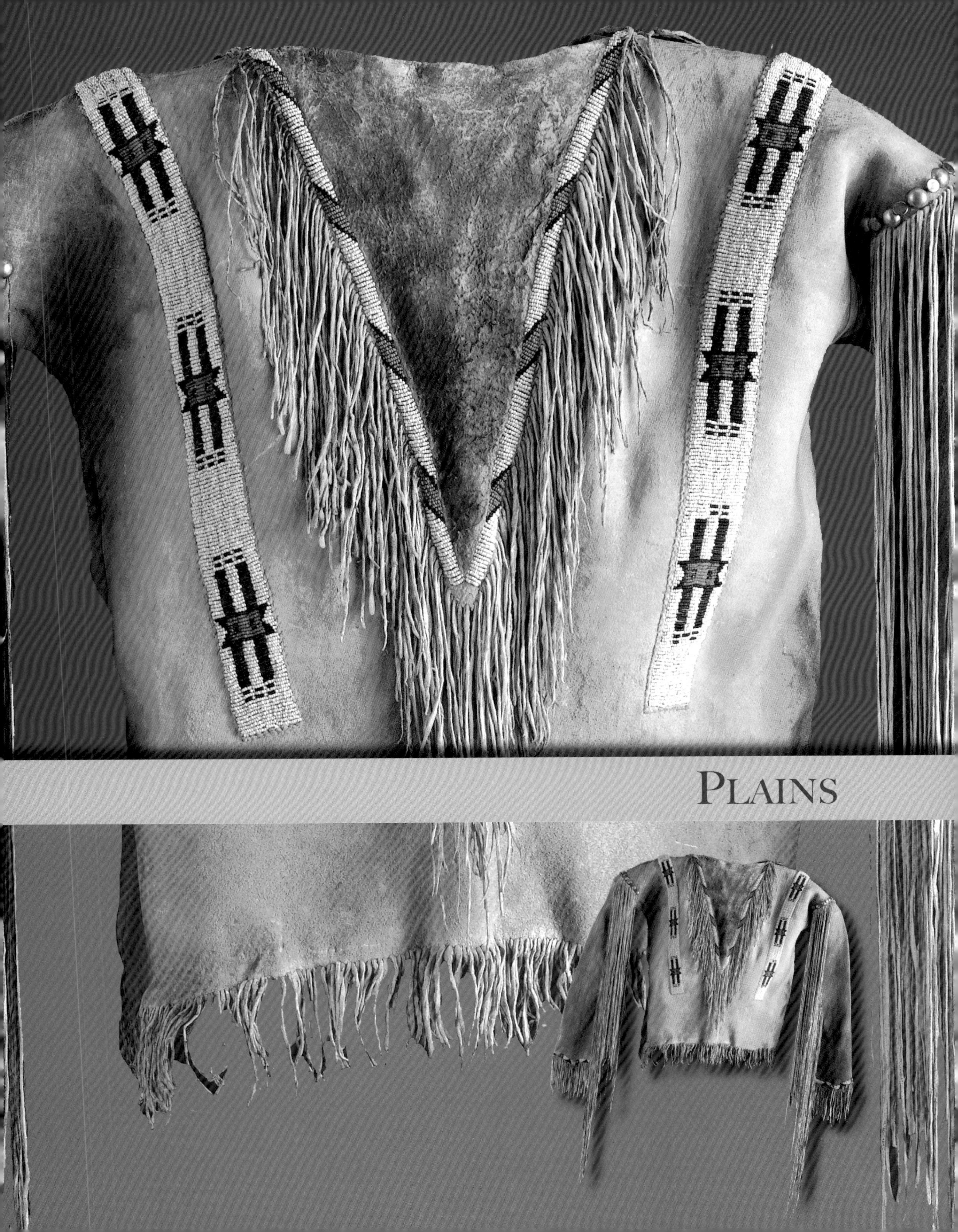

48086

EASTERN SIOUX COUNCIL PIPE WITH ORNATE LEAD INLAID STEM AND BOWL

Circa 1865
Length 47 in. overall

This council pipe has a flat and slightly tapering ash wood stem, elaborately decorated along its length with lead inlay in a pattern of acorns and leaves. The catlinite "T" shaped bowl is inlaid with two bands of crosses, their form reminiscent of Christian crosses made by Montreal silversmiths for the Indian trade.

Before the advent of fixed ammunition Indian people needed lead bullets for their muzzle loading firearms. Traders supplied both bullet molds and lead to meet this demand. Lead has a low melting point (621° Fahrenheit) so native people easily mastered the technology. Lead inlay was a common decorative element on pipe bowls. However, there are almost no examples of lead inlay being applied to pipestems. This stem is notable for its unique and lavish inlay.

Provenance
Ralph Olson, Deerfield, Illinois.

Estimate: $10,000-$15,000

48087

EASTERN SIOUX PIPE BOWL AND STEM

Circa 1870
Length 28½ in. overall

The ash wood stem has been carved in an even spiral pattern its entire length. An elbow shaped catlinite bowl is fitted to the stem. An open hand is carved in relief on the front of the bowl and a scalloped pattern on the underside.

Spiral carved or "twisted" pipestems were popular in the western Great Lakes (Chippewa, Potawatomi, Menominee, and Winnebago) and extended to both the Eastern Sioux (Dakota) and Western Sioux (Lakota). Contrary to some references and conjecture, the wood stem was not steamed and twisted. Rather, it was patiently worked, the artist taking care not to break into the smoke channel. Fine examples such as this represent the sophisticated product of the carver's art.

Provenance
Brant Mackley, Hummelstown, Pennsylvania.

Estimate: $6,000-$8,000

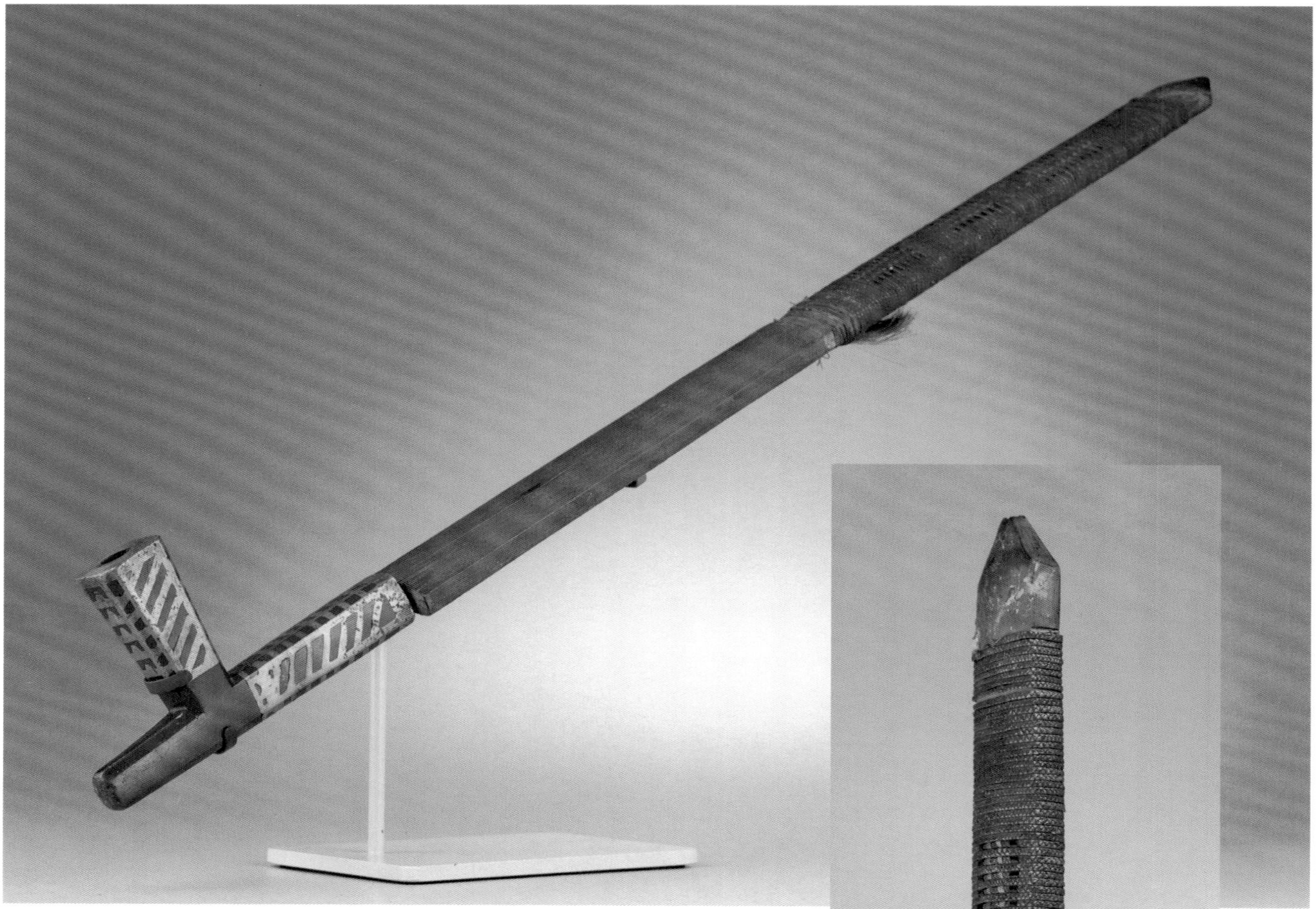

48088

SIOUX PIPE BOWL AND STEM

Circa 1875
Length 27¼ in. overall

The ash wood stem is decorated with finely plaited porcupine quillwork in red dyed quills. A simple design pattern has been created on the upper side as the black and yellow quills cross over and under the two thread red quill bands in alternating rows. A tuft of dyed red horsehair decorates the underside. The stem is fitted to a catlinite "T" shaped bowl with extensive lead inlay set in a pattern of diagonal stripes and small squares.

Provenance
Collected by Milford Chandler before 1926. His collection numbers painted in red on the pipe bowl and stem—C647 and C494.

Estimate: $4,000-$6,000

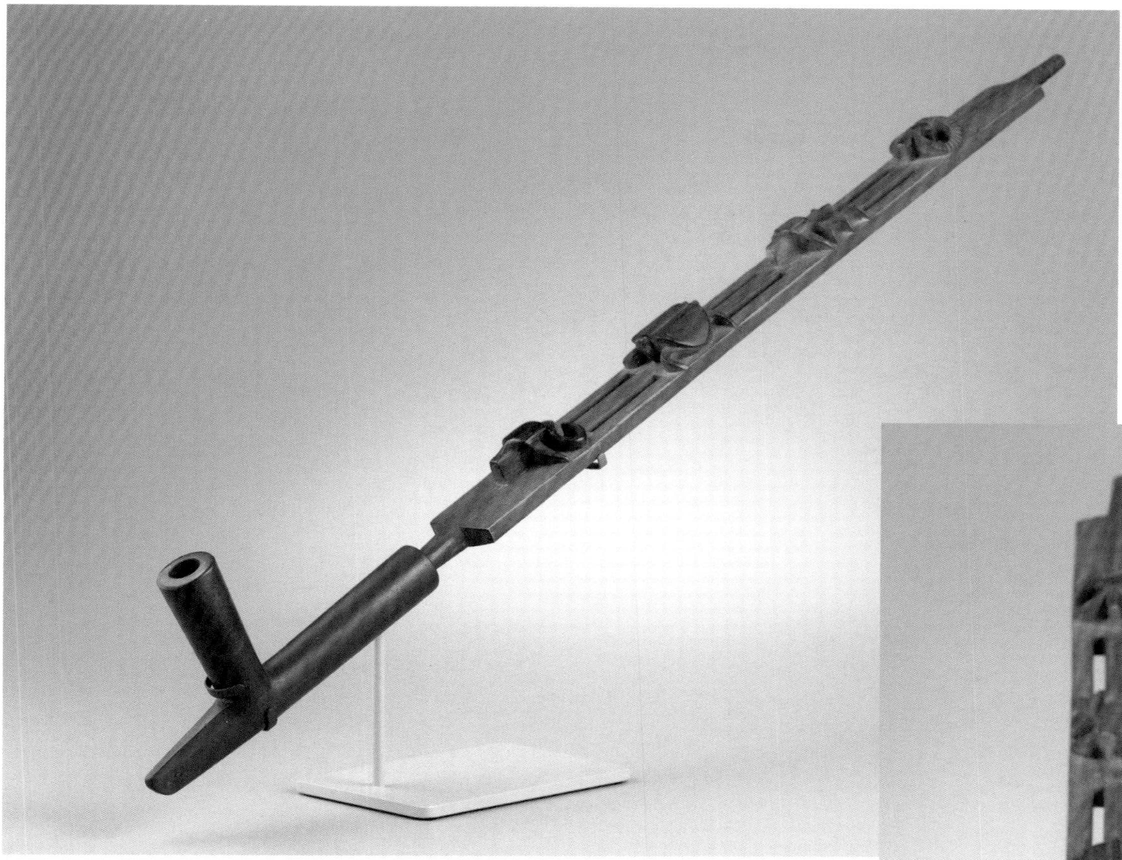

48089

SIOUX PIPE BOWL AND EFFIGY CARVED STEM

Circa 1885
Length 30 in. overall

This ash wood stem is finely carved in high relief along its length with a big horn ram head, an elk head, a turtle, and a buffalo head. The stem is pierced with six narrow, rectangular cutouts. A plain catlinite "T" shaped bowl accompanies the stem.

This distinctive type of pipestem is frequently associated with the Standing Rock Indian Reservation. John Ewers comments upon them in *Plains Indian Sculpture*. In reference to a similar example he writes, "After viewing a photograph of this pipestem, Beatrice Medicine, the Hunkpapa Sioux ethnologist, told me that this was the kind of work done by Crazy Bear, a Sioux on Standing Rock Reservation." Numerous stems exist in public and private collections with slight variations on the basic design concept exemplified here. Some examples have partially quill wrapped stems and fewer figures. Examination indicates that several carvers were at work and their manufacture probably extended to other reservations in the Dakotas. These pipestems enjoyed widespread popularity among Indian people and were eagerly sought by early collectors. This stem can be compared with one held by the Sioux Chief No Neck in two George Spencer cabinet card photos in this sale (Lot 48214 and Lot 48215).

Provenance
Gallery West, Tucson, Arizona.

Reference
Ewers, John C., *Plains Indian Sculpture*, Smithsonian Institution Press, Washington, D.C., 1986, pp. 112 and 113.

Estimate: $6,000-$9,000

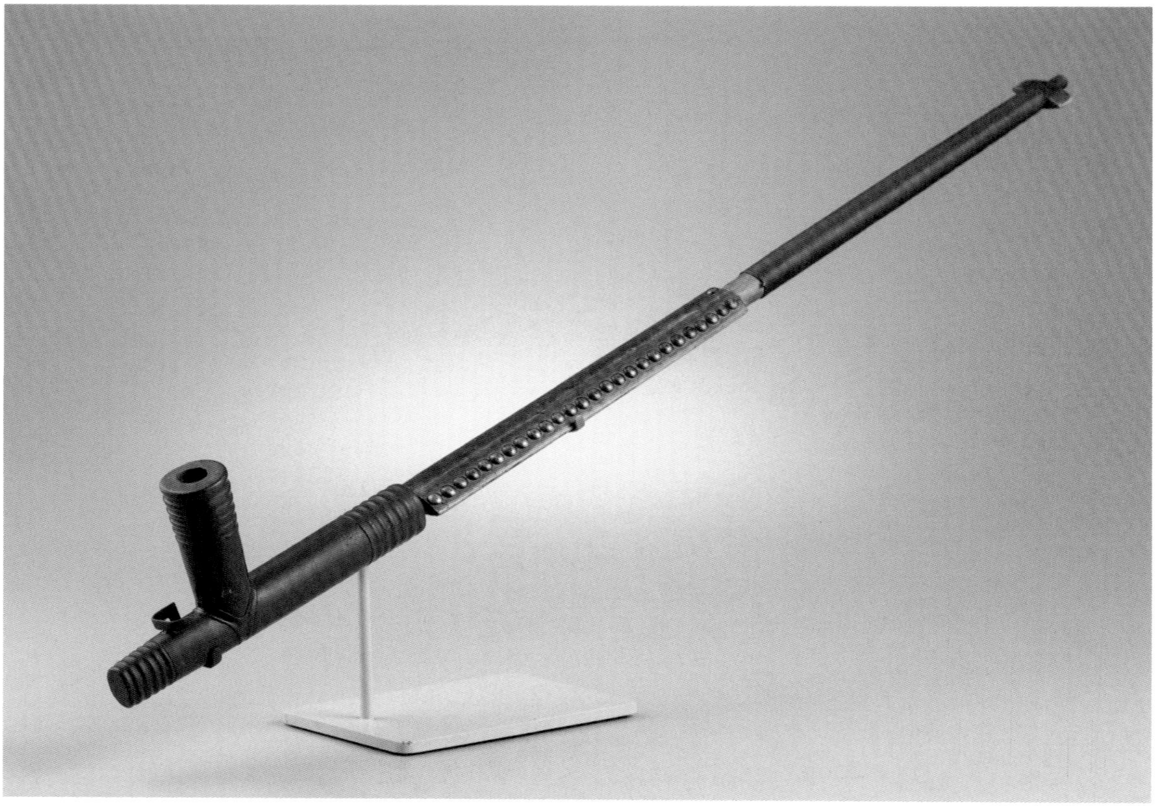

48090

SIOUX PIPE BOWL AND STEM WRAPPED WITH COPPER TELEGRAPH WIRE

Circa 1880
Length 28½ in. overall

The ash wood stem is wrapped with copper wire along half its length. A row of brass upholstery tacks decorates the flat section. The stem is accompanied by a catlinite "T" shaped bowl artfully carved with circular decorative bands. Brass wire was a coveted item and Indian traders made an effort to have quantities available. Brass wire was even included in annuity payments to the tribes. It was used to make earrings, bracelets, and armbands for both men and women. Tomahawk handles and pipestems were occasionally wrapped with brass wire for decorative effect. Copper, however, was used for telegraph wire and it is interesting to speculate on the source of wire for this pipestem.

Provenance
James Hart, Acquisition, Inc., Maple Shade, New Jersey.

Reference
Hanson, James. *Metal Weapons, Tools, and Ornaments of the Teton Dakota Indians.* University of Nebraska Press, Lincoln, 1975, pp. 98-100.

Estimate: $3,000-$5,000

48091

AN INTACT AND COMPLETE ALBUM OF 30 WALTER BONE SHIRT DRAWINGS
PINE RIDGE RESERVATION, SOUTH DAKOTA

c. 1887-88
Leather album, colored pencil, and ink
$5 \times 7\frac{7}{8}$ inches

Provenace
Marcy Burns, New York, New York
Gallery West, Tuscon, Arizona

Estimate: $400,000-$600,000

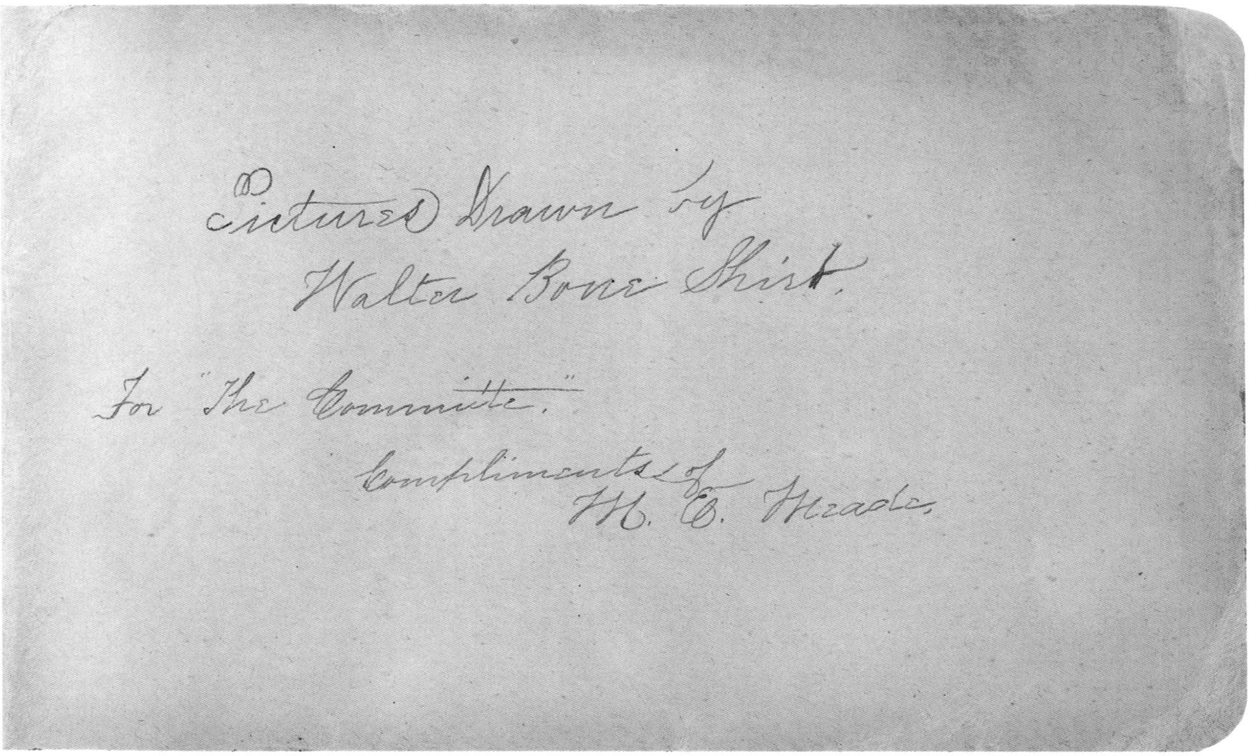

Dedication Page

1

2

3

4

5

6

7

8

9

10

11

12

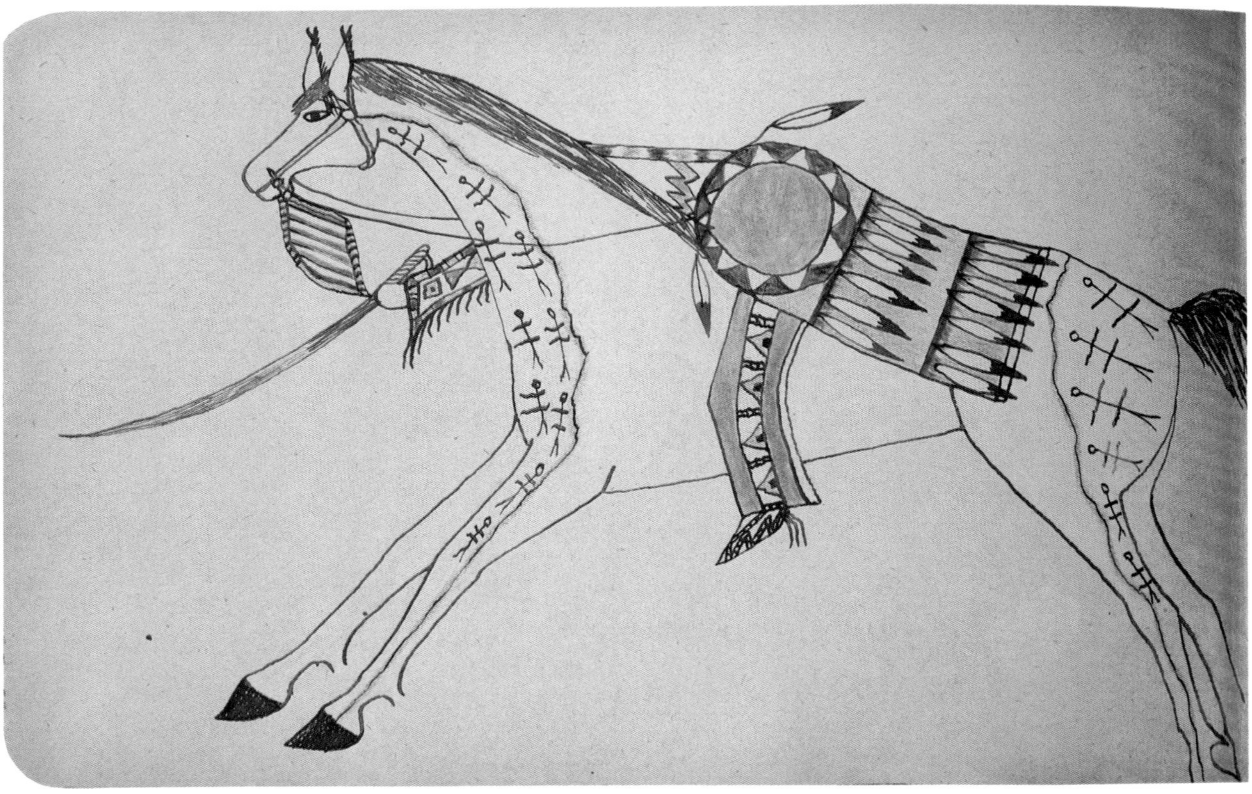

13

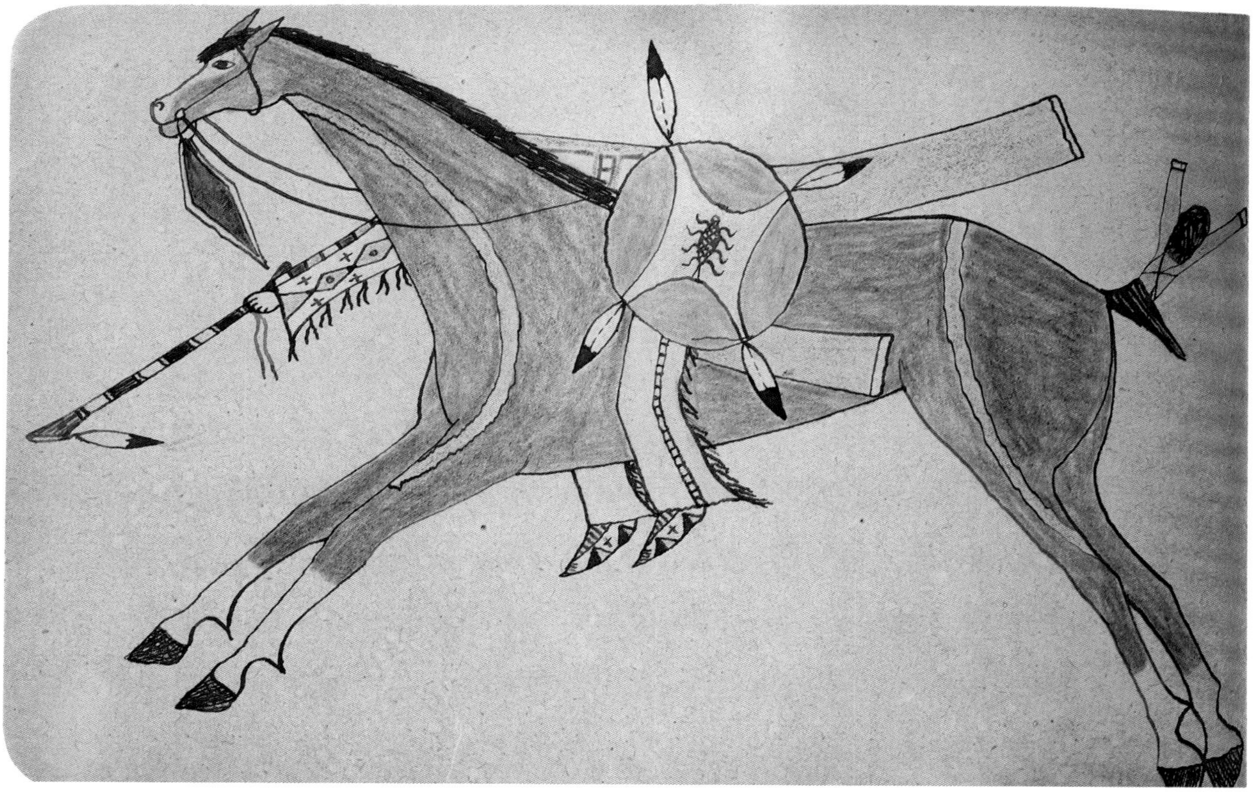

14

15

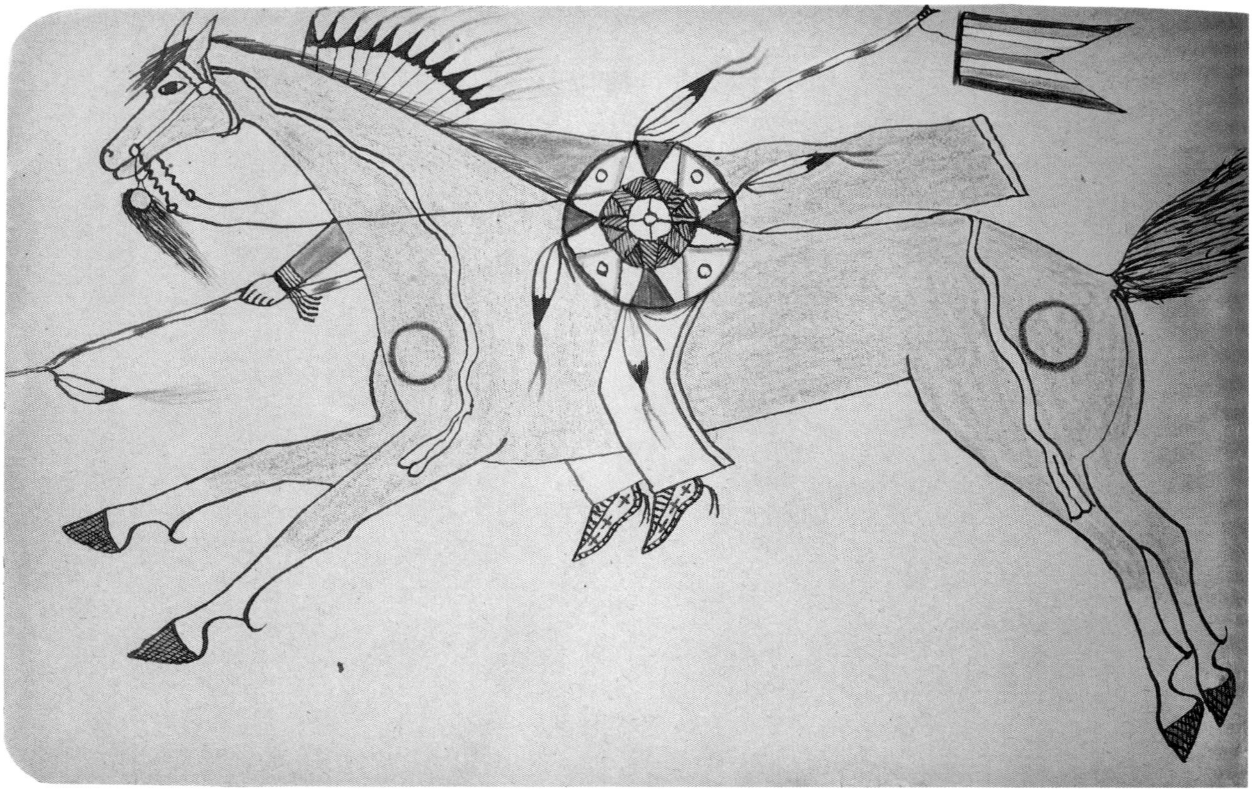

16

17

18

19

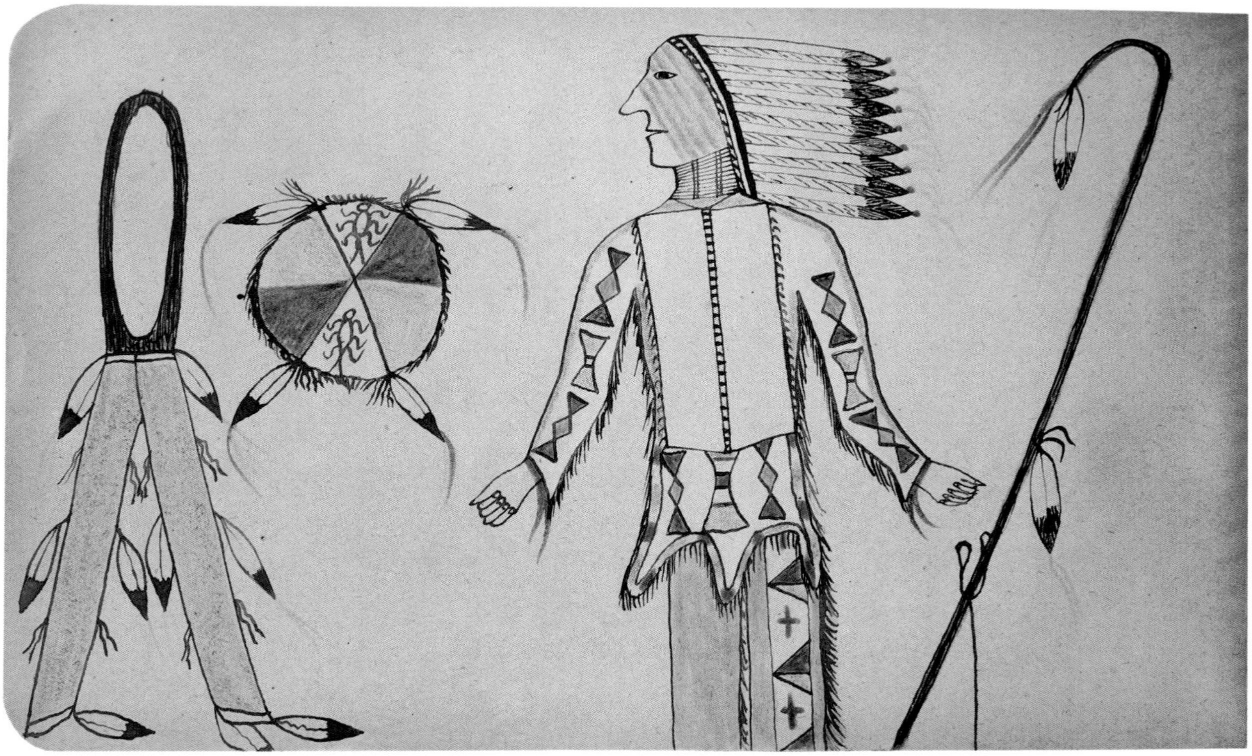

20

21

22

23

24

25

26

27

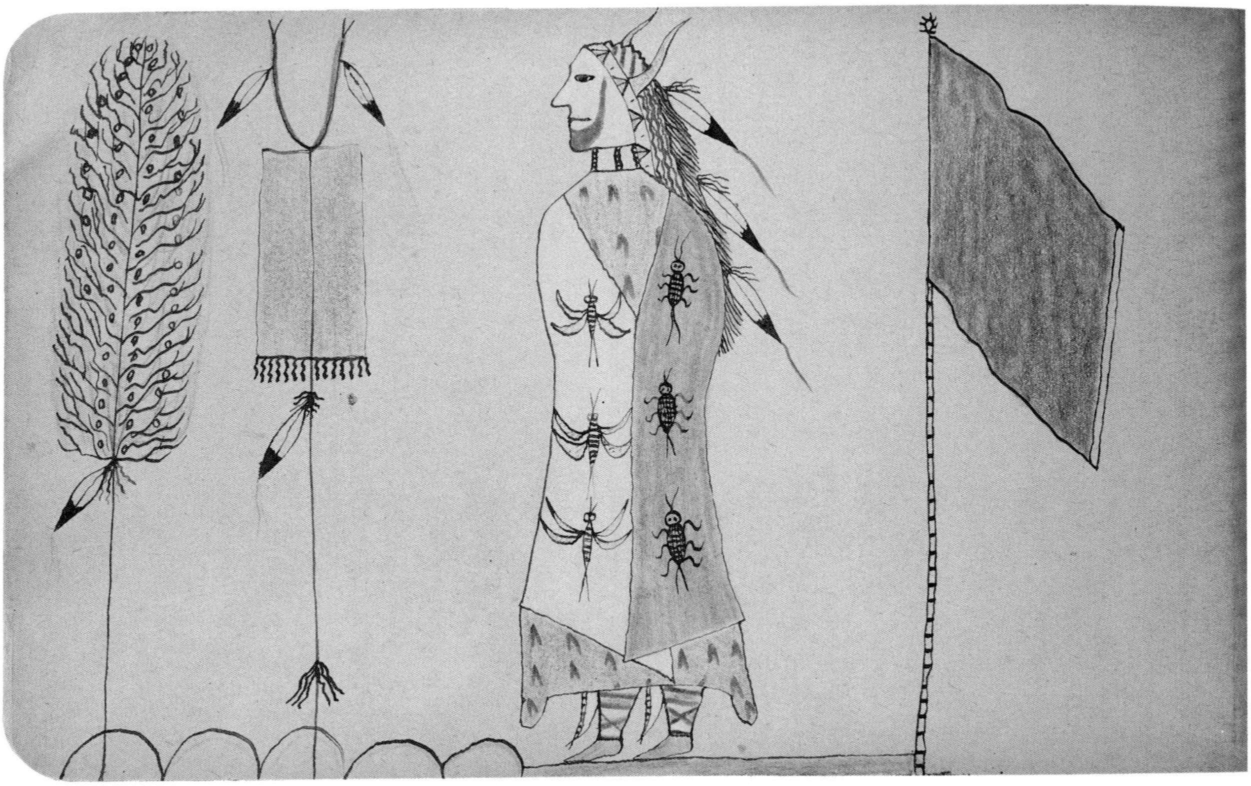

28

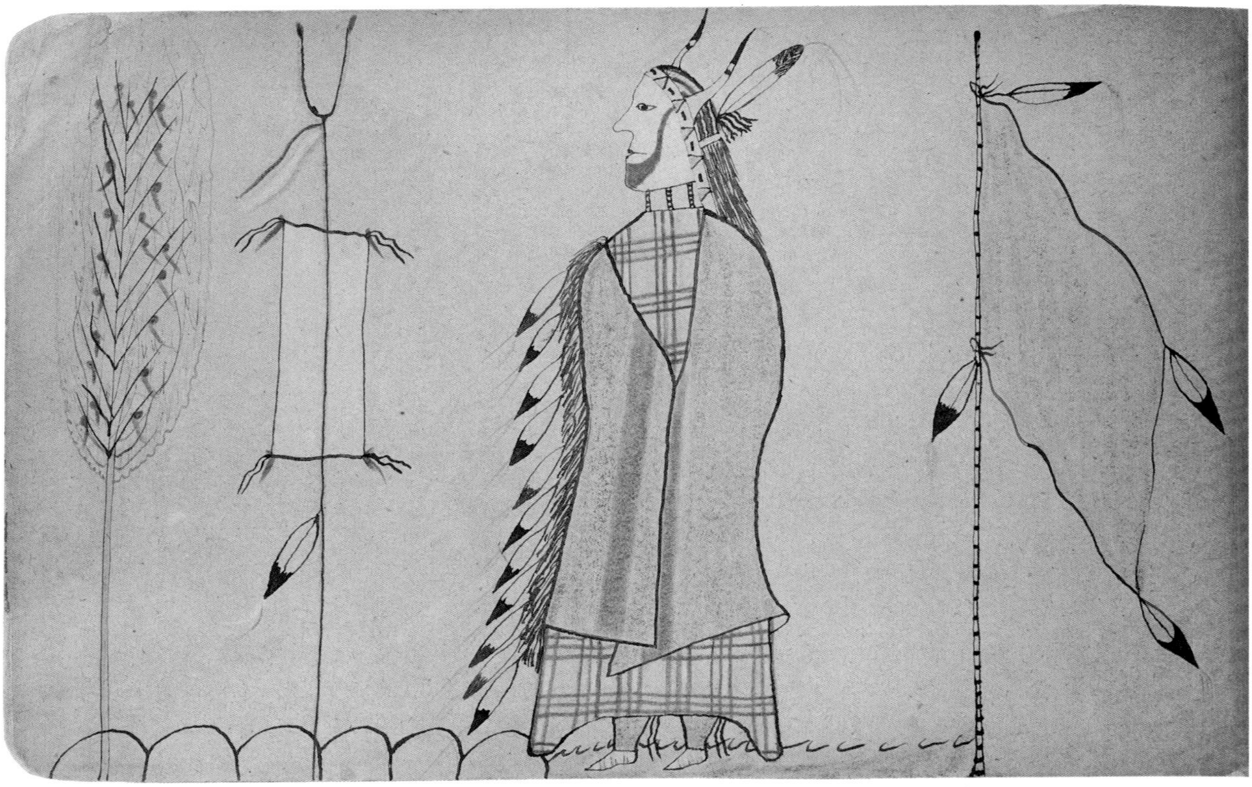

29

30

THE SUN DANCE LEDGER OF "NEVER MISSES," CALLED WALTER BONE SHIRT

IDENTIFYING THE ARTIST

The flyleaf of this book of drawings is inscribed by "M.E. Meade". Despite the spelling discrepancy, this is believed to have been Mary Eliza Mead, whose husband operated a trading post on the Pine Ridge Reservation, South Dakota. In a memoir of her life Mary wrote: "When we lived at the Agency, I made a collection of Indian bead work, porcupine quill work and other Indian handiwork, buckskin beaded women's dresses, men's buckskin and cloth shirts beaded and fringed, tobacco sacks, pipestone pipes and tomahawks, war clubs, bows and arrows, beaded gun cases, bow and arrow quivers, children's beaded and fringed jackets, which I hung from the walls and ridge poles of the house. They were much admired" (*Western Nebraska Churchman*, April & May, 1927). Mary Mead and her husband moved to Pine Ridge in the 1880s, and were present through the chaos of 1890-91.

Three other collections of drawings by this artist are known to survive. In the University of Montana Libraries, Missoula, 18 drawings were received without documentation from the daughter of Lt. John S. Parke, who obtained them while serving as military commander at the Rosebud Reservation, South Dakota, in 1890-91, during the Ghost Dance uprising (see: www.lib.umt.edu/research/digitalcollections/ledger.htm). Another 18 drawings now in the Detroit Institute of Arts, also undocumented except as to location of origin, were collected directly from James G. Wright, who was Agent of the Rosebud Reservation 1889-96. A third collection of 13 drawings in the same, distinctive style is in the Gilcrease Museum, Tulsa, Oklahoma. This is entirely undocumented, save for written inscriptions in Lakota and English on two of the pages saying that "This book belongs to Charles Good Boy," and the Lakota nickname *Can Wohn*.

Figure 1. Red Warrior *(Akicize Luta)*, called Alfred John Bone Shirt, a younger brother of the artist, while performing with the Pawnee Bill Wild West Show. Photo by Erwin E. Smith, Boston, Massachusetts, June, 1908. Erwin E. Smith Collection of the Library of Congress on Deposit at the Amon Carter Museum, Fort Worth, Texas, Neg. No. LC-S6-331.

The important book of 30 drawings addressed herewith is accompanied by a dedicatory page which attributes them as the work of "Walter Bone Shirt". This also identifies the artist of the other collections. The 1900 U.S. Federal Census of Meyer County, South Dakota (later divided into parts of present Mellette and Todd counties, and incorporating the Rosebud Reservation) lists three "Heads of Household" by the name of Bone Shirt, a father and two sons. The elder man, identified simply as "Bone Shirt," (*Hohu Ogle* in the Lakota language, which refers to a breastplate of tubular, bone beads called "hairpipes", such as those shown in **Figs. 1 & 12**) was born in 1830, and was married to Plenty Bugs, (*Wabluska Ota*, called Anna Bone Shirt, b. 1835). Their eldest son, identified on the census as "Junior Bone Shirt", was born in 1856, and was married to War Bonnet Woman (b. 1863). No children resided with them. Neither "Junior" nor his wife (nor the Bone Shirts, Sr.), could speak, read or write English. A second son Red Battle, or Red Warrior (*Akicize Luta*—see **Fig. 1**), called Alfred John Bone Shirt (b. 1875) was married to White Cow Goes Out (called Susie Bone Shirt, b. 1877). Both could read, write and speak English, indicating they had been through a program of schooling. They had one son, Thomas, born in 1898. A third son, the same age as Alfred John—they may have been twins—is listed as "David Bone Shirt" on the 1890 census of Rosebud Reservation. His Lakota name is given as *Kahna Wanica* (Has No Shavings). It seems very likely that the inscription on the Gilcrease collection was made by this son. In struggling to frame the Lakota syllables in Roman characters, *Can Wohn* was David's best solution. And as one brother was "Alfred John," the other was "David Charles."

Figure 2. Two Strike (*Num Capa*), Head Chief of the Brule Lakota. Photo by Alexander M. Gardner, 1872. Amon Carter Museum, Fort Worth, Texas, P1967-3159.

It is extremely unlikely that the elder Bone Shirt could have been the artist, because none of the 79 known drawings depicts any battle exploits. To document one's battle prowess, (and by extension, one's social position) was the primary purpose of drawing for all Lakota men who lived during the mid-19th century. The fact that this artist shows NO battle exploits denotes that he must have been too young to have acquired any.

Similarly, it is unlikely that either of the youngest Bone Shirt brothers could have been the artist, because both were only 14 or 15 years old in 1890-91, when most of these drawings were obtained. They may have been created several years earlier, so the two younger sons were probably too young to have acquired the intense experience of the Sun Dance ceremony which is detailed throughout these collections.

The elder son therefore, called Junior Bone Shirt, is the most likely candidate. A traditionalist, full-blood Lakota, three of his grandparents were Brule, and his maternal grandfather was a Blackfeet Lakota. Junior Bone Shirt was 34 years old in 1890. He might actually have been named "Walter" (either in files of the Rosebud Agency; or the Episcopal or Catholic church), but everyone in the community just called him "Junior," which in the Lakota language would be *Cinca* (pronounced CHEEN-cha), meaning "son of". On a partial census conducted at Spotted Tail Agency in 1877, the Lakota name of Bone Shirt's eldest son is given as "Never Misses" (Federal Archives and Records Center, Kansas City, Record Group 75. We are indebted to William Wierzbowski for this important detail).

Where Junior Bone Shirt lived is also significant. Subsequent to the assassination of Spotted Tail in 1881, the senior chief of the Brule Lakota tribe was Two Strike (*Num Capa*—**Fig. 2**). On the 1900 census, Two Strike is listed as "Head of Household #43;" and Junior Bone Shirt was "Head of Household #46." Several children of Iron Shell, another, noted Brule chief, are listed on the same page of the 1900 census as Junior Bone Shirt, indicating extensive connections at the highest level of Brule society. It was traditional for Brule men to join the family group of their wife. It is likely, therefore, that Never Misses, called Junior Bone Shirt, was married either to a daughter of Two Strike, or of Iron Shell, and by that connection was related to both chiefs.

Junior Bone Shirt was only 14 years old when Spotted Tail and his lieutenant Two Strike took their people to the White River Agency in 1870. Later they moved to "Spotted Tail Agency", now the Rosebud Reservation. This ended the active period of warfare for most Brule males—certainly for the families of both chiefs—so Junior Bone Shirt is unlikely to have had any opportunity to go to war. This would account for the absence of personal battle exploits among his compositions.

In addition to being the senior Brule political leader, Two Strike was also a Sun Dance sponsor and leader. His great-great-grandchildren *still* sponsor a well-attended Sun Dance ceremony each summer at the Two Strike Community, near St. Francis, South Dakota. As Junior Bone Shirt was a close adherent, and probably a relative of Chief Two Strike, it is likely that he was an established *Itancan* (Ee-TAWN-chon), or priest of the Sun Dance ceremony. Certainly he was old enough to have participated many times. In the collection of 18 "Bone Shirt" drawings at Detroit Institute of Arts, two compositions (pages 3a & 19) are identified as Sun Dance leaders, and may be self-portraits. Similar drawings exist in this collection (**Plates 7 – 10**).This clarifies how Bone Shirt could have had the intimate knowledge necessary to produce drawings of this cultural content and detail.

HISTORICAL CONTEXT

During the Wounded Knee troubles in 1890-91, after the assassination of Sitting Bull on December 15, 1890, the Two Strike *tiyośpaye* (or extended family community) fled westward from Rosebud to join the traditionalist "hostiles" in the badlands of the Pine Ridge Reservation. In fact, Brules from Two Strike's camp were the first relief party to arrive at the Wounded Knee battlefield, and bring back a few, badly-injured survivors (Utley, 1963: 231-32). This historical certainty places Junior Bone Shirt at precisely the time and location that the M.E. Mead collection of Walter Bone Shirt drawings was acquired.

Figure 3. Two Strike informing members of his band that they would surrender, and move from their camp in the Badlands to Pine Ridge Agency. Photo by Northwestern Photo Company, January 30, 1891. Denver Public Library, Western History Collection, Neg. No. X-31289.

Two weeks later, Two Strike was centrally involved in arranging the surrender of the hostile camp. He was photographed by the Northwestern Photo Company giving the surrender oration (**Fig.3**). Although we do not have an identified portrait of Junior Bone Shirt, he certainly was one of the people in that assemblage. At that sensitive and dangerous time, Two Strike may personally have been the conduit by which the drawings of his relative were perhaps presented to an Army officer, who later conveyed them to Mary Eliza Mead. Or after the surrender, the drawings may have been given or traded to Mrs. Mead directly at her husband's Pine Ridge store. The Brules were interned at Pine Ridge through the late spring of 1891 (**Fig. 4**).

When the Two Strike exiles returned to Rosebud, they were taken in charge by the military commander there, Lt. John S. Parke, whose *other* collection of Bone Shirt drawings now reside at University of Montana Libraries, Missoula (see McCrea, 2006). Again, it is likely that Two Strike personally was responsible for presenting an elegant gift to smooth the homecoming of his band.

Figure 4. Members of the Two Strike band, while interned at Pine Ridge Agency. Photo by Solomon D. Butcher (?), spring 1891. Denver Public Library, Western History Collection, Neg. No. X-31767.

The other, known Bone Shirt drawings now in the Chandler-Pohrt collection at Detroit Institute of Arts, were obtained by Milford G. Chandler from James G. Wright, who was Agent at Rosebud, 1889-1896, and was the *other* government official with whom Two Strike needed to establish good relations upon his return in 1891 (on Wright's tenure, see Foreman, 1942: 120-121; and Hamilton & Hamilton, 1971: 88-89).

The circumstances of acquisition for three of the four Bone Shirt collections, therefore, suggest that these beautiful drawings may have played a role in mitigating the very desperate plight of the Brule people, immediately following the massacre at Wounded Knee.

HISTORICAL SEQUENCE AND APPROXIMATE DATES

All four of the Walter Bone Shirt collections depict Sun Dance scenes, but each shows a unique assemblage of participants, and variant activities. This suggests that each collection is the individual record of a particular ceremony, in different years. In the 19th century it was unusual for an individual to pledge participation in the grueling ceremony more than once (a requirement was abstention from food and water for long periods in temperatures often above 100 degrees). The fact that Bone Shirt was involved in multiple years is further, direct evidence that his role was as one of the *Itancans*, or spiritual leaders.

Three of the Bone Shirt collections passed into White ownership in early 1891. The three, annual ceremonies these drawings document, therefore, occurred no later than 1888-1890. Though one or another may have been slightly earlier, probably all occurred post-1885. Progression in the artist's style suggests the order in which the three collections were created, and therefore reasonably close dates of their origin.

The horse figures in the Meade collection, while beautifully drawn, are more tentative and less polished than those in the collections at Detroit, Missoula and Tulsa. Bone Shirt was still experimenting with proportion, so that the horses in the Meade compositions are all rather long bodied. The poses are also repetitive, without the innovative positions achieved in some of his later compositions (compare Feder, 1972: 84; and Penny, 1992: 290-293). The Meade drawings are, therefore, the earliest of the Bone Shirt collections, created ca. 1887-88. In this writer's opinion, the Detroit collection was created next, ca. 1888-89. The Missoula drawings are the most polished, and hence a bit later, recording the Brule Sun Dance ceremony of 1889 or 1890.

The 13 drawings in the Gilcrease collection are very similar to those at Missoula, done in Bone Shirt's most mature style. In the opinion of this author they were made a few years later still, during the mid-1890s, and given by Junior Bone Shirt to his younger brother David Charles, who then inscribed them. Ration records for Rosebud Reservation indicate that on March 27, 1894, Junior Bone Shirt joined the Pawnee Bill Wild West Show for its first tour of the eastern United States. The drawings now in the Gilcrease collection may have been a homecoming gift for his younger brother in that period.

THE SUN DANCE CEREMONY

The Sun Dance is an overwhelming spectacle of religious devotion in which sacrifice for the benefit of one's family, friends, community and the Earth itself is a primary theme. It occurred about the time of Summer Solstice, in an open, circular structure of erected poles and cross rafters which was built anew for each, annual ceremony (**Figs. 5, 6 & 7**). It is the Sun Dance, with its many diverse activities, which Bone Shirt chose as the theme for every one of his 79 drawings that are known to exist. The first ten of the Bone Shirt drawings in the Meade Collection are distinguished by beautifully drawn and subtlely-colored panels across the top of the composition. What these represent are the cloth awnings draped across the rafters around the outer perimeter of the circular Sun Dance lodge, to provide shade for the hundreds of spectators (**Figs. 5 & 6**). Throughout most of the 19th century, several prominent families might be honored during a Sun Dance by being asked to loan their buffalo skin tipi covers, and the interior linings or "draft screens," to be draped across the lodge rafters to provide this shade (see Powell, 1992: Fig. 2; and Maurer, 1992: Cat. No. 155, for examples).

Figure 5. Oglala Sun Dance ceremony witnessed at Red Cloud Agency, Nebraska, July 1874, by the artist Jules Tavernier. From *Harper's Weekly*, January 2, 1875. Note the cloth offering banners (shown as red in hand-colored issues of the newspaper); and the cloth awnings laid across the rafters. Denver Public Library, Western History Collection, Neg. No. Z-3283.

By the 1870s, however, through reservation traders like Mary Mead and her husband, the Sioux had access to printed calico cloth by the bolt. In a multitude of bright colors and intricate patterns, such cloth panels provided not only shade, but added a completely new design element to the Sun Dance structure, itself. With the bright, prairie sun blazing above, these cloth awnings added an effect much like stained glass windows in a church. Spectators and participants alike assumed an ethereal aspect as their bodies were mottled by these diffused patterns of projected color. Under this "Big Top", shadows gained contour; and movement gained texture. Undoubtedly, the fact that it was the *Sun* which created this mystical "paint", made the effect even more appealing.

It is this evocative "light show" which Bone Shirt has documented with such lavish care in ten of his drawings. Using the most sophisticated shading found anywhere in Plains Indian art of the 19th century, he has rendered cloth of pale blue speckled with designs of stars, spots, stripes and arabesques. Often, his pale patterns are so subtle as to escape notice, unless one can peer at them from a distance of a few inches. See **Fig. 8**, for a selection of details. Incredibly, Bone Shirt even succeeded in using yellow to over-pattern blue (**Plates 4, 5 & 7**). Again, the especial attention he devoted to this structural aspect of the ceremony suggests he may have been one of the primary leaders, a man who helped to design and build the national cathedral, year after year. It also reveals him as an artist of unusual skill and sophistication.

Figure 6. Oglala Lakota Sun Dance ceremony near Red Cloud Agency, Nebraska, July 1882. Note the large pile of offering cloths laid at the foot of the Center Pole; and the two horses being given away, at the right. Amon Carter Museum, Fort Worth, Texas, P1967-646.

In **Plates 2, 5 & 6**, the scalloped lower edges of the suspended cloth panels indicate that they had previously been in use as draft screens, or decorative liners inside individual family tipis. In a continuation of the earlier tradition, these have been loaned temporarily for the ceremony. The tie laces along the "upper" edge are indicated in **Plates 5 & 6**, now become decorative "pendants" with the liners inverted. **Plate 2** illustrates the lower edge of a lodge liner, with the holes by which it was staked to the ground when in use inside a tipi. To each of these stake-holes the loaning family has added an eagle-feather pendant as a respectful accent to the Sun Dance lodge. Like the cloth banners, such feathers were continually stirred by the wind, adding peripheral motion to the ambience of the ceremony. For a photograph showing Chief Two Strike posed before another Brule tipi liner also decorated with eagle feathers, see Hamilton & Hamilton, 1971: 277. It was the tension, between the staked-down bottom edge of these cloth tipi liners, and the tie thongs along the top edge by which the panel was attached to the poles of a tipi, which over time stretched the cloth liners out of shape, creating the scalloped contours depicted by Bone Shirt.

Among the most common of offerings in the latter-19th century were banners of expensive and colorful cloth. Suspended from sticks carried in the hands (**Plates 1 & 7**), or the same sticks erected in the earth (**Plates 9, 17, 21, 27, etc.**), or worn to accent a headdress (**Plates 8 & 11**), or on an implement (**Plate 16**), or tied to the posts of the main structure itself (**Fig. 5**), these offering banners danced on the omnipresent prairie winds, sculpting the visual field, in complement with the sacred, resonant hymns of the ceremony, which lift the heart, and lead the soul. The wind is the breath of the Earth, which these banners make manifest. Into a corner of each banner a separate, prayerful bit of tobacco, a sacred plant for the Lakota people, was tied as an additional offering at the tips of the banners shown in **Plates 19, 21 & 27**. After four days of use, perhaps soaked with the sweat of the dancers—the most elemental of offerings; or steeped in blood (Plate 21), these banners were carried to the foot of the Center Pole by each participant and abandoned as personal tokens of gratitude to the Deity (**Fig. 6**).

Figure 7. Brule Lakota Sun Dance ceremony at the Two Strike community, near St. Francis, South Dakota, ca. 1920. Note the cloth offering banners planted at the foot of the Center Pole. Denver Public Library, Western History Collection, Neg. No. X-31670.

The Sioux concept of physical sacrifice was eloquently expressed in 1911 by a Yanktonai man named Chased By Bears: *"A man's body is his own, and when he gives his body or his flesh he is giving the only thing which really belongs to him...I might give tobacco or other articles in the Sun Dance, but if I gave these and kept back the best, no one would believe that I was in earnest. I must give something that I really value to show that my whole being goes with the lesser gifts; therefore I promise to give my body"* (Densmore, 1918: 96).

The Sun Dance involved four, main types of physical sacrifice, each of which was a personal choice of the individual dancer (see Walker, 1917: 116-117). The first form did not involve blood sacrifice, but consisted entirely of dancing from sunrise to sunset (about 15 hours) for two days without food or water, in temperatures often in excess of 100 degrees. This was a grueling ordeal for anyone, especially for women or the elderly, who might be praying for the health of a relative. This form of sacrifice is depicted by Bone Shirt in **Plates 27 – 30**.

A second form of sacrifice involved the skin of the dancer's back being pinched up, then pierced with a knife over each shoulder blade, and a wooden skewer run through each wound. To these skewers rawhide ropes were attached, and many, heavy buffalo skulls were tied to these, which the dancer must drag around the open circle of the Sun Lodge, until the skewers were torn out. Bone Shirt depicts a man painted to receive this form of torture in **Plate 10** (see further, below).

A third form of torture required four piercings, two over the shoulder blades, and one on each breast. Four stout saplings were planted in the ground about eight feet apart, marking a square, and a rope from one sapling was tied to each of the four pierced skewers, forcing the dancer onto his toes as he was tautly suspended from the four points. Only when his sagging weight increased the play in the ropes, could he struggle sufficiently against them to tear himself free. This might take many hours. One drawing in the Detroit collection depicts this form of Sun Dance sacrifice.

In the fourth and best-known form of flesh sacrifice, a dancer was pierced through the skin of each breast. Ropes tied to the two skewers were attached to the top of the Center Pole, and the dancer strained back against these bonds, until the wounds tore through. Bone Shirt depicts this type of sacrifice in **Plate 21**.

The first six drawings in this collection are distinguished by a green ground line under the feet of the subjects, representing the renewed, and grass-covered Earth. Bone Shirt returns to this convention in **Plates 27-30**.

PLATES, BY CATEGORY

Charging the Tree: 13, 14, 15, & 16
Smoothing the Ground Dance: 3, 4, 5, 6, 18, & 19
Sun Dance *Itancans*: 7, 8, & 9
Buffalo Dancers: 1, 2, 11 (steer), 12, & 17
Sweat Lodge Ceremony: 20 & 22
Male Sun Dancers: 10 & 21
Female Sun Dancers: 27, 28, 29, & 30
Women Leading Giveaway Horses: 23, 24, 25, & 26

Charging the Tree — Plates 13, 14, 15 & 16

Elaborate ceremonies were associated with the selection and felling of the tree used as the Center Pole for the Sun Dance Lodge. It represented an enemy, surrounded, cut down, dismembered and carried into the camp. The *Itancans* had selected and marked the tree they wanted beforehand; but on the morning of the second day of the ceremony four distinguished warriors were selected as scouts to ride out and "discover" the enemy. Four of the Bone Shirt drawings in the collection at Detroit depict these scouts.

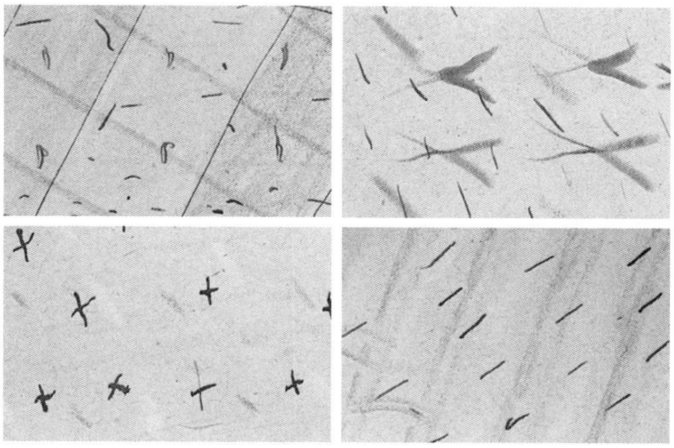

Figure 8. Details of Plates, showing the very subtle color patterns achieved by Bone Shirt.

"Drums beating and drummers singing, the scouts form in single file and ride four times around the [camp circle], then away toward the timber, accompanied for a distance by a legion of horsemen dashing around and around them" (Curtis, 1908: 91-92). Perhaps half a mile from the camp the crowd of riders halted, to wait while the scouts proceeded on to locate the "enemy", and mark the tree with paint or banners. After a while, the scouts were seen returning toward the crowd of mounted men, who represented the members of a war party. When the approaching scouts directed their horses in a zigzag movement, which signaled an enemy had been sighted, *"with one impulse the restless steeds of the impatiently waiting young men leap toward the returning party, sweeping around them four times in a great, seething circle. Then back wheels the whole tumultous horde, thundering down upon the 'enemy.' War-bonnets stream; weapons are brandished aloft; horses strain eagerly forward. Loud and shrill the war cry fills the air. For the moment the most ardent wish of every horseman is to reach the goal first, and no risk of reckless riding is too great to be taken in the effort, for he who*

is first to strike [the tree]...feels himself assured of achieving an honor of the highest class in his next battle" (Curtis, 1908: 92).

Plates 13-16 in the Mead Collection are devoted to showing individuals participating in this charge on the cottonwood tree that would become the Center Pole of the Sun Dance Lodge. Note that all of the horses have been elaborately painted, as they would be for war. Two have a scalp suspended below the bit; and two others have a silk scarf in this location.

The shields in **Plates 14 & 15** are painted with larval insect forms, which will be discussed in the section on "Sun Dance *Itancans*". Here, we need only note that these distinctive talismans identify their bearers as acolytes of Bone Shirt, and demonstrate that he was a noted shield maker, among his other abilities. These are clients of his services, probably relatives from the Two Strike *tiyo'spaye*. The trailing double sash depicted in **Plate 15** is an insignia of the Miwatanni warrior society. Similar sashes are shown in **Plate 20** and **Fig. 9**.

Figure 9. Miniconjou Lakota member of the *Miwatani* Warrior Society. Note the distinctive headdress and trailing sash of wool cloth (seen crossing the chest diagonally), which are characteristic of this organization. Similar sashes are depicted in **Plates 15 & 20**. Unknown photographer at Cherry Creek, South Dakota, September, 1909; Rosemary Lessard Collection.

There are three, similar compositions in the Detroit collection; one at Missoula; and at least two in the Gilcrease collection.

Smoothing the Ground Dance — Plates 3, 4, 5, 6, 18 & 19

After the Center Pole had been cut down, carried into the camp, and erected in the Sun Dance Lodge, a final labor was necessary to level the ground, and prepare it for the bare feet of the votaries who would commune there. Wisely, the Sioux turn a *community labor project into a party. "[The] men have painted their faces, and donned war-bonnets and scalp-shirts, if they have attained to that dignity. At the cry of the herald these come trooping into the lodge in single file for the performance of the Dance That Smooths the Ground. As the musicians drum and sing, the participants dance toward the pole... retreating and advancing alternately..."* (Curtis, 1908: 94). *"The warriors should continue to dance the victory dance, stomping and striking uneven places on the uncovered space [the large, central area within the shaded perimeter] until it is made sufficiently level to dance upon easily"* (Wissler, 1917: 110). In a short time, several hundred men enthusiastically dancing over an area will have trampled any clods, and leveled the grass and weeds. That is what Bone Shirt has depicted in this series of plates. Note that the elaborately depicted cloth awnings denote that the locale is within the Sun Dance Lodge.

According to Walker (1917: 109), it was during the Smoothing the Ground Dance that rawhide effigies representing a male enemy, a buffalo and sometimes a horse, which had been hung to the Center Pole, were brought down by a volley of arrows and gunfire. These symbolized tribal success in warfare, hunting and raiding during the coming season. The enemy and horse effigies are shown by Bone Shirt in **Plate 10**. Actual effigies of this type are shown in **Fig. 10**. All three were used in the 1882 ceremony depicted in **Fig. 6**.

In one of the drawings at Missoula, and another at Detroit, Bone Shirt depicted the enemy and buffalo effigies hanging from the Center Pole. In another drawing at Detroit, he shows a rawhide horse effigy hanging from the wrist of a Sun Dancer, perhaps the man who succeeded in shooting it down during the Smoothing the Ground Dance.

Figure 10. Painted, rawhide cut-outs representing a buffalo and a male enemy. These were obtained in 1882 by the ethnologist Alice C. Fletcher, at the Oglala Sun Dance ceremony shown in **Fig. 6**. Courtesy of the Peabody Museum of Natural History, Yale University, New Haven, Connecticut, USA, Cat. Nos.: buffalo, 82-45-10/27497; male enemy, 82-45-10/27498.

Sun Dance *Itancans* — Plates 7, 8, 9 & 10

In **Plates 7 – 9**, and perhaps **Plate 10**, Bone shirt depicted *Itancans*, or leaders of the Sun Dance ceremony. Their hair is flowing loose, each is naked except for a colorful and costly cloth skirt wrapped around his lower body, and each would be dancing barefoot. The upper body of each man is elaborately painted. Although the design employed by each is unique, the first three feature similar insect depictions which indicate either that the same visionary painted them all; or that these are three depictions on different days of the same man who had painted himself. It is nearly a certainty that this painting of the dancers' bodies was done by Bone Shirt, and this is the strongest direct evidence that he was, in fact, an *Itancan*. Similar insect figures appear prominently throughout all four of the Bone Shirt collections, on war shields and robes as well as body paint, indicating a broad clientele, each of whom would have paid the visionary artist for his services.

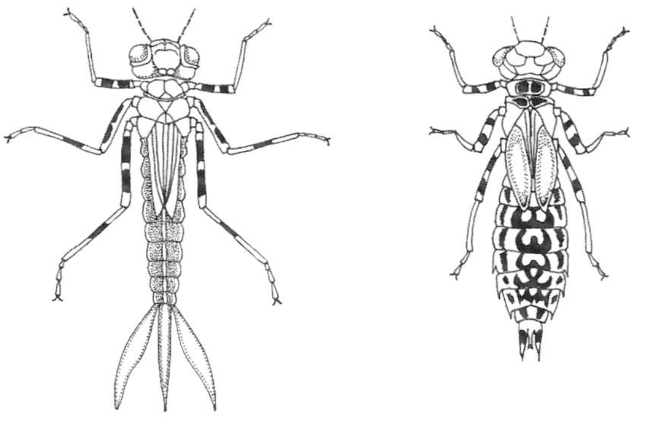

Figure 11a & b. Mayfly and dragonfly nymphs, which are the insect figures depicted by Bone Shirt in **Plates 7, 8, 9, 12, 14, 15, 20, 27, & 28**. Note the tail appendages, which are gills in the larval forms, allowing them to breathe under water. Drawings by author.

What these insects represent are the nymph forms of dragonflies and related species (**Fig. 11a & b**). Lakotas were, and remain, very close observers of the natural world around them. Among the mind-boggling mysteries of our environment are creatures which transcend different physical realms, in ways that human beings cannot. Lakota religious philosophers observed that dragonflies began their existence in the water, as crawling creatures which could neither fly, nor survive if taken into the open air. Yet as they matured, these seeming "lowly" entities one day would crawl out of the water, attach themselves to some reed, then "die". Their whole body would crack open, and apparently remain as a husk attached to the reed; but from within would emerge a *new*, air-breathing form of being with wings, that could dodge erratically, was almost untouchable, and hence nearly invulnerable. This metaphor of "life coming from death," and its evasive abilities, made the dragonfly in its various forms a potent protective symbol, of deep significance to warriors who risked themselves in battle; or who in the Sun Dance would thirst and nearly die for two days together. It is clear from his many drawings that Bone Shirt had established a visionary understanding of this transformative power, and many other Lakotas sought his assistance and advice in acquiring the same.

In **Plates 7 & 8**, adult dragonflies are painted flying outward along the arms; while the nymph forms are depicted on the torso. The forked appendages shown at the tail are diagnostic of what these insect forms really are: they represent the gills which allow the nymph to breath underwater. In **Plate 9**, the nymphs are shown painted on the arms. In **Plate 28**, three underwater nymphs are painted on the green half of a robe, while three adult dragonflies soar in yellow sunlight. The dragonfly's lesson of Life in triumph over Death infuses the war shields shown in **Plates 14, 15 & 20**. A similar ensign appears in the Gilcrease collection.

Buffalo Dancers — Plates 1, 2, 11 (steer), 12 & 17

The Sun Dance, as has been noted, is a difficult physical challenge for those who participate. Frequent periods of brief rest are required, for the dancers to husband their strength, and recuperate a bit before the next trial. During these intermissions, various of the Lakota "dream" societies might enact their visions for the benefit of the spectators. This was part street theater and also, in a society that survived by hunting, an important promise of survival and future success. It was believed that game animals voluntarily sacrificed themselves for their "relatives", the Lakota people. Other tribes believed the same, with themselves as the beneficiaries. Men who were successful hunters had therefore been "adopted" by the prey, and to such men their animal brethren often sent dreams of successful hunts, which were considered as promises waiting to be fulfilled. These fortunate dreamers shared this intelligence with their neighbors by donning costumes of the adoptive animals, and pantomiming the progress and expected outcome of the anticipated chase. One of the primary accounts of Lakota mystical associations notes:

> Buffalo Cult
>
> *There was a group of men and occasionally a few women, known as the Buffalo Dreamers...In the regular ceremonies while the drumming is going on, the members bellow like buffalo and some stamp a foot leaving buffalo tracks upon the ground* (Wissler, 1912: 91-92).

Black Elk, a Buffalo Dreamer, recalled: *"I had horns on, and was painted red all over my body...The people were all eager to see me. In this act I represented the relationship between the people and the buffalo. From the buffalo, people had reared their children up. I went around acting like [a] buffalo..."* (Neihardt,1984: 240-41).

This is precisely what Bone Shirt has depicted in **Plates 1, 2, 12 & 17** of this collection. The buffalo tracks mentioned by Wissler are painted in **Plate 1** on the dancer's legs, showing that the prey have consented to follow him. The lightning bolts painted on his arms denote his ability to dispatch them. Those among the spectators who wisely follow him whenever the hunt is later announced, will share in the largesse he has been promised. The Lakota People, relatives of the Buffalo Nation, will survive.

In such performances *"a shaman would appear in the head and skin of a buffalo* [Plate 2]. *As he ran about the camp a nude young man stalked him, while the [other buffalo dancers] followed singing. At the proper time the hunter discharged an arrow deeply into a spot marked on the buffalo skin. The shaman would then stagger, vomit blood and spit up an arrow point...Later, another shaman would use* [herbal] *medicine (pejuta), pull the arrow out and at once the wound was healed"* (Wissler, 1912: 91; see also the graphic depiction in Bad Heart Bull, 1967: 277).

If an extensive animal-drive pantomime with many actors was necessary, such a performance was staged outside the Sun Dance lodge, as shown in a panoramic drawing by the Oglala, Standing Bear (Powell, 1992: Fig. 2). The crowd simply followed the actors "outside", then returned to the Sun Dance lodge when the main ceremony resumed. Bone Shirt's drawings make clear that similar performances by one or only a few visionaries also occurred within the lodge itself. This is denoted specifically by the overhead panels of colored cloth in **Plates 1, 2 & 17** (where the edge of the cloth is indicated, but not colored in). The Buffalo Dreamer shown in **Plate 12** apparently performed outside the Sun Dance lodge. The fact that five drawings depicting these animal dancers are scattered among seventeen compositions probably indicates that they occurred separately, perhaps on different days. **Plate 12** documents a "Long-horn Cow Dreamer", an innovation of the late-1880s, when such cattle were being imported to the Sioux reservations (see the 1889 photographs in Hamilton & Hamilton, 1971: 98-100, for examples at Rosebud).

Three other Buffalo Dancers are shown in the Bone Shirt Collection at Missoula, in combination with two Elk Dancers. Black Tail Deer (mule deer) Dancers appear in the collections at Missoula, Detroit and Tulsa. Each of these groups, as well as heyokas, or Thunder Dreamers, who are the sacred clowns of Lakota society, performed during intermissions in the main ceremony.

Sweat Lodge Ceremony — Plates 20 & 22

"On the morning of the Sun Dance those who were to take part in the ceremony were allowed to eat a full meal, after which they entered the vapor lodge while the following song was sung:

> *A voice I will send.*
> *Hear me.*
> *All over the land I am sending my voice.*
> *Hear me.*
> *I will survive.' "*

The *Inipi* or Sweat Lodge ceremony is in itself another of the seven sacred rites of the Lakota People, always performed before engaging in one of the more elaborate rituals (Powers, 1977: 89-91; Brown, 1953: 31-43). Its purpose is to cleanse an individual, both inside and out. The framework of the structure is created from green willow withes stuck into the ground, bent into supporting arcs, then lashed together. After the frame was covered with buffalo robes, or later with canvas or quilts, stones heated red-hot were carried inside, and dashed with cold water, producing effusive clouds of purifying steam. With a ground covering of aromatic sage plants, the effect is much like the inhalation therapy of the present day, though more effective.

The domed shape of the sweat lodge is shown at the lower

left in **Plate 22**. Behind the structure rises a sapling to which are suspended an offering of blue cloth, and a cylindrical container of painted parfleche (semi-tanned rawhide), of the sort often used to protect and transport personal talismans worn into combat. One of the votaries huddled within the ceremonial structure has hung it aloft to be infused with the empowering essence of the Sun.

Occupying the center of the composition is an elaborately painted horse that has an expensive silver bridle and Mexican trade bit with *coscojo* suspensions. A costly blanket of blue wool cloth with a decorative strip of beadwork is draped over the horse's back. This animal, having been blessed by the prayers offered within the sweat lodge, will later be taken into the center of the Sun Dance Lodge, and perhaps tied to the rope by which its owner has been pierced, so that its struggles may aid him in tearing free. Afterward, some deserving elder will be called forth by the dancer's family, and this horse, together with its expensive outfit, will be given away to commemorate the dancer's sacrifice. Such a presentation, with two horses, is occurring in the 1882 photograph shown in **Fig. 6**.

Before the reservation period, immediately following the Sun Dance ceremony war parties would depart in all directions. One purpose of the ceremony was to "recharge" the weapons and protective insignia of the various warrior societies, before their owners carried these against the enemy. In **Plate 20**, an otter-wrapped "crooked lance" of the *Cante T'inza*, or Strong Heart society, is shown at the right; and at the left is a sash and war shield of a member of the *Miwatanni* society (compare **Fig. 9**). This drawing is probably associated with the sweat lodge ceremony, the insignia being arrayed near the domed structure during that prayer ceremony, like the elevated parfleche case shown in **Plate 22**.

Male Sun Dancers — Plates 10 & 21

"...After their vapor bath, the dancers were painted by the men whom they had selected for that purpose" (Densmore, 1918: 123-124). Wissler was told "Each Mentor should paint his candidate's feet and hands red. Then he should place the symbolic color of the Sky on him so as to indicate the form of the dance he is to do. If he is to dance the second form [dragging buffalo skulls] , a stripe of blue should be painted across his shoulders..." (Wissler, 1917: 112). This is what Bone Shirt has depicted in **Plate 10**. It is not clear whether this man is an *Itancan*, or one of the dancers. It was not uncommon for an *Itancan* also to perform one of the sacrifices, so this individual may fill both categories. His body is painted red, as Wissler specifies, and the blue stripes on his shoulders show where he will be pierced in the back with wooden skewers to which ropes will be attached, and heavy buffalo skulls, which he then will drag around inside the circular Sun Dance Lodge, until the splints tear out of his skin.

Plate 10 is an innovative composition, combining both lateral and overhead perspectives of the action. The dancer, Center Pole and offering banners are seen in lateral view; while the right ¼ of the drawing shows from overhead the curved, inner edge of the open dance area, with the panels of colored cloth forming the perimeter awnings extending to the right.

The dancer shown in **Plate 21** has been pierced through the skin of each breast with wooden skewers. Rawhide ropes attached to these bind him to the Center Pole. His sacrifice shall be to pull back against these wounds, until the skewers tear loose. Rather than being painted red, the priest who dedicated this man has covered him in the yellow paint which represents the Sun. Blood from the wounds streaks down his torso. The offering banners probably are his personal gifts, placed before he began the sacrifice. When he has torn free, these will be gathered up and laid at the foot of the Center pole, as shown in Fig. 6, making way for the next votary.

Here, Bone Shirt includes another important detail of the ceremony, the tribal offering which was tied into the fork of the Center Pole, before it was raised into position. This bundle was composed of *"four times four wands of chokecherry wood* [representing a prayer for bountiful fruits], *and enclosing...a wisp of sage* [and] *sweetgrass* [sacramental plants that figure prominently in all Lakota ceremonies], *and a tuft of shed buffalo hair* [representing the essence or spirit of all buffalo, which were believed attracted by a ceremony sincerely performed]" (Wissler, 1917: 109).

Female Sun Dancers — Plates 27, 28, 29 & 30

> *"Women sometimes took part in the Sun Dance by fasting and standing beside some relative who was dancing, or by assuming part of the obligation of a vow made by some relative and permitting their arms to be cut...Women whose relatives were fulling vows* [by being pierced during the ceremony] *frequently danced beside them during part of the time.* ***Ta'sinaskawin*** *(White Robe)* [took] *part in a Sun Dance in which her brother was fulfilling a vow. As the result of a successful raid against the Crows, he brought home many horses which were divided among his relatives, she receiving part of the number. He had vowed that if he were successful he would be suspended from the pole and would also have 200 cuts made on his arms. She and her sister assumed one half of this number, each having her arms cut fifty times. She and his other female relatives danced while he was dancing"* (Densmore, 1918: 132 & 135).

All four of these women are wearing horned headdresses characteristic of the *Cante T'inza*, or Strong Heart, warrior society. This means that the male relatives whom they are supporting by their presence belong to that organization, and the women are in turn being simultaneously honored for their assistance by temporarily being allowed to wear this war clothing. Since Bone Shirt has here depicted four family members of the Cante T'inza, it is likely that he was himself also a member.

In **Plates 28 & 29**, leafy saplings are shown erected at the left, and the small dots throughout the leaves represent tiny offerings of tobacco tied in small pieces of cloth. In **Plate 30**, similar tobacco offerings wrapped in blue cloth are tied to a sheaf of sticks, and this is hung together with a banner painted with horse tracks which represents an ardent prayer for success in acquiring the same. At the conclusion of the ceremony these would be laid at the foot of the Center Pole.

The forked implements hung with eagle feathers and offering banners in **Plates 28-30** represent the badge of office of a young boy appointed as "water carrier" for a war party during his first venture into the dangerous business of being a warrior. A small "bucket" made from the pericardium of a buffalo was laced to the open, forked end of such a staff. With this tool the eager young lad would dip water from every creek or spring the party encountered, and carry it around to refresh his seniors. It was a proud badge of maturity (see Wissler, 1912: 60; and Bad Heart Bull, 1967: 111). In any battle, the "water boy" might use his emblem to count coup on any enemy encountered. If he enjoyed success, he might choose to use a similar implement in battle throughout his career, for luck. Here, the warriors to whom these ensigns belong have erected them while they pay, in blood, for past or future success.

Women Leading Giveaway Horses — Plates 23, 24, 25 & 26

"The gifts distributed by relatives of the dancers and the feasts given in their honor were also the work of the women" (Densmore, 1918: 132). The family of every Sun Dancer staged elaborate giveaways to distinguish their relative, and fix his particular sacrifice in the community's memory. What is depicted in these four drawings are women hauling these expensive gifts to the vicinity of the Sun Dance Lodge, where a herald would call out the names of those invited, and the presentations would be made before hundreds of surrounding witnesses. Two of the horses are dragging tipi poles, indicating that decorated lodges, as well as the horses—in effect, "a house and a car"—will be part of the presentation. Each horse has a decorated saddle and crupper. Pairs of beaded, soft-leather storage bags atop the saddles hold prestigious gifts, such as quill or bead-decorated clothing, and feather headdresses. Painted parfleche cases slung at the horses' sides would hold additional gifts, or dried foods such as pemmican and chokecherry cakes, for a traditional feast. The woman in **Plate 26** is carrying a rolled-up backrest—a traditional "chair"—across her back. Note that the horse depicted in Plate 25 with a dark mane is a dun roan: a yellow phase with black points. The stripes indicated on the legs are natural "war paint" of the Spanish Barb, very much coveted by Lakota horsemen.

A POSSIBLE PORTRAIT OF THE ARTIST

Figure 12 shows an unidentified Brule Lakota man traveling with the Pawnee Bill Wild West Show in 1908. Junior Bone Shirt was 52 years of age in that year. His younger brother was a member of the troupe (**Fig. 1**), and Junior is known to have traveled with Pawnee Bill previously. An 1894 list of ration recipients at Rosebud Reservation, for example, shows him as then absent, with the Pawnee Bill Show. If Junior Bone Shirt was with his brother in 1908, this portrait shows the only unidentified member of the troupe who is old enough. There is a strong similarity between the face of this man, and the younger Bone Shirt. Compare especially their noses and mouths, and the lines in the cheeks enclosing those features. It is possible, therefore, that this man was the artist of the drawings considered here.

Figure 12. Unidentified Brule Lakota man traveling with the Pawnee Bill Wild West show in June, 1908. Photo by Erwin E. Smith, at Boston, Massachusetts. Erwin E. Smith Collection of the Library of Congress on Deposit at the Amon Carter Museum, Fort Worth, Texas, Neg. Nos. LC-S611-808 and LC-S611-810. For reasons discussed in the essay, it is possible this man is Junior Bone Shirt, creator of the drawings considered here.

CONCLUSION

His family named him Never Misses, a hopeful invocation of success both in hunting and in war. By the quality of his life, the eldest son of Bone Shirt earned honor of another kind, to light his name across the ages. With unerring skill in creating this comprehensive record of his people's greatest religious ceremony, the artist truly "never missed." A leader and innovator of his own generation, he found a way to outdistance Time and Death, preserving the knowledge that had informed his own life, and passing it down with skill and rare beauty, to Lakota generations yet unborn.

— Mike Cowdrey
San Luis Obispo, California

ACKNOWLEDGEMENTS

David Penny, Curator of the Detroit Institute of Arts, and Kim Roblan, Interim Library Coordinator at the Gilcrease Museum, Tulsa, provided comparison images, and information about the Bone Shirt drawings in their collections. Marcy Burns, who first realized the importance of the "Walter Bone Shirt" collection of drawings, and Beverly Twitchell-Marchant of Marshall University, who made the connection to Mary Eliza Mead of Pine Ridge, have been gracious in sharing some of their notes and research with Richard Pohrt, Jr., and the author. William Wierzbowski, Assistant Keeper of American Collections at the University of Pennsylvania Museum of Archaeology and Anthropology generously shared his research notes concerning early Brule census lists in the Federal Archives and Records Center, Kansas City. We are grateful to them all.

BIBLIOGRAPHY

Bad Heart Bull, Amos (Helen, H. Blish, ed.). *A Pictographic History of the Oglala Sioux.* Lincoln: University of Nebraska Press, 1967.

Berlo, Janet Catherine, ed. *Plains Indian Drawings, 1865-1935: Pages from a Visual History.* New York: Harry N. Abrams, 1996.

Brown, Joseph Epes. *The Sacred Pipe.* Norman: University of Oklahoma Press, 1953.

Curtis, Edward S. *The North American Indian, Vol. 3: "The Teton Sioux".* Cambridge: Harvard University Press, 1908.

Densmore, Frances. *Teton Sioux Music.* Washington, D.C.: Bulletin 61, Bureau of American Ethnology, 1918.

Dorsey, James Owen. "A Study of Siouan Cults," *Annual Report 11,* pp 351-544. Washington, D,C,: Bureau of American Ethnology, 1894.

Feder, Norman. *Two Hundred Years of North American Indian Art.* New York: Frederick A. Praeger Publishers, 1972.

Foreman, Grant. "J. George Wright, 1860-1941", *Chronicles of Oklahoma,* Vol. 20, No.2:120-123, 1942.

Hamilton, Henry W. and Jean Tyree Hamilton. *The Sioux of the Rosebud: A History in Pictures.* Norman: University of Oklahoma Press, 1971.

McCrea, Donna. "The Walter Bone Shirt Ledger." Missoula: Maureen and Mike Mansfield Library, The University of Montana, Archives and Special Collections, 2006.

http://www.lib.umt.edu/research/digitalcollections/ledger.htm

Maurer, Evan M. *Visions of the People: A Pictorial History of Plains Indian Life.* Minneapolis: Minneapolis Institute of Arts, 1992.

Mead, Mary. "Mrs. Mary Mead, A Pioneer", *Western Nebraska Churchman,* April and May 1927.

Neihardt, John G. (Raymond J. De Mallie, ed.). *The Sixth Grandfather: Black Elk's Teachings, Given to John G. Neihardt.* Lincoln: University of Nebraska Press, 1984.

Penny, David W. *Art of the American Indian Frontier: The Chandler-Pohrt Collection.* Seattle and Detroit: University of Washington Press, 1992.

48092

SOUTHERN ARAPAHO WARRIOR'S SHIRT

Circa 1880
Length 26 in. Width across the arms 59 in.

This native tanned deerskin shirt is decorated with beaded shoulder strips and a long triangular bib, painted dark green and heavily fringed. The body of the shirt is heavily rubbed with yellow ochre and long fringe extends from the shoulders and elbow, short fringe from the cuffs and along the bottom. Brass studs and small German silver conchos are sewn alongside the shoulder fringe. This shirt well represents the Southern Plains aesthetic. Hide clothing is characterized by minimal bead decoration, extensive fringing and the overall painting of garments.

Provenance
Sotheby's, Sale 7228, Lot 383, December 2, 1998.

Estimate: $20,000-$30,000

48093

KIOWA PAINTED AND FRINGED MOCCASINS

Circa 1885
Length 10¼ in.

This pair features native tanned and painted deerskin uppers with rawhide soles. The moccasins are characterized by hide fringe extending along the outer side of the vamps, long heel fringe, short bifurcated tongues, and rectangular shaped cuffs. They are painted a deep green overall, the vamp and heel fringe done in dark blue.

Provenance
Brant Mackley, Hummelstown, Pennsylvania.

Estimate: $4,000-$6,000

48094

KIOWA STRIKE-A-LIGHT CASE COLLECTED FROM THE CHEYENNE CHIEF WHITE HORSE

Circa 1880
Length 9½ in. overall; Length 6¼ in. case proper

This classic example is beaded on saddle leather with geometric designs including a "house" pattern in navy blue with a red "door". In addition, there are triangles done in navy blue and a zigzag band done in cranberry red, all against the white bead background. The cover flap is decorated with a German silver concho and tin cone fringe. The bottom is decorated with tin cones and twisted fringe. The reverse has two lanes of beadwork along the bottom.

Aside from their utilitarian function, strike-a-light cases and awl cases were popular costume accessories. Kiowa beadworkers excelled at making these small masterpieces. Men often tied them to their bow case and quiver sets (see Lot 48152). Girls and women used them as belt ornaments and they can be noted in historic photographs (see Lot 48227).

Provenance
Purchased from White Horse, a Cheyenne Indian, along the Cimarron River in Oklahoma by H.C. Schilling in January, 1890. Schilling was from Rogers, Arkansas, and hunted in Indian Territory. A letter dated January 25, 1890 written from Guthrie, Indian Territory, detailing the collecting circumstances and signed by Schilling accompanies this lot. The Cheyenne Chief White Horse was a signatory to the Medicine Lodge Treaty of 1867.

Estimate: $4,000-$6,000

48095

KIOWA STRIKE-A-LIGHT CASE

Circa 1885
Length 9¾ in. overall
Length 6 in. case proper

This typical example is beaded on saddle leather with a central "house" motif in navy blue, blue, red, green, and yellow against a white background. The cover flap and bottom of the case are decorated with tin cones. The laces for the flap are embellished with two short bone hairpipes, tin cones, and a German silver crescent likely salvaged from earrings. The fringes at the bottom corners are decorated with tin cones, brass beads, and brass buttons.

Estimate: $3,000-$5,000

48096

SIOUX PAINTED BUFFALO ROBE [NORTHERN TETON, PROBABLY HUNKPAPA OR BLACKFEET SIOUX (*SIHA SAPA*)]

Circa 1865
Height 90 in. Length 109 in.

Estimate: $120,000-$160,000

48096

SIOUX PAINTED BUFFALO ROBE [NORTHERN TETON, PROBABLY HUNKPAPA OR BLACKFEET SIOUX (*SIHA SAPA*)]

Across the Great Plains and throughout much of North America hide robes were the typical outer garment. They were worn with the thick animal hair lying against the skin, providing protection from the cold. Hides with the hair removed were worn in the warmer seasons. The Plains Indians wore their robes with the head of the animal to the wearer's left and the longer dimension wrapped around the body. Most robes, like the present example, retain the stake holes through which pegs were driven during the dressing process. The finely-grained skin of the tanned hide made a more than suitable canvas for artistic expression. A number of conventionalized designs became popular within the Plains Indian cultural milieu. Examples and their descriptive terms include box and border robes, border and hourglass robes, feathered circle robes, etc. However, the most dramatic painted robes are those depicting the war exploits of the owner. Recognition and status within the tribe were best achieved through prowess in battle. The pictographic robe was a reminder to all of the wearer's success on the war trail.

The earliest documented example of a painted pictorial robe is one collected by Meriwether Lewis and William Clark from the Mandan and shipped to President Thomas Jefferson. William Clark's journal entry for April 3, 1805 states: "we are all ingaged packing up Sundery articles to be sent to the President of the U.S." The itemized list for "Box No. 2" includes "1 robe representing a battle between the Sioux and Ricara's, Minetarras and Mandans." This famous robe is in the collections of the Peabody Museum of Harvard University, Cambridge, Massachusetts.

The present example falls squarely within the same tradition as the Lewis and Clark robe. The painting is done with mineral and trade pigments, fixed in a binder of animal skin glue, on brain tanned buffalo hide. There is minor abrasion to the painted surface, due to age and wear, but the images are intact, without restoration, and the colors are quite vibrant. There is minor discoloration due to long display in a museum frame.

There are a number of markers on this robe which identify it as Sioux. This robe has previously been published and a Cheyenne attribution assigned. (See: *American Indian Art Magazine*. Volume 27, Number 1, Winter 2001, inside front cover.) It is useful to compare some of the relevant details surrounding Cheyenne and Sioux pictographic art. The former identification was largely made on the basis of the Dog Soldier figure which appears in the second tier from the bottom, second figure from the left. However, other tribes allied with the Cheyenne–the Arapaho and Sioux–also had warrior societies with officers who wore headdresses and sashes similar to those of the Cheyenne Dog Soldier Society. Among the Sioux, the relevant association was the *Miwatani* Society. (See: Amos Bad Heart Bull. *A Pictographic History of the Oglala*

Here two teams of mules are being run off, one team still drawing a military caisson. This image is a significant reference to the events occurring on the robe - the fighting between the Sioux and the troops of Colonel Samuel Walker and Colonel Nelson Cole in the summer and fall of 1865.

The two pipes and the horse tracks indicate the owner of this robe "carried the Pipe" - that is, acted as war leader, on two horse raids. On one occasion six horses were captured, on the second only two. Note the mounted figure to the upper left. He is wearing a cloth "war cape". These capes can be noted in Sioux ledger book art and help to reinforce the Sioux attribution. (See: Berlo, Janet Catherine (ed.). ***Plains Indian Drawings 1865 – 1935***. New York: Harry N. Abrams, Inc., 1996, pp. 184, 213, 215.

Sioux. Lincoln: University of Nebraska Press, 1967, pp. 106-107.) A characteristic feature of Cheyenne warfare depictions is that many individuals and their horses were represented with extensive designs of protective body painting. Aside from the *Miwatani* Society figure, only minimal face painting appears among the other figures, strongly indicating that the tribal identity of the artist cannot be Cheyenne. The rider in the top tier, second from the right, wears a horned headdress with feathered trailer typical of the Sioux *Cante T'inza* (Strong Heart) Society. (See: Bad Heart Bull, p.104.) The rider in the top tier, far right, carries an otter fur wrapped crooked lance typical of the Sioux *Ihoka* (Badger) Society. (See: Bad Heart Bull, p.109.) Cloth "war capes" of the type worn by two figures on this robe are also typical of the Sioux, but not the Cheyenne.

It is important to realize that although the mass of figures on this robe gives the impression of a single, large melee, actually many separate events are depicted which all probably occurred within a single season. Note, for example, that the *Miwatani* Society warrior wears only a breechcloth–indicative of summer activity; while the dismounted figure to the left wears a white-wool blanket capote, a garment for cold weather. Also, in the second tier from the bottom, below the rider with red cape, two pipes are represented, in conjunction with horse tracks. These are not to be understood as "lying on the ground", where they would be trampled by the charging horses. Instead, they symbolize two occasions when the owner of this robe "carried the Pipe", or acted as leader of separate horse raids. On one occasion, six horses were captured; on the second occasion, only two were obtained.

A combination of features represented on this robe suggests that the events depicted occurred during the fighting between the Northern Tetons, and the Cole-Walker expedition (Colonel Nelson Cole and Colonel Samuel Walker) along the Powder River, Montana during the summer and autumn of 1865. The U.S. military force consisted of both infantry and cavalry, with artillery support units. No recorded battle with U.S. troops during the 1870s involved artillery. Two U.S. infantrymen and a civilian teamster are depicted being overcome in the top tier of figures. Two bearded civilians, perhaps scouts, are being attacked near the tail of the robe. Many of the captured horses have clearly-represented McClellan saddles, used by the U.S. Cavalry. The group at lower center even have the canteens represented behind the saddles.

Two mules drawing an artillery caisson are shown in the bottom tier, being captured at far left. This probably represents

The mounted figure at the upper left is wearing the headdress of the Miwatani Society and its attendant "No Retreat" sash. "The wearer of the headdresses were very important and their position was most precarious, for, in the front of battle, they were obligated to stake themselves down (with the stake pin through the small hole in the end of the sash ...) and so remain unless a fellow member could fight back the enemy sufficiently to pull up the stake and release his comrade. The Miwatani are generally considered to be the first to institute this no flight regulation." (See: Bad Heart Bull, Amos. ***A Pictoraphic History of the Oglala Sioux***. Lincoln: University of Nebraska Press, 1967, p. 106.) Four army horses with McClellan saddles are being run off, the soldiers' canteens represented behind the saddles.

events that occurred on September 1, 1865: "...Missouri River Sioux–Minniconjous, Sans Arcs, Hunkpapas and Blackfeet Sioux ... had discovered the trail of the columns on the Little Missouri and, three-hundred strong, they had followed the trail to the powder where, on the morning of the first, they went down into the deep valley, surprised the troops and stampeded part of the cavalry herd ... Little fights were fought on both sides of the river ... The troops recaptured some of the stolen horses, but the Sioux succeeded in getting away with most of them, and at one point they set a trap for (the detachment led by Captain E.S. Rowland of the Second Missouri Light Artillery. He was saved by the arrival of Cole's column, but all of his men were lost)". (See: George E. Hyde and Savoie Lottinville (ed.). *Life of George Bent, Written From His Letters*. Norman: University of Oklahoma Press, 1968, p.235 and footnote 14, same page.)

The mounted warrior at the upper right is wearing a horned headdress with feathered trailer typical of the Sioux Cante T'inza (Strong Heart) Society. (See: Bad Heart Bull, p. 104.) The figure directly in front of him is attacking an infantryman who is armed with a pistol. The riding quirt suspended above the soldier's head indicates the warrior counted coup. Striking an armed opponent was considered the bravest of deeds.

Much of the draftsmanship on this robe is extraordinarily fine. The two teams of mules drawing the caisson are represented with such precision they are readily distinguished from the horses shown elsewhere.

The encounters between Sioux and Cheyenne and the troops of Cole and Walker are well described in the literature. It can be mentioned that Sitting Bull, age 34 during the fall of 1865, participated in a subsequent attack on September 8, 1865. Some four -hundred Sioux attacked Walker's troops that day but did not try to hold the field after Cole came forward with his troops to assist. Sitting Bull was armed only with bow and arrows and a single shot muzzle loader and during this encounter he failed to count coup. The troops staggered into Camp Connor (located at the junction of the Bozeman Trail and Powder River) on September 20, 1865 having lost most of their horses and mule teams to starvation and exposure–the result of severe weather and cold.

Provenance

Pitt-Rivers Collection (Mrs. Stella Pitt-Rivers), Oxford University, England. Merton Simpson, Paris and New York. George Terasaki, New York. Trotta-Bono, Shrub Oak, New York.

References

1–Ewers, John C. *Plains Indian Painting*. Stanford: Stanford University Press, 1939, pp. 8 -13. 2–Moulton, Gary E. (ed.). *The Journals of Lewis and Clark, Volume 3*. Lincoln: University of Nebraska Press, 1987, pp.329-330. 3–Bad Heart Bull, Amos. *A Pictographic History of the Oglala Sioux*. Lincoln: University of Nebraska Press, 1967, pp. 104, 106, 107, 109. 4–Hyde, George E. and Lottinville, Savoie (ed.). *Life of George Bent, Written From His Letters*. Norman: University of Oklahoma Press, 1968, p.235 and footnote 14, same page. 5–Vestal, Stanley. *Sitting Bull: Champion of the Sioux*. Norman: University of Oklahoma Press, 1957, pp. 76-82. 6–Berthrong, Donald J. *The Southern Cheyennes*. Norman: University of Oklahoma Press, 1963, pp. 245-256.

— Thanks to Mike Cowdrey, San Luis Obispo, California, for his great assistance with this essay.

The frenzied action suggests the Sioux surprised the soldiers. Here, they move swiftly and purposefully through their opponents' lines, counting coup, killing the enemy, and capturing horses.

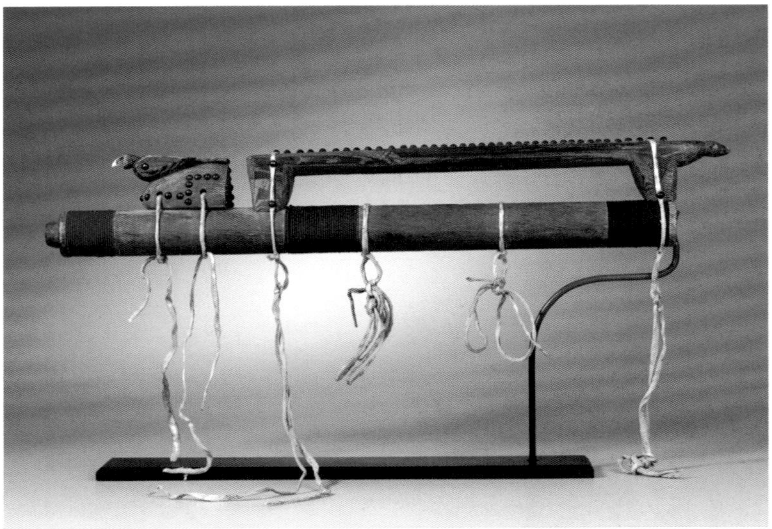

48097

NORTHERN PLAINS COURTING FLUTE

Circa 1880
Length 25¼ in.

The flute is made of red cedar, the pith removed. The flute is remarkable for its elaborate superstructure. An avian figure serves as the stop and an elongated quadruped straddles the six flute holes. Brass upholstery tacks decorate both figures.

Courting flutes were used by young men to serenade their sweethearts. Many stories are told of love calls played at night from the edge of camp to arrange a rendezvous. The carved figures may represent animals or birds whose behavior was interpreted in amorous or erotic terms. (For related examples see: Conn, Richard; *Native American Art in the Denver Art Museum*, Denver Art Museum, 1979, p. 136; Vincent, Brydon, Coe (Eds.), *Art of the North American Indians: The Thaw Collection*, New York State Historical Association, Fenimore Art Museum, 2000, p. 143; and Hail, Barbara, Hau, Kóla, Haffenreffer Museum of Anthropology, Brown University, Providence, 1980, p. 184.)

Provenance
Collected by Charles Henry Parker in Montana during the 1890's. Descended in the family to Mrs. Virginia Ward Golding, Pontiac, Michigan, 1979. Chandler-Pohrt Collection. Morning Star Gallery, Santa Fe, New Mexico.

Estimate: $4,000-$6,000

48098

SIOUX PIPE BOWL

Circa 1885
Height 4¼ in. Length 8½ in.

This classic catlinite "T" shaped bowl is carved with pleasing proportions, a flat base, and a funnel shaped bowl. Painted on the side in 19th century script—"Dr. Van Velsor", who may have practiced medicine amongst the Sioux.

Estimate: $400-$600

48099

GREAT LAKES PIPE BOWL

Circa 1800
Length 4¼ in.

This cast brass pipe from the fur trade era has a bowl that screws into the base. The pipe is of a style made by Europeans and traded to Indian people in the Great Lakes region. (For a similar example see Vincent, Gilbert T., Brydon, Sherry, and Coe, Ralph T. (Eds.); *Art of the North American Indians: The Thaw Collection*, New York State Historical Association, Fenimore Art Museum, 2000, p. 67, item T645, identified as Ottawa.)

Estimate: $800-$1,200

48100

SIOUX WARRIOR'S SHIRT DEPICTING AMERICAN FLAGS

Circa 1890
Length 38½ in.

This shirt is tailored in typical Plains fashion and made to be worn poncho style. There are hide tie laces along the open sides and the sleeves are sewn together from wrist to elbow. The shirt is decorated with beaded shoulder and sleeve strips, the outer edges fringed with long hair locks. "In theory, at least, a lock of hair was added for each recognized deed in war: as, coup, capturing a horse, taking prisoners, getting wounds, saving the life of a friend, etc., but eventually the fringed shirt became simply the conventional regalia of the four grand councilors and finally a style of dress for anyone." The beaded strips feature classic Sioux colors and geometric motifs including crosses, chevrons, and triangles in red, green, yellow, and blue. Matched pairs of American flags are integrated into the design scheme. Further, the shirt is painted in blue green and yellow.

The American flag became a popular design element with the Western Sioux during the last quarter of the nineteenth century and into the twentieth. Its significance is subject to differing interpretations and meanings might be layered. The flag could be viewed as a power symbol, a protective device, or an expression of loyalty to new authority. It may also be a reflection of Sioux beadworkers interest in new design concepts and changing fashions of the times. This phenomenon has been explored in several studies. (See: Pohrt, Richard, *The American Indian/The American Flag, Flint Institute of Arts*, 1975; and Herbst, Toby and Kopp, Joel, *The Flag in American Indian Art*. Cooperstown: New York State Historical Association, 1993.) For similar examples see: *The American Indian/The American Flag*, figure 93, p. 82; and again in *Art of the North American Indians: The Thaw Collection*, figure T72, p. 131. Another shirt can be noted in Thompson, Judy, *The North American Indian Collection: A Catalogue*. Berne Historical Museum, 1977, figure 120, p. 176.
Over time "war shirts" became less emblematic of specific rank or society affiliation. Nevertheless, they would only have been worn by important, well respected Lakota men.

Provenance
Acquired from a Pennsylvania family by Roy Harrelson. James Hart, Acquisition, Inc., Maple Shade, New Jersey.

Reference
Wissler, Clark, "Societies and Ceremonial Associations of the Oglala Division of the Teton-Dakota," *Anthropological Papers of the American Museum of Natural History*, Vol. XI, Part 1, New York, 1912.

Estimate: $45,000-$65,000

48101

SIOUX DRESS WITH FOUR BEADED CROSSES

Circa 1890
Length 54 in. Width 55 in.

This native tanned hide dress is tailored in typical fashion with two hides utilized for the skirt and a third hide for the yoke. The large yoke is fully beaded, front and back, with four large crosses in navy blue against a light blue background. A series of geometric motifs decorates the border and neatly frames the central design. Hide fringing extends from the yoke sleeves, along the skirt side seams, and along the bottom.

Provenance
G. Gernower Estate, Litchfield, Connecticut, said to have been collected in the Black Hills of South Dakota around 1892. Sotheby's, New York, Lot 36, June 21, 1985.

Estimate: $15,000-$20,000

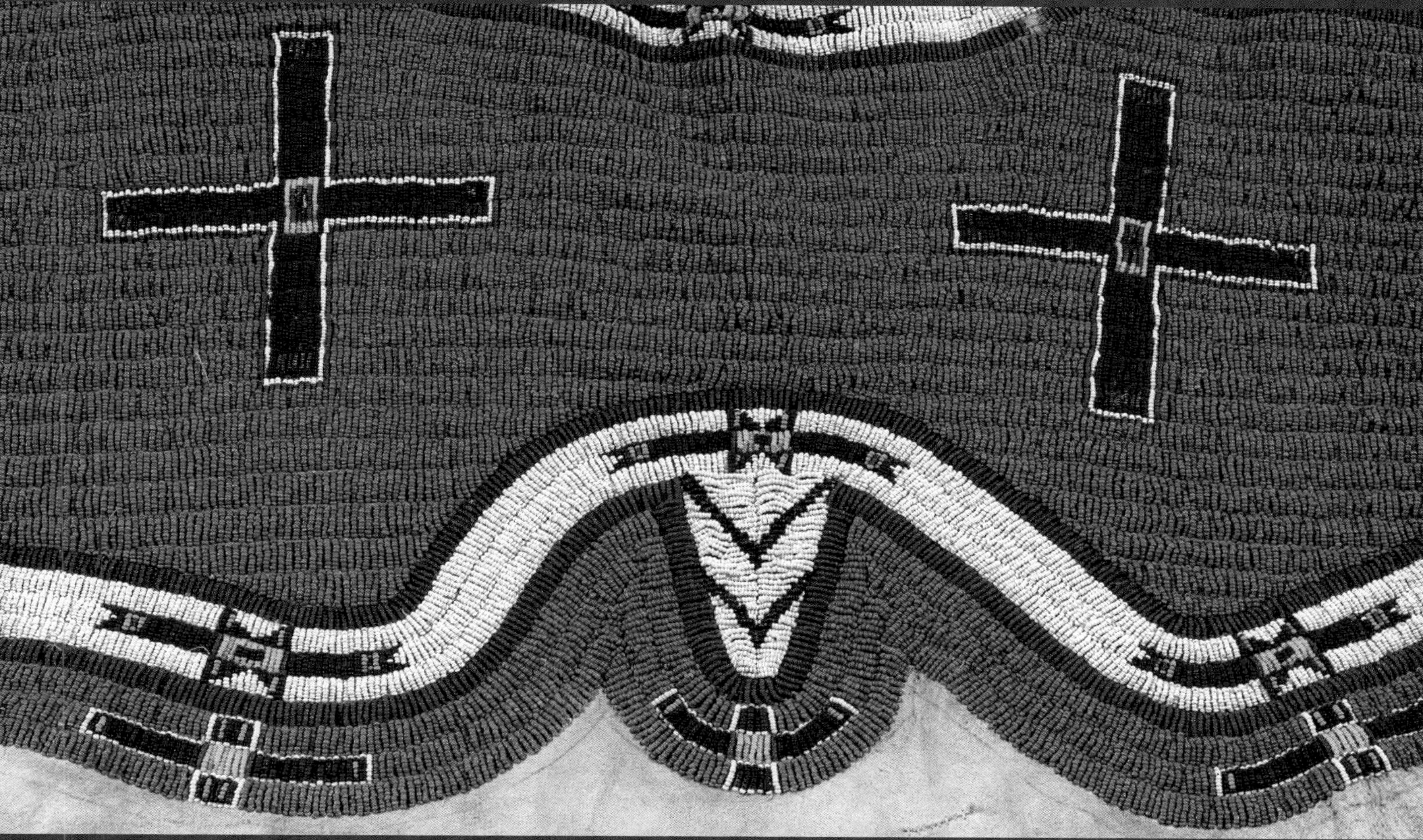

48102

SIOUX BABY CARRIER

Circa 1880
Length 22 in. as mounted

This native tanned hide cradle is fully beaded in lazy stitch with a pattern of stepped diamonds and triangles in red, green, yellow, and navy blue together with navy blue and yellow squares all against a blue background, sinew sewn. A navy blue wool cloth panel serves to extend and enclose the wrap. This portion is decorated with tubular glass beads in a star pattern. The interior surface is lined with calico. Numerous brass hawk bells are tied to the fringes of the beaded rawhide flap and along the base of the beaded area.

Estimate: $5,000-$7,000

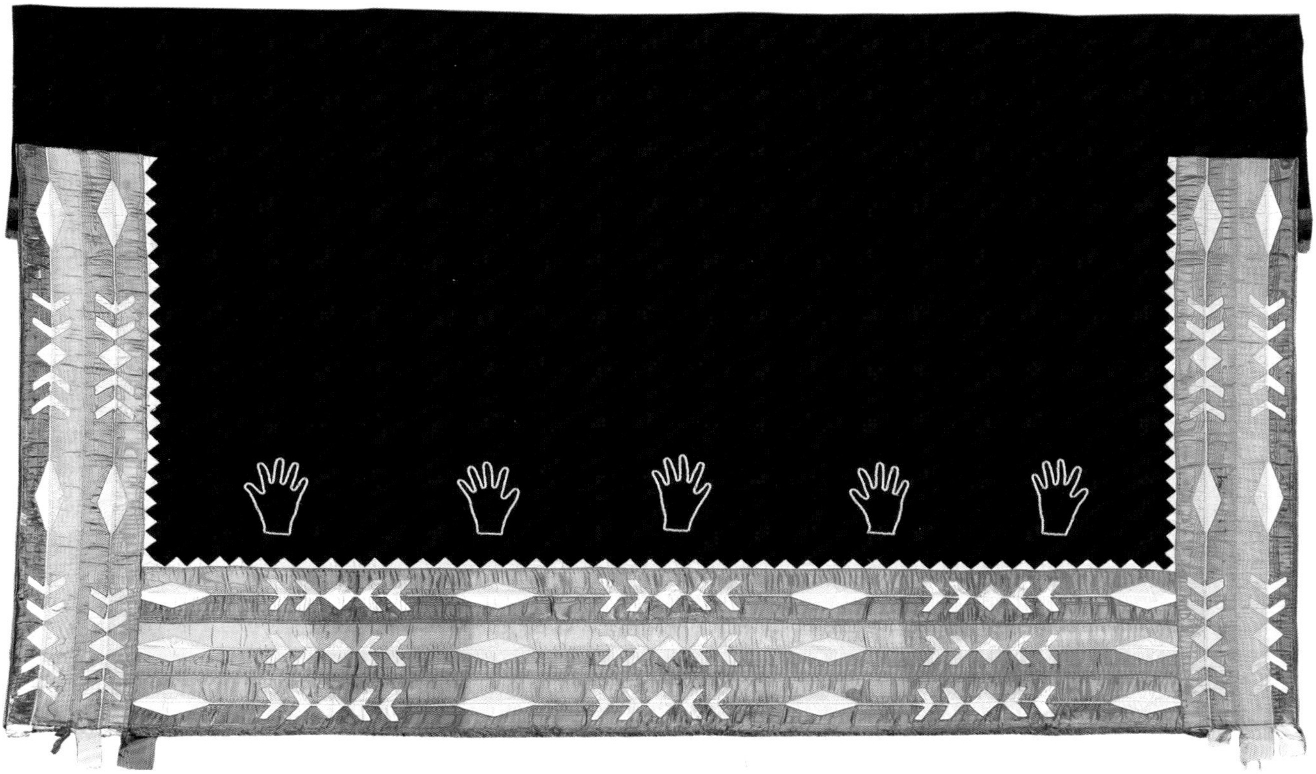

48103

OSAGE WOMAN'S FRIENDSHIP BLANKET

Circa 1900
Length 55½ in. Width 68½ in.

The navy blue wool blanket is decorated with silk ribbon appliqué work using traditional Osage geometric designs. Vertical bands of ribbon work decorate the sides of the blanket and the pattern is repeated across the bottom. The blanket is further decorated with five red silk hands outlined with white beads. Commenting on a similar example Ralph T. Coe states: "Large wearing blankets with silk ribbon appliqué borders developed in Oklahoma around the turn of the century, particularly among the Osage and Oto peoples. They reached a peak in production during the height of the oil boom in Oklahoma in the 1920s and 1930s. Osage families made fortunes from the oil on their lands, and their lifestyle became increasingly comfortable. Accompanying this extravagance was an elaboration in dress that marks a high point in Osage couture, and beautifully patterned wearing blankets such as this one became de rigueur. They are still worn by prominent Osage women at important occasions. Draped across the back, they are folded across the shoulders. The beaded hand symbols on this example, a special feature not always included, signify friendship."

Provenance
Morning Star Gallery, Santa Fe, New Mexico.

Reference
Coe, Ralph T., *The Responsive Eye*, Yale University Press, New Haven, 2003, p. 241.

Estimate: $5,000-$7,000

48104

SIOUX MAN'S WEARING BLANKET

Circa 1890
Length 68½ in. Width 99 in.

This "skunk" blanket is fashioned from two pieces of navy blue wool cloth with white selvage. The term is an obvious reference to the wide, central stripe created by the bands of white selvage. These blankets are also referred to as "courting" blankets. Courtship scenes are commonly depicted in ledger art with a man and a woman enveloped in a similar blanket. The center of the blanket is decorated with a beaded strip, sinew sewn on hide, then stitched to the blanket. The blanket strip is composed of five panels and four rosettes. The panels are decorated with an *u-ma-ne* symbol in red, yellow, navy blue, amber, and metallic beads against a blue bead background. The *u-ma-ne* symbol, frequently seen in Sioux beadwork and quillwork, represents the unappropriated life or power of the earth (which man may obtain). The square or oblong with four radiating lines is interpreted to represent the earth and the four directions. The rosettes are divided into quadrants, alternating in red and blue, outlined in navy blue.

Provenance
Bonhams and Butterfields, Sale 7477E, Lot 3275, December 8, 2003.

Reference
Dorsey, James O., "A Study of Siouan Cults" *Eleventh Annual Report of the Bureau of Ethnology 1889-1890*, Smithsonian Institution, Washington, D.C., p. 451.

Estimate: $4,000-$6,000

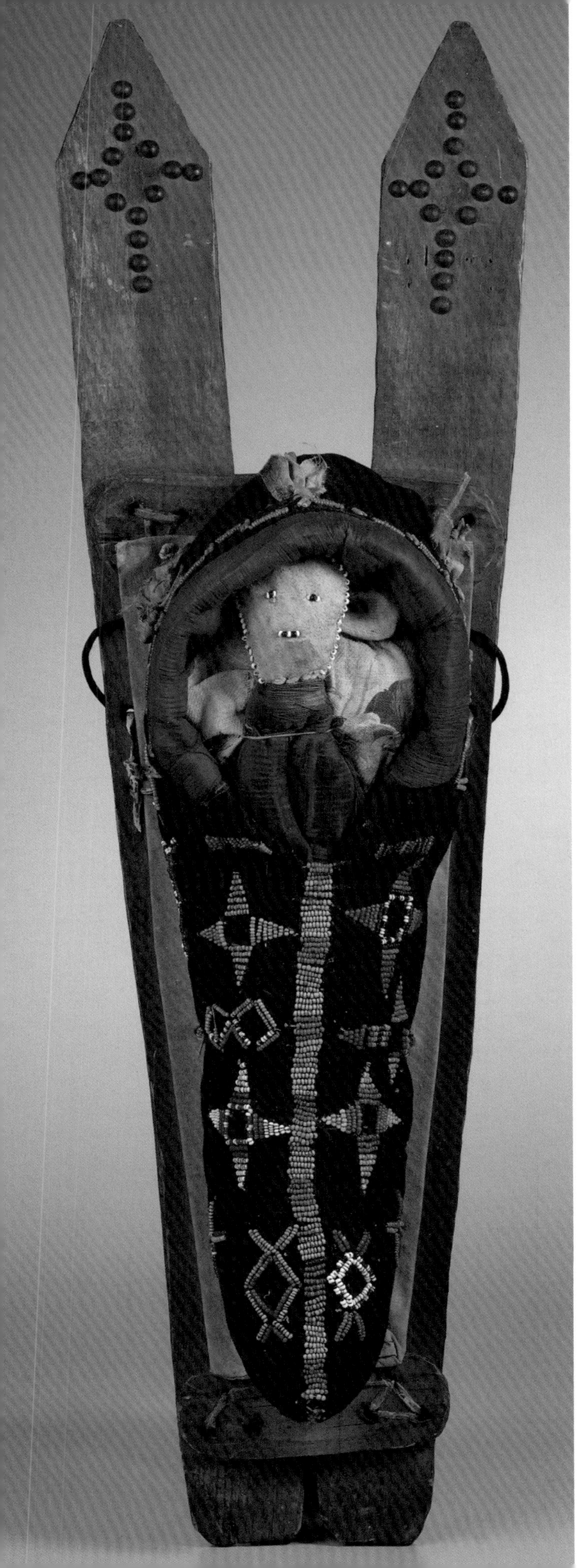

48105

KIOWA TOY CRADLEBOARD

Circa 1895
Length 22 in.

This model cradleboard is made of wool cloth that is partially beaded with four point stars, diamonds, zigzag bands, etc. in various colors set against the black cloth background. Three small muslin pouches, possibly containing tobacco offerings, are sewn to the top of the cradle. A simple hide and cloth doll is fitted into the pouch. The cradle is supported by two wood backboards that are painted red at their peak and decorated with a morning star symbol in brass tacks.

The wood backboard is signed on the reverse "Geronimo's daughter made this, Lawton, Okla."

Provenance
Skinners Auctioneers, Sale 2237, Lot 110, May 22, 2004.

Estimate: $5,000-$7,000

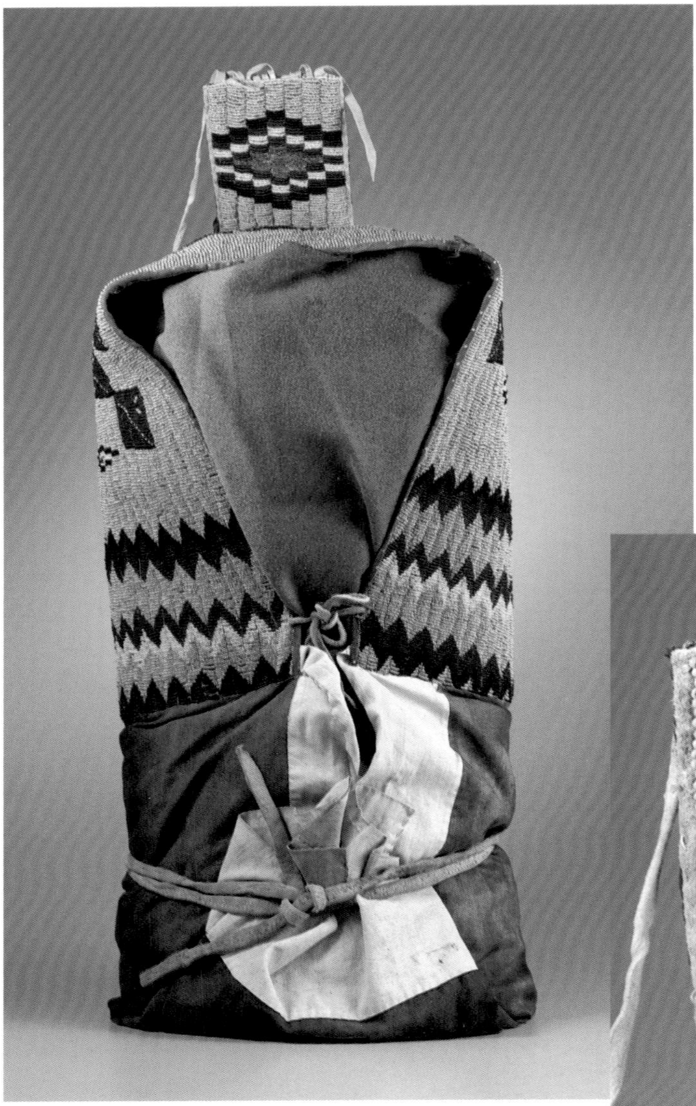

48106

SIOUX BABY CARRIER

Circa 1880
Length 23 in. as mounted

This native tanned hide cradle is fully beaded in lazy stitch with a variety of geometric designs including zigzag bands, crosses, squares, rectangles, and a stepped diamond in red, green, yellow, navy blue, and metallic beads against a blue background, sinew sewn. A cotton cloth wrap has been added below the beaded area.

Provenance
Eleanor Tulman Hancock, New York, NY; Chris Peck, Memphis, TN.

Estimate: $5,000-$7,000

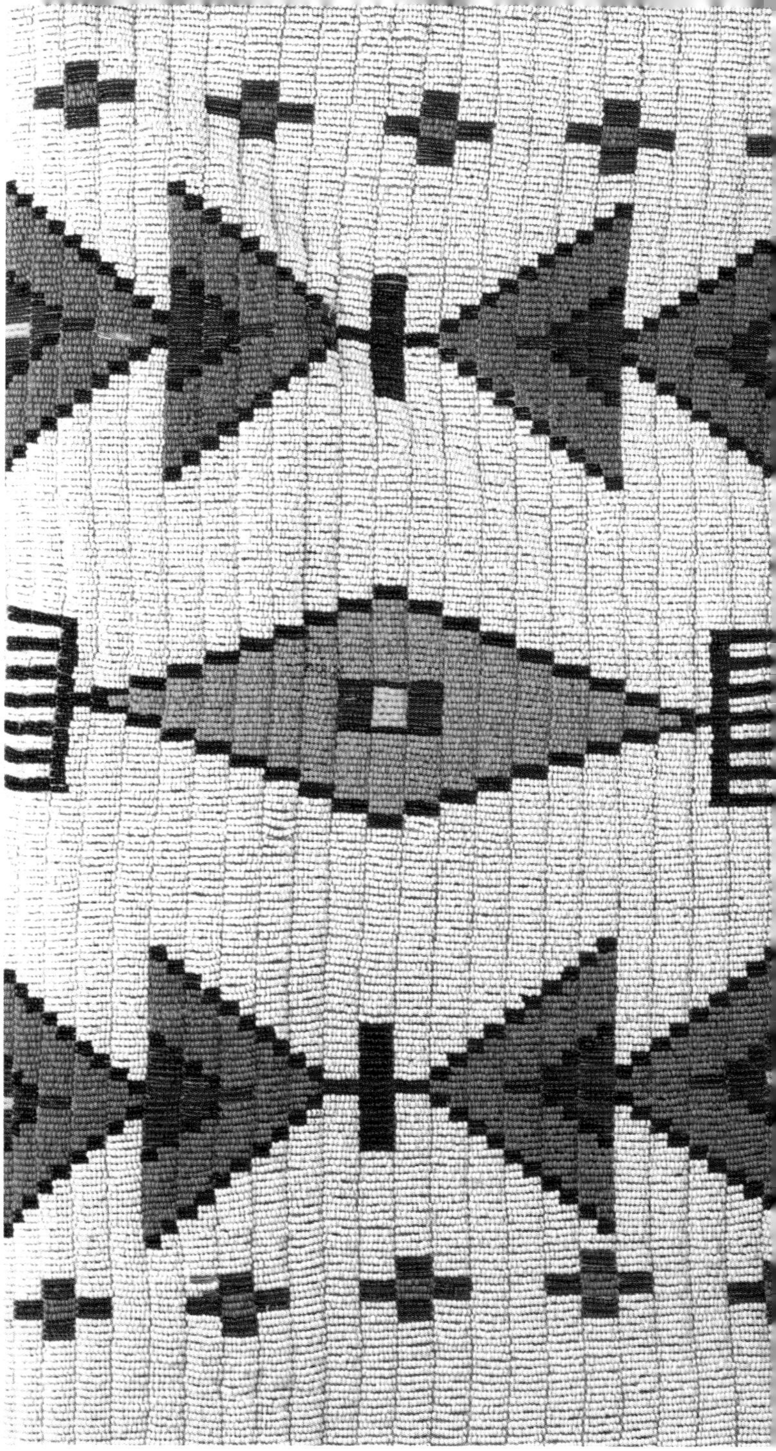

48107

SIOUX BABY CARRIER

Circa 1890
Length 28 in. as mounted

The native tanned hide cradle is fully beaded in lazy stitch with a variety of geometric designs including stepped triangles, stepped diamonds, small squares and crosses, done in green, blue, navy blue, red, and metallic beads against a white background, sinew sewn. Brass hawk bells decorate the rawhide flap and the edges of the opening. A section of wool blanket cloth has been sewn to the base.

Cradles served a variety of roles within Sioux culture. "1-Cradles functioned as child care tools, to keep babies warm, safe, restricted in their movements and easy to carry about. 2-Cradles functioned as art objects. 3-Cradles were cultural products, artifacts of Lakota material culture, identifying the maker and the user as Lakota. 4-Cradles strengthened relationships as gifts made by one woman to give to another to whom she was related by blood or by marriage. 5-Cradles advertised craftswomen's expertise. 6-Cradles were status symbols, designators of rank, indicators of status, re-enforcers or enhancers of status and reflections of a family's prestige."

Reference
Lessard, Rosemary, "Lakota Cradles" in *American Indian Art Magazine*, Volume 16, Number 1, Winter 1990, pp. 44-53.

Estimate: $6,000-$9,000

48108

PAIR OF SEMINOLE DOLLS

Circa 1930
Height, Male 22 in. Height, Female 24¼ in.

This matched pair of male and female dolls is dressed in typical cotton patchwork clothing. The bodies and heads are made of palmetto fiber. The male doll is wearing tanned hide pants. These dolls were made in great quantity over the years to meet tourist demand. Dolls made of palmetto fiber appear as early as 1918. It is rare to find a male and female pair, especially of this large size. The construction of the male doll required extra work time to fabricate the arms and legs and proportionally fewer were made.

Reference
Blackard, David, *Patchwork and Palmettos*, Fort Lauderdale Historical Society, 1990, pp. 56-57.

Estimate: $800-$1,200

48109

UTE TOY CRADLEBOARD

Circa 1880.
Length 21½ in.

This classic miniature is made with native tanned hide covering the wood backboard. The cradle is beaded in lazy stitch with geometric designs in a semi-circular band across the top. A doll made of muslin fits into the pouch. The hide covering has been painted with yellow ochre indicating it was intended for a girl. It is fringed at the bottom and along the top on the reverse. This toy cradle is a finely detailed model of the full sized examples prevalent in Ute culture. (For related examples and a discussion of Ute cradleboards see: Wroth, William (Ed.), *Ute Indian Arts and Culture*, Taylor Museum of the Colorado Springs Fine Arts Center, 2000; pp. 134-141 and 166-168).

Provenance
Skinners Auctioneers, Sale 2265, Lot 185, January 29, 2005.

Estimate: $2,000-$3,000

48110

APACHE SHAWL NECKLACE

Circa 1890
Length 9¾ in. Width 21 in.

The upper portion consists of a cloth panel fully beaded with a step pattern in navy blue against a white background. The edges are fitted with hook and eye clasps. A decorative panel of netted beadwork with a zigzag design in blue and white against a navy blue background drapes below. These elaborate necklaces were commonly worn by a girl during puberty ceremonies and at other important public functions. Other nearby peoples including the Mojave, Pimas, and Paiutes made similar netted beadwork collars. (For similar examples see: Ferg, Alan (Ed.), *Western Apache Material Culture*, University of Arizona Press, Tucson, 1987, p. 106; and Furst, Jill Leslie, *Mojave Pottery, Mojave People*, School of American Research Press, Santa Fe, 2001, pp. 116 and 117.)

Estimate: $1,000-$2,000

48111

CROW FEMALE DOLL

Circa 1890
Height 6¼ in.

The doll is wearing a wool dress embroidered with white seed beads in imitation of classic Crow elk teeth dresses that were the predominant fashion for many years. Materials on this doll include wool and cotton cloth, glass seed beads, tanned hide, and horsehair.

Provenance
Gallery West, Tucson, Arizona.

Estimate: $750-$1,000

48112

SIOUX DOLL DRESS

Circa 1880
Length 11¼ in. Width 8 in.

This native tanned deerskin doll dress is decorated across the yoke with two lanes of beadwork in green, blue, red and white, sinew sewn. The skirt is painted with red triangles outlined in green. Hide fringe decorates the side seams, the ends of the yoke, and hem. This dress is an accurate representation of a full-size woman's dress.

Provenance
Skinners Auctioneers, Sale 2237, Lot 119, May 22, 2004.

Estimate: $400-$600

48113

NORTHERN PLAINS BEADED BALL

Circa 1890
Diameter 2 in. Length with strap 7½ in.

This beaded hide ball with wrist strap is decorated with a striped pattern in pink, yellow, and navy blue against a light blue background. In addition, this example has a number of faceted beads.

Provenance
Skinner Auctioneers, Sale 2237, Lot 106, May 22, 2004.

Estimate: $200-$400

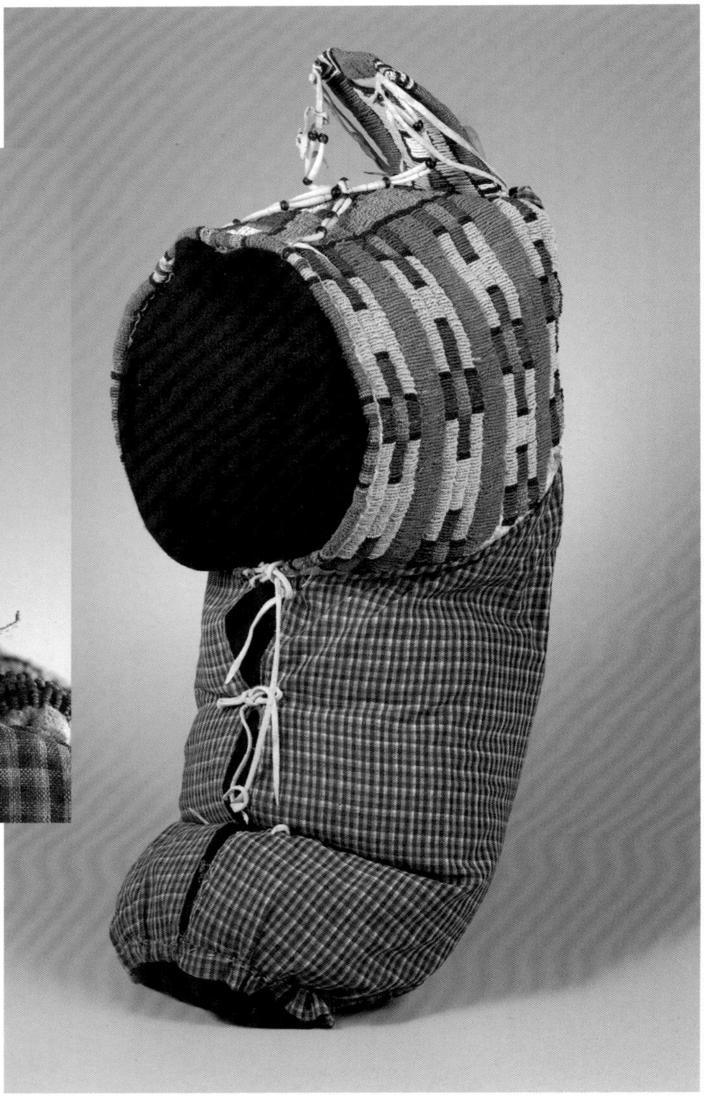

48114

SIOUX BABY CARRIER, WITH TREE DWELLER FIGURE BEADED ON FLAP

Circa 1890
Length 28 in. as pictured

This typical example is made of native tanned cowhide, glass seed beads, dentalium shells, calico cloth, and is sinew sewn. The cradle is beaded with a repetitive pattern of crosses in red, navy blue, and sky blue arranged in bands against a yellow background, then separated by wide green lanes. A section of calico is sewn to the base of the cradle along with hide laces. An interesting and perhaps unique element is the horned figure beaded on the reverse side of the top flap. This may be *Canotida*, the "tree dweller" or "little forest dweller" well known in both Dakota and Lakota mythology. "He is usually malevolent and often 'loses' people in the woods or hills. He sometimes appears to people in visions, however, and if he is secured by a person as a spirit helper in this manner he can be summoned to work for the good of the visionary by performing the proper ceremony."

Provenance
Dennis Lessard, Santa Fe, New Mexico; Butterfields, Sale 7307E, Lot 5248, March 25, 2002.

Reference
Howard, James, "The Tree Dweller Cults of the Dakota"; *Journal of American Folklore*, Volume 68, Number 268, April/June, 1955, p. 170.

Estimate: $4,000-$6,000

48115

OMAHA WOMAN'S SEWING BAG

Circa 1865
Length 8 in. Width 11¾ in.

This rectangular shaped bag is made of native tanned buffalo hide with the hair attached. Bags of this type were commonly used by women to store their sewing tools and materials. This example is beaded along each side with seed beads and across the scalloped cover flap in pony beads. It is a fine example from the pre-reservation era. (For similar examples see: Hanson, James A., *Little Chief's Gatherings*, The Fur Press, Crawford, Nebraska, 1996, pp. 68 and 69; and in Thompson, Judy; *The North American Indian Collection: A Catalogue*, Berne Historical Museum, Switzerland, 1977, p. 160.)

Provenance
Collected by Milford Chandler before 1926. Chandler-Pohrt Collection #3152.

Estimate: $1,000-$1,500

48116

PAWNEE PAINT BAGS (2)

Circa 1860
Length 10¾ in.

These two native tanned buffalo hide pouches were used as containers for dry paint. The longer of the two bags is fringed and has traces of a painted design. This suggests the material was salvaged from a painted robe. The two bags are stored in a calico cloth pouch.

Provenance
Collected from the Pawnee by Milford Chandler before 1926. Chandler-Pohrt Collection #3237.

Estimate: $400-$600

48117

CROW TOBACCO BAG

Circa 1885
Length 26¼ in. Width 5 in.

This native tanned deerskin bag is partially beaded on each side with stylized floral designs in navy blue, sky blue, red, and yellow, all outlined in white. The bag has been rubbed with yellow ochre overall; hide fringing decorates the bottom. The beading is typical of Crow floral designs that became popular toward the end of the 19th century. These stylized floral patterns can also be noted on vests, coats, trousers, gauntlets, and moccasins from the period. (For examples of this art form, well documented to place and time, see: O'Connor, Nancy. *Fred E. Miller: Photographer of the Crows*, University of Montana, Missoula and Carnan VidFilm, Malibu, 1985, plates 25, 35, 65, 67, 77 and 78.)

Estimate: $3,000-$5,000

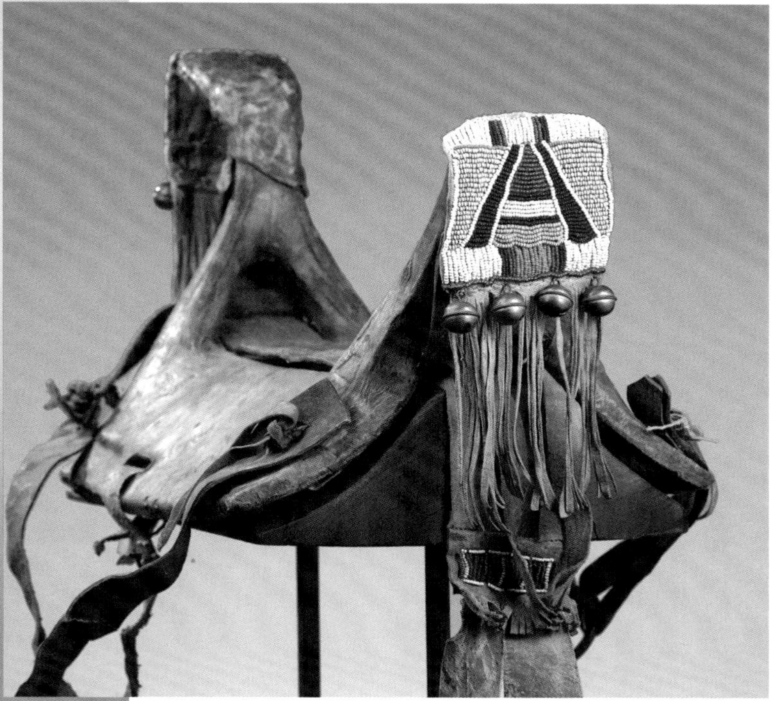

48118

CROW SADDLE

Circa 1875
Length 17 in.

This wood frame saddle with buffalo hide covering is complete with crupper, stirrups, and cinch straps. The pommel and cantle are decorated with beaded panels using classic Crow geometric designs and color preferences. The panels are fringed and brass hawk bells are attached.

Provenance
Christie's, Sale 1389, Lot 272, June 23, 2004.

Estimate: $3,000-$5,000

48119

OJIBWA SHAMAN'S RITUAL MATERIAL

Circa 1880

This group contains an assortment of ceremonial regalia and associated artifacts including a hand drum, several rattles, pipes, charms, herbal medicines, weasel skins, and a series of native pen drawings. This collection was acquired in the 1920s by Alfred A. Allorecht from Johnny Martin at the Plains Ojibwa community of Swan Lake in southern Manitoba. This was during a period when the Canadian government suppressed native religious ceremonials, and when many elderly Indians discarded their ceremonial regalia. This collection consists of at least two groups of objects, each associated with a different religious cult. The heavily fringed costume and the mask with its long crooked nose is the typical outfit of a *Windigokan*, aka Cannibal, Clown, or Fools dancer. The *Windigokanek* was a society of masked dancers who represented cannibalistic ice giants, believed to live in the far north, and prominent in Plains Ojibwa folklore. The leaders of this cult were people who had dreamed of these giants or of thunderbirds, the latter referred to by the large crooked nose of their masks. By means of their dance this cult group was believed to exorcise the demons of disease, who used to invade the Indian camps in wintertime. The *Windigokan* also used their herbal medicines in curing sick people. The many small moccasins attached to this particular costume may refer to success in curing children. This costume, made of tanned and smoked hide, may pre-date the late nineteenth century, since when *Windigokan* costumes were commonly made of old pieces of canvas. Part of this group of objects is an additional long-nosed mask made of canvas, the drum with its cloth cover, the bulbous rattles, and perhaps some of the herbal medicines. The second group of artifacts consists of some beadwork decorated charms or scapulars, the weasel skins, pipes, a pouch filled with sticks, a roll of birchbark, the flat circular rattle, and perhaps the roots. These objects were associated with the *Metawin (Midewiwin)* or Grand Medicine Lodge, the most important religious institution of the Ojibwa, with branches or "lodges" from Wisconsin westwards as far as Saskatchewan. This organization instructed its members in herbal and shamanistic knowledge, used in the securing of a healthy life. The Plains Ojibwa ascribed the origin of the *Metawin* to Nanapus a legendary culture hero who interceded between human beings and the spirits. The organization consisted of four degrees, each with increasing levels of esoteric knowledge transmitted to its members. The beadworked black cloth panels in this collection have small pockets at the back, each containing a small cowrie shell, and each shell referring to magical power transferred to the owner during the rituals of this society. These scapulars were worn on the breast by the initiated members. On one of these scapulars a human figure is pictured with its elbows and knees indicated. This is the scapular of a *Metawin* member of the second degree, on account of having had magic shells placed on his joints, thereby giving him clairvoyance in hunting. The beadwork on the large scapular pictures the spirits of bear and underwater monster, two of the most important *manitos* in the *Metawin* rituals. The two thunderbirds pictured on the strap most probably indicate that the owner of this scapular in his dreams had been adopted by a married couple of thunderbirds.

Provenance

Acquired from Johnny Martin by Alfred A. Allorecht at Swan Lake, Manitoba in the 1920s. Arnold Alderman Collection, Hamden, Connecticut.

References

Howard, James H. *The Plains Ojibwa or Bungi*. Vermillion: South Dakota Museum, University of South Dakota, 1965.
Skinner, Alanson. "Political Organization, Cults, and Ceremonies of the Plains Ojibway and Plains Cree Indians." *Anthropological Papers of the American Museum of Natural History Volume XI*. New York, 1914.

— Ted Brasser, Peterborough, Ontario, June, 2006.

Estimate: $20,000-$40,000

48120

NORTHERN PLAINS MOCCASINS / POSSIBLY FORT PECK ASSINIBOIN

Circa 1890
Length 10¾ in.

This pair features native tanned hide uppers with rawhide soles. The vamps are partially beaded with stylized floral designs. The moccasins have been rubbed overall with an orange ochre. A single lane of beadwork circles the border.

Estimate: $1,000-$2,000

48121

CHEYENNE MOCCASINS

Circa 1890
Length 9½ in.

This pair features native tanned hide uppers with a "U" shaped panel in red, white, navy blue, and sky blue beads decorating the vamps; sinew sewn. The rawhide soles have been removed and replaced with commercial leather soles, complete with heels. This modification probably took place after the pair left Indian hands.

Estimate: $1,000-$1,500

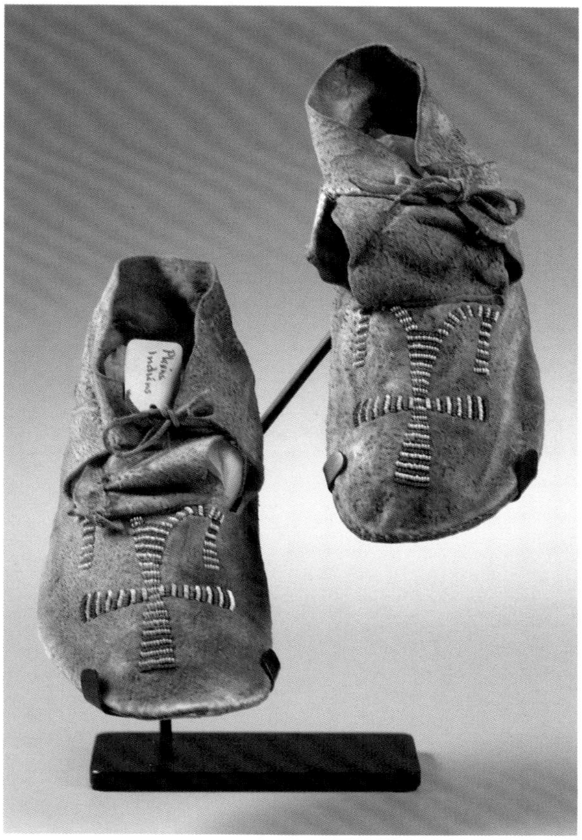

48122

SIOUX MOCCASINS

Circa 1880
Length 7¾ in.

The moccasins have tanned deerskin uppers with rawhide soles. The vamps are decorated with a cross pattern in red, green, and white beads, sinew sewn, and colored overall with yellow ochre.

Estimate: $300-$500

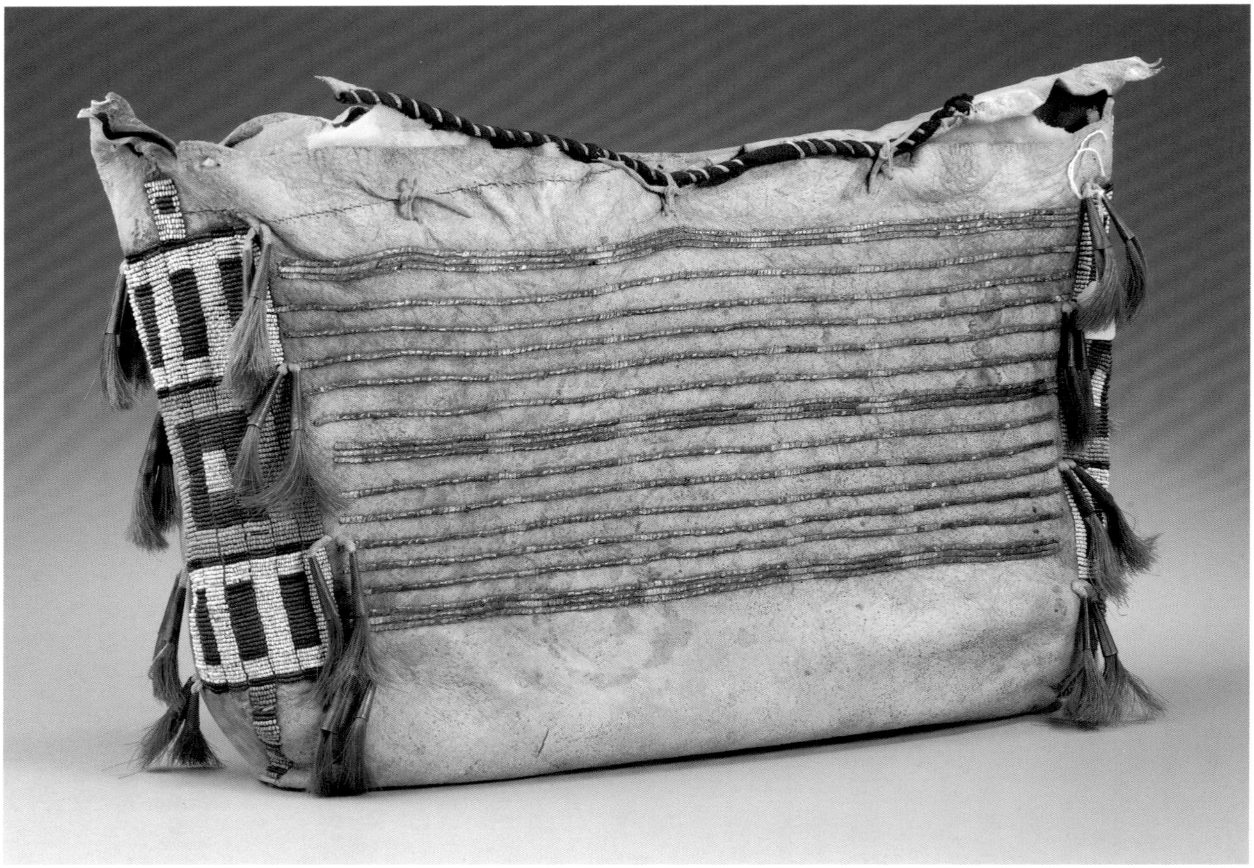

48123

SIOUX TIPI BAG

Circa 1875
Length 13½ in. Width 21½ in.

This native tanned buffalo hide bag is decorated across the front with narrow horizontal bands of red and yellow dyed porcupine quillwork. The sides are beaded with wide panels using geometric patterns in red, green, yellow, blue, and white. The beaded area is edged with tin cones and dyed red horsehair accents.Tipi bags, sometimes referred to as storage bags or possible bags, were all purpose containers and were originally made in matched pairs.

Provenance
Merrill Domas, Old Chatham, New York.

Estimate: $3,000-$5,000

48124

SOUTHERN PLAINS PEYOTE RATTLE

Circa 1900
Length 12½ in. Length overall with fringe 24 in.

The gourd rattle was part of the ritual paraphernalia used by members of the Native American Church (sometimes referred to as the Peyote Cult). The gourd is painted and delicately engraved with a sun image and lightning bands. The wood handle has been covered with hide and bead wrapped. The hide fringe is decorated with brass beads.

Provenance
Bonhams & Butterfields, Sale 7307E, Lot 5302, March 25, 2002.

Estimate: $750-$1,250

48125

UNITED STATES SCOUT PIN AND CABINET CARD PHOTOGRAPH OF AN INDIAN SCOUT

Circa 1880
The pin: Length 1¾ in. Width 2¾ in.
The photograph: Length 6½ in. Width 4¼ in.

This rare cast metal pin was made as an insignia for Indian scouts employed by the Army. The design features the letters USS (United States Scout) above a pair of crossed arrows. This pin is accompanied by a cabinet card photo by Lancaster and Corey, Cedar Falls, Iowa, depicting a Plains Indian holding an eagle feather fan and with a similar USS insignia fixed to his cavalry hat (lying on the fur draped chair to his right).

Estimate: $1,000-$2,000

48126

PLAINS / PRAIRIE ROACH

Circa 1890
Height as pictured 7¼ in. Length 6 in.

This classic example is composed of dyed red deer hair and porcupine hair. The relatively short length, together with the all hair base, is characteristic of late 19th century examples.
The term "roach" for this style of headdress apparently resulted from its resemblance to the roaching or clipping of a horse's mane, which was fashionable in the 19th century.

Estimate: $500-$700

48127

PLAINS / PRAIRIE ROACH

Circa 1920
Height as pictured 7 in. Length 9 in.

This typical example is composed of dyed red deer hair and porcupine hair. The roach is constructed with an all hair base and the chin strap is attached. The roach continues to be an important component of men's traditional and fancy dance outfits.

Estimate: $500-$700

48128

SIOUX BUFFALO HORN ORNAMENT

Circa 1895
Height 8¼ in. Width 12½ in.

This whimsical decoration is composed of two buffalo horns and a central beaded panel in red, green, white, and navy blue against a crystal background. Beginning in the late 19th century, the Sioux produced a variety of non-traditional items to meet the demands of traders, visitors, and curio dealers. The sale of these objects coupled with that of traditional items provided a much needed source of income.

Estimate: $400-$600

48129

EASTERN SIOUX QUILLED AND FRINGED BUFFALO HIDE KNIFE SHEATH

Circa 1850
Length 11¾ in.

This native tanned buffalo hide case is partially decorated with porcupine quillwork. Floral designs executed in red, white, and blue quills are bordered by alternating rows of plaited quillwork in blue and white and blue and red. Quill wrapped hide fringe decorates the upper and lower edge. The sheath is fitted with a buffalo rawhide liner.

Provenance
Deaccessioned from the Memorial Hall Museum, Deerfield, Massachusetts. This knife case is listed as number 19 in the collection of relics as published by the Pocumtuck Valley Memorial Association in Deerfield (1920). The knife case was collected by Francis Thompson, a local judge and historian from Greenfield, Massachusetts (1833-1916). This lot is accompanied by documents from the museum.

Estimate: $8,000-$12,000

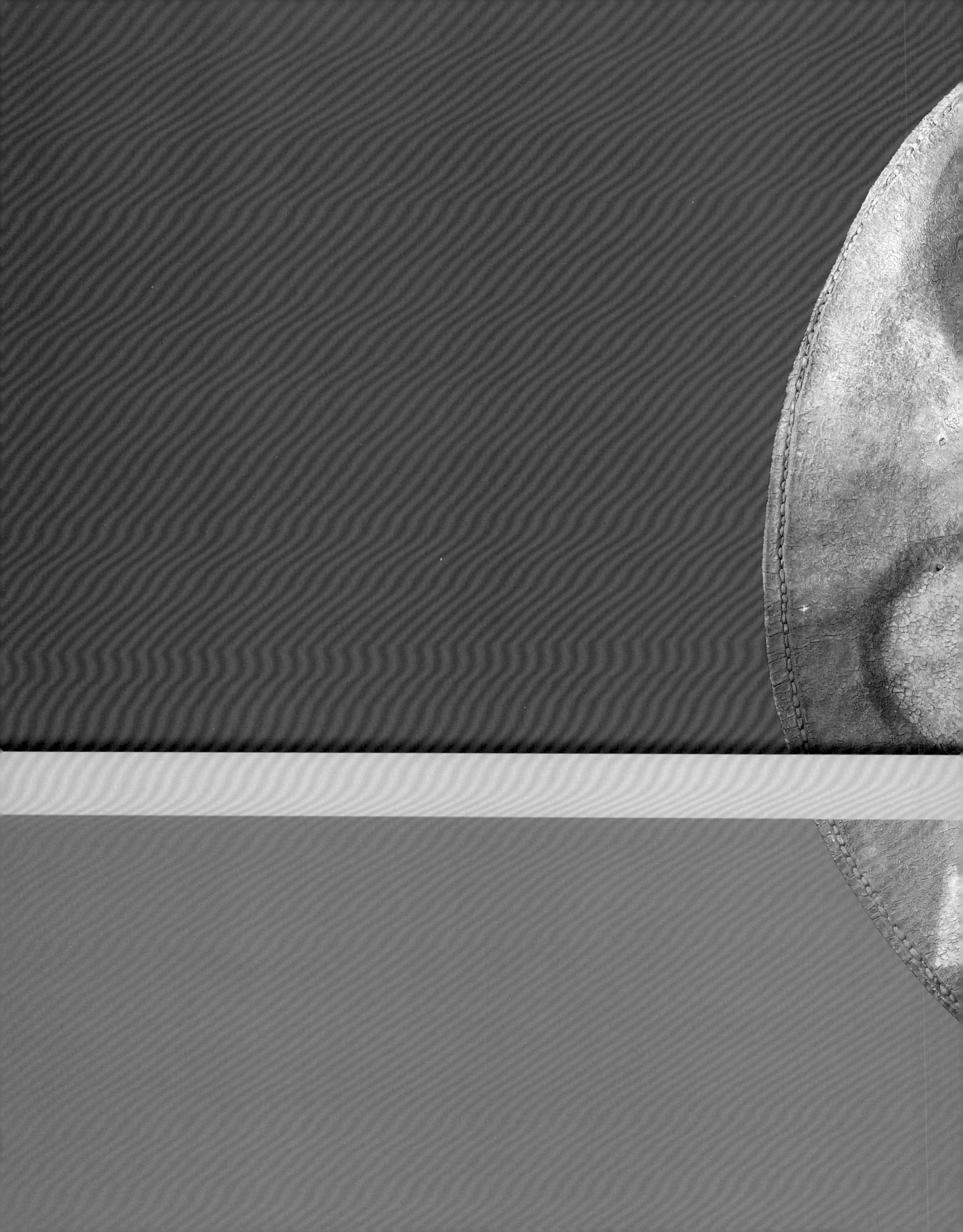

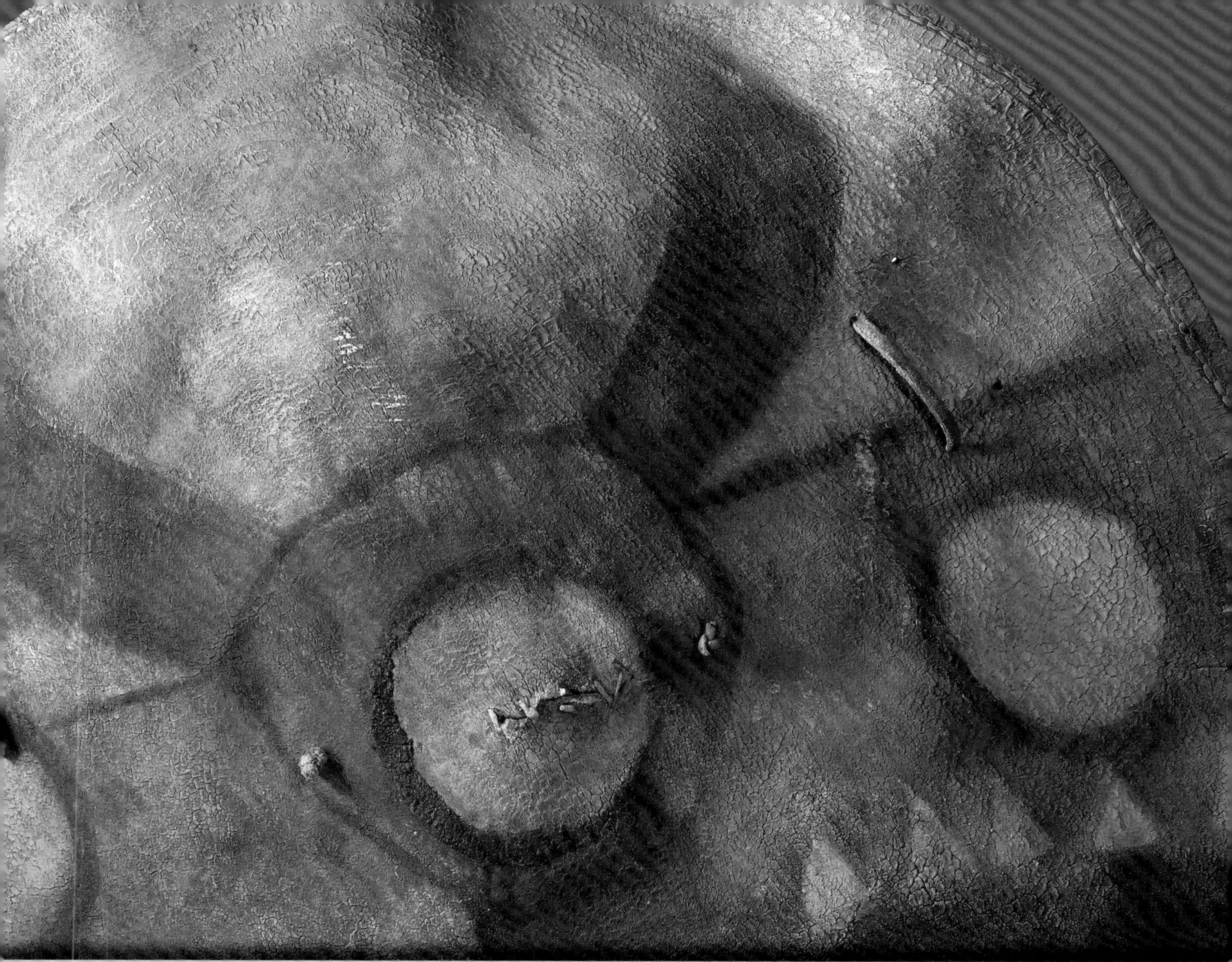

Weapons

48130

OMAHA GUNSTOCK CLUB

Circa 1850
Length 28 in.

This classic gunstock club is made of pinewood and engraved on each side with single line designs, most painted with vermilion. The club is fitted with a double edged steel blade that is anchored to the stock with a metal pin and a lead collar. The handle is decorated with two brass tacks and there is hot file branding on the hand grip. The club has a fine, deep brown patina.

Provenance
Ex-Museum of the American Indian, Heye Foundation with collection number painted on the stock in black 19/5093. The club was de-accessioned by exchange in November, 1963.

Estimate: $10,000-$15,000

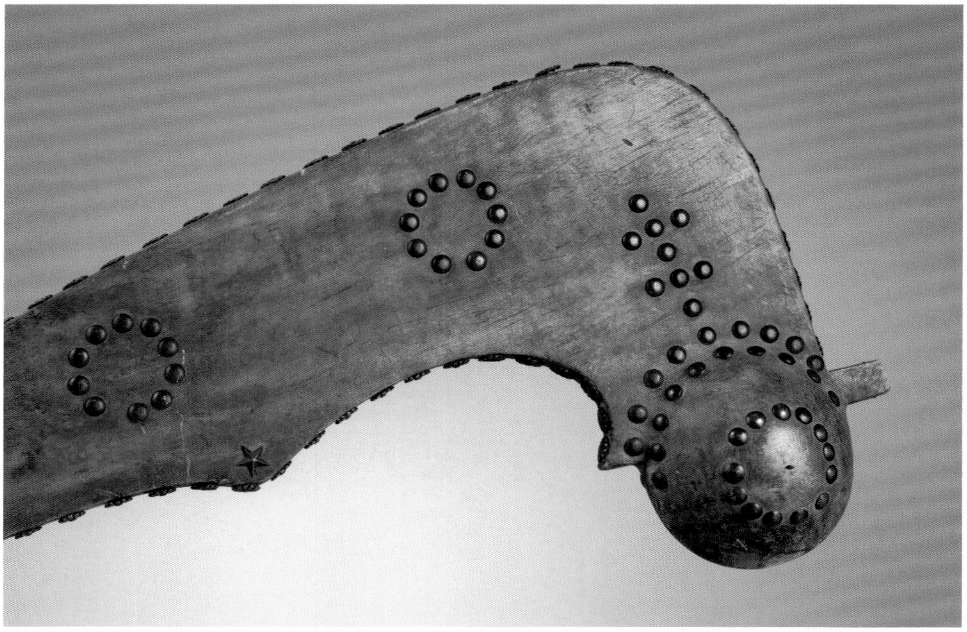

48131

SIOUX BALL HEAD WAR CLUB

Circa 1850
Length 33 in.

This relatively large war club is gracefully carved with the pleasing proportions so characteristic of the form. The wood club is decorated with brass upholstery tacks on both sides of the handle, around the ball head, and along the inner and outer edges. The grip is wrapped with a wool braid.

The ball head club was well known throughout the Eastern Woodlands, Great Lakes and Prairie. It was a formidable weapon, highly effective in hand-to-hand combat. This club compares favorably with an example in the Denver Art Museum collections, no doubt made by the same hand. (See: Conn, Richard, *Native American Art in the Denver Art Museum*, Denver Art Museum, 1979, p. 116; and again in Conn, Richard, *Circles of the World*, Denver Art Museum, 1982, p. 107.)

Provenance
Sotheby's, Sale 6853, Lot 130, May 21, 1996.

Estimate: $20,000-$30,000

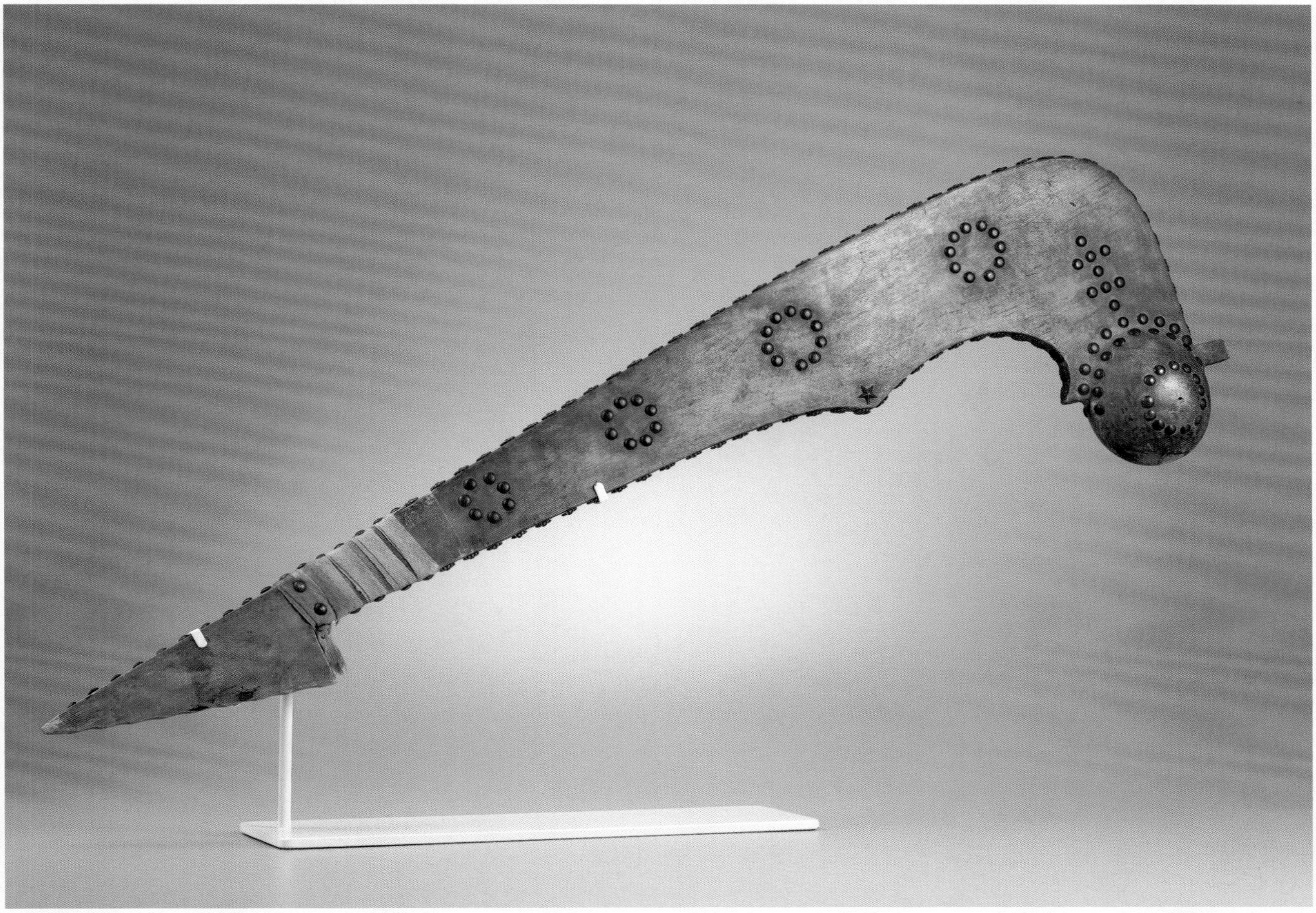

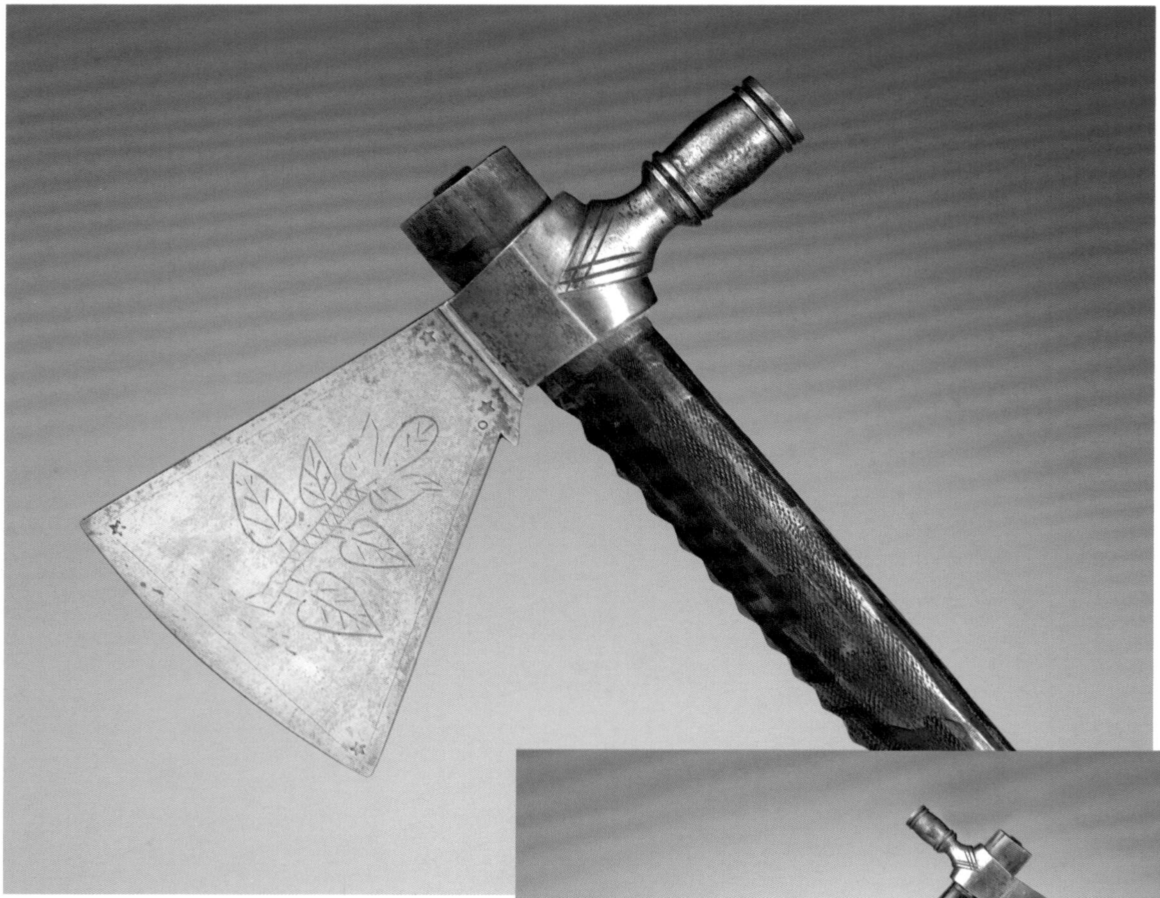

48132

PIPE TOMAHAWK BY J. WILSON

Circa 1850
Length 23 in. overall; Length 8½ in. the blade

The hand forged iron blade is decorated on one side with a brass inlaid foliate motif and cold stamped five point stars at the corners. The opposing side is rocker engraved with a similar foliate design and the same cold stamped stars. The blade is fitted to an ash wood handle with a carved scallop pattern near the top, hot file branding overall, and a deep brown patina. The majority of pipe tomahawks were made by frontier blacksmiths who labored in obscurity. By and large, little is known about them and their craft. Wilson embellished the classic features of the Plains tomahawk with stamping, engraving, and inlay. His tomahawk blades are quite distinctive and readily identifiable. Examples are present in a number of important collections. Harold Peterson illustrates two Wilson tomahawks in his classic study (See: Peterson, Harold, *American Indian Tomahawks*, Museum of the American Indian, Heye Foundation, 1971, item 188, p. 118 and item 198, p. 120). Both tomahawks are in the collections of the National Museum of the American Indian. Another example is rocker engraved with the words "Made by J. Wilson" along the edge of the blade. This tomahawk was collected from an Omaha Indian around 1860. (See: Baldwin, John, *Tomahawks and Pipe Axes of the American Frontier*, Early American Artistry Trading Company, West Olive, Michigan, 1995, p. 103.)

Provenance
Chandler-Pohrt Collection, catalogue number 618.

Estimate: $10,000-$15,000

48133

PIPE TOMAHAWK BY J. WILSON WITH BEAD AND COIN PENDANT

Circa 1850
Length 19½ in. overall; Length 8 in. the blade

This hand forged iron pipe tomahawk is decorated on the blade and eye with rocker engraving in a variety of floral and foliate motifs. The blade is fitted to an ash wood handle that is decorated with brass tacks and hot file branding. The handle exhibits a deep brown patina. There are two short strands of faceted cobalt blue beads, each ending with an Indian head cent, tied to the handle.

Provenance
Chandler-Pohrt Collection, catalogue number 905.

Estimate: $10,000-$15,000

48134

CROW BEADED AND FRINGED RIFLE SCABBARD

Circa 1875
Length 51 in.

This native tanned buffalo hide gun case is decorated at the muzzle end and butt end with geometric patterns using both glass seed beads and red wool trade cloth as design elements. The muzzle end has long buffalo hide fringe in typical Crow fashion. This gun case is emblematic of the lavishly ornamented accoutrements of the Crow warrior.

Provenanace: Chandler-Pohrt Collection. Lynn Brooks, Auburn, Indiana.

Estimate: $12,000-$15,000

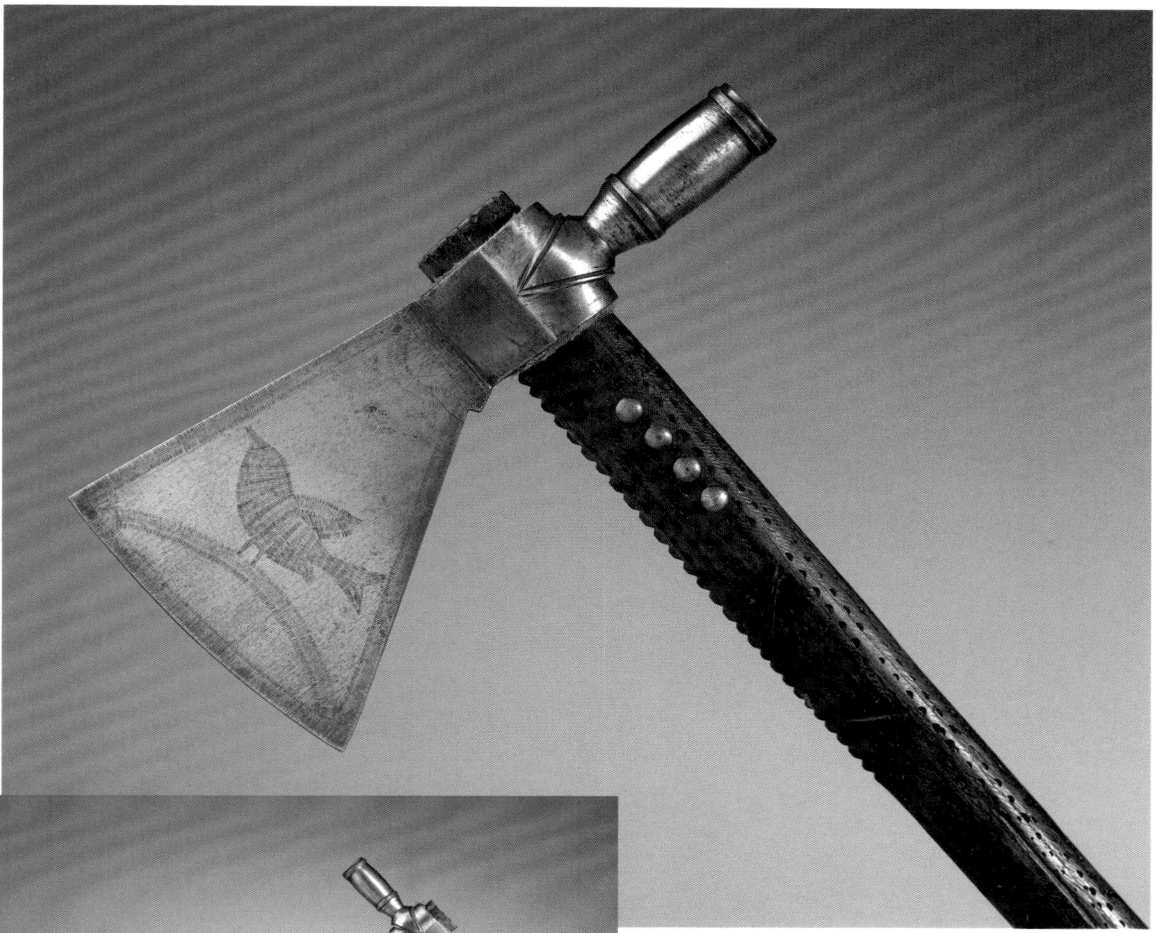

48135

PIPE TOMAHAWK BY J. WILSON

Circa 1850
Length 23¾ in. overall; Length 8¼ in. the blade

This hand forged iron pipe tomahawk is decorated with rocker engraving. One side of the blade contains a floral design while the opposing side depicts a bird perched on a branch. The blade is fitted to a wood handle decorated with brass upholstery tacks and hot file branded with a coarse rasp. The handle has scallop carving for approximately six inches below the eye of the blade.

Provenance
Chandler-Pohrt Collection, catalogue number 879.

Estimate: $10,000-$15,000

48136

CROW TOMAHAWK WITH HEART CUTOUT AND BEADED AND FRINGED PENDANT

Circa 1890
Length 51¼ in. overall; Length 8½ in. the blade proper

The hand forged iron ceremonial blade with heart cutout is fitted to an ash wood handle decorated with brass tacks and hot file branding in a chevron pattern. The handle is wrapped with red wool cloth and hide lacing to secure the triangular shaped drop. The drop is beaded with classic Crow colors and geometric designs. The long hide fringe is decorated with basket beads.

Provenance
Drew Bax Collection, Denver, Colorado.
Sherwoods Spirit of America, Santa Fe, New Mexico.

Estimate: $10,000-$15,000

48137

SIOUX TOMAHAWK, BEADED PENDANT WITH HORSETRACK DESIGNS

Circa 1870
Length 46 in. overall; Length 9½ in. the blade

This hand forged iron blade is of the classic western Plains form, likely fabricated from an old gun barrel. The blade is fitted to an ash wood handle decorated with nine brass tacks. A decorative beaded drop is secured to the handle by a section of fringed hide and red wool braid. The triangular shaped pendant is beaded with a series of horse tracks in navy blue against the light blue background. Twisted hide fringe, four brass hawk bells, and a piece of red wool trade cloth with white selvage finish the ornament. The hide is backed with calico.

Provenance
Tom Haas, Riverton, Utah

Estimate: $15,000-$20,000

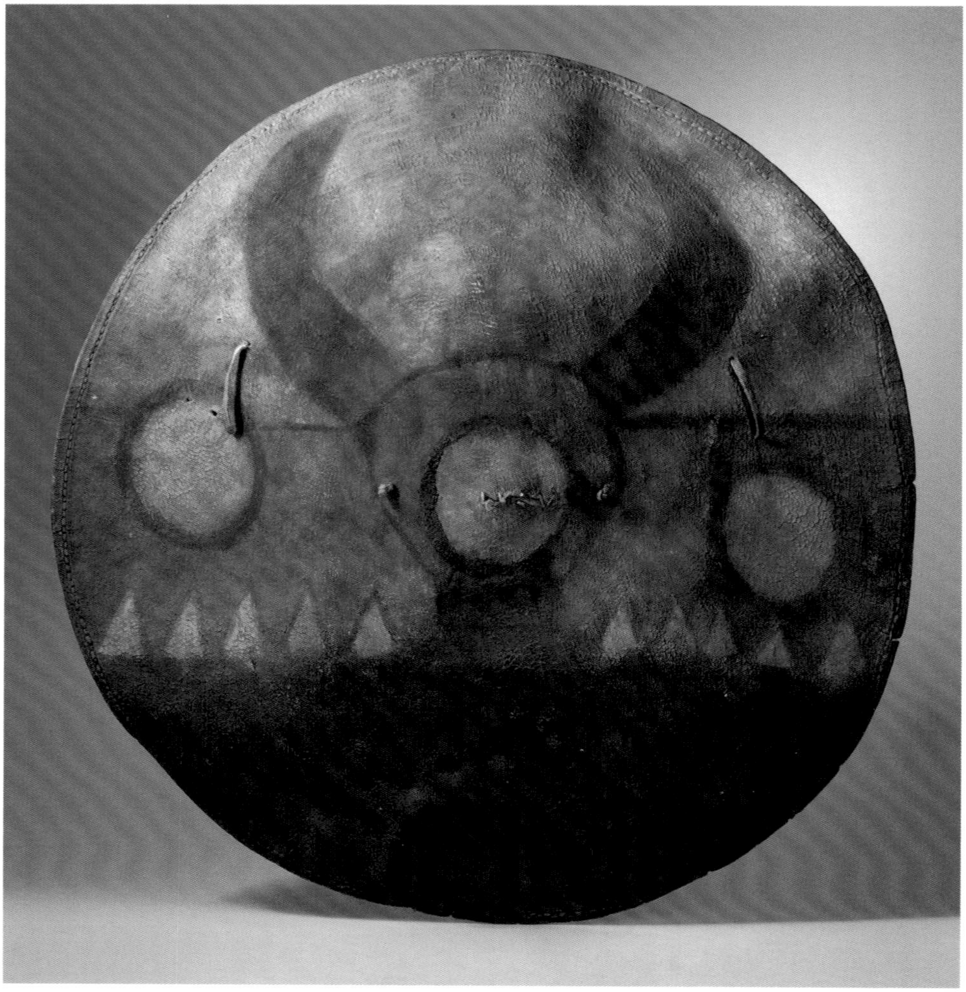

48138

PUEBLO BUFFALO RAWHIDE WAR SHIELD

Circa 1800
Diameter 23 in.

This early, slightly convex war shield is composed of two layers of buffalo rawhide, the perimeter finely and tightly stitched along the rim. A horned figure dominates the center of the shield. A series of yellow triangles emerge from the horizon line that marks the lower third of the shield. Three yellow spheres move across the center. The reverse is undecorated and vestiges of the carrying ties remain.

The Pueblo people fought primarily on foot and used the shield as a true defensive device. Its effectiveness was enhanced by supernatural protection afforded by the painted symbols.
This shield is stylistically similar to a number of documented shields collected at Jemez Pueblo in the early years of the 20th century. (See: Wright, Barton; *Pueblo Shields*, Northland Press, Flagstaff, Arizona, 1976, pp. 48-61.)

Provenance
Christie's, Sale 1332, Lot 53, June 12, 2004.

Estimate: $15,000-$25,000

48139

PUEBLO BUFFALO RAWHIDE WAR SHIELD

Circa 1800
Diameter 14 in.

This thick buffalo rawhide shield is finely painted with a pair of avanyus (water serpents), a central vertical band in black, green, and red, and with small green circles spread over the white background. A short wood handle, usually associated with Pima shields, is tied to the reverse. (For similar examples in size and design see: Wright, Barton; *Pueblo Shields*, Northland Press, Flagstaff, Arizona, 1976, figure 17, p. 30 and figure 27, p. 40.)

Provenance
From the estate of Paul Peralta-Ramos, founder of the Millicent Rogers Museum in Taos, New Mexico.
Sotheby's, Lot 146, June 24, 2004.

Estimate: $10,000-$15,000

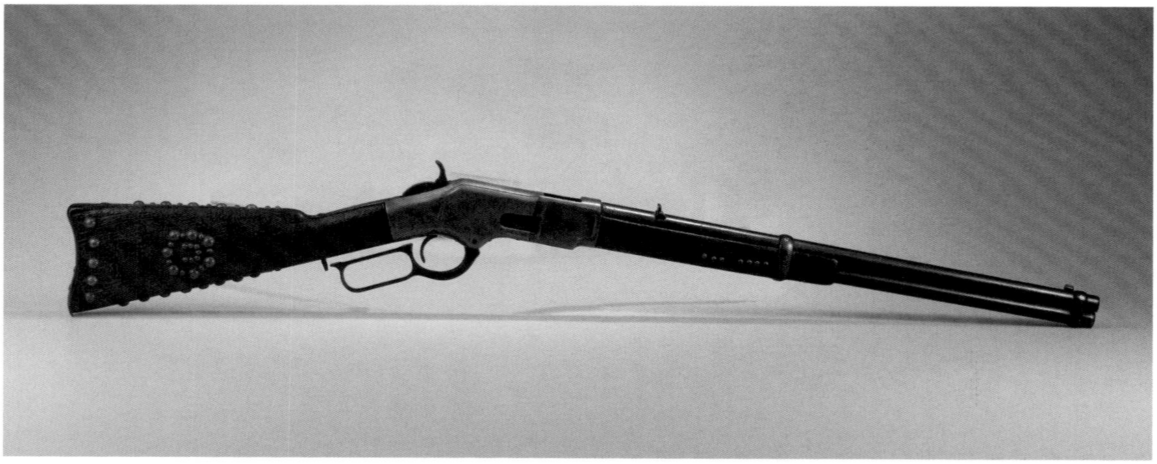

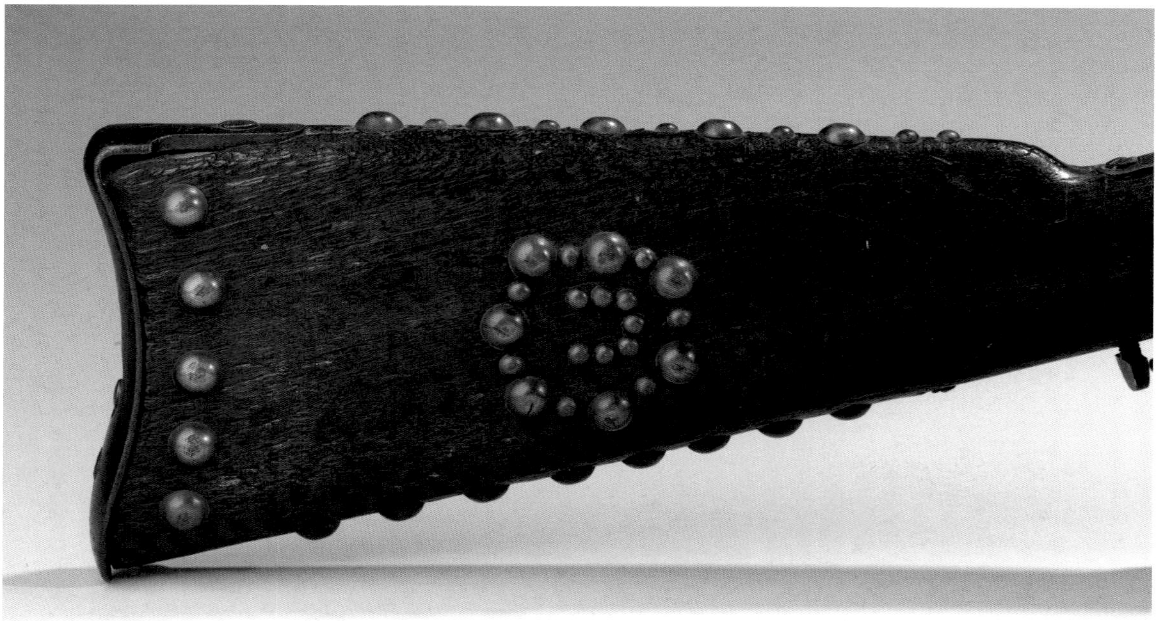

48140

TACKED WINCHESTER MODEL 66 SADDLE RING CARBINE FROM BLACKFEET CHIEF CURLEY BEAR

1871
Length 38½ in.

This gun bears the serial number 76622 and was manufactured in 1871. The stock is decorated with brass and copper tacks including a horse track motif. This model is commonly known as a "Yellow Boy". This gun was originally collected from Curley Bear, a Blackfeet Indian, leader of the Siksika Blackfeet Indians.

Provenance
Sherwood's Spirit of America, Santa Fe, New Mexico.

Estimate: $3,000-$5,000

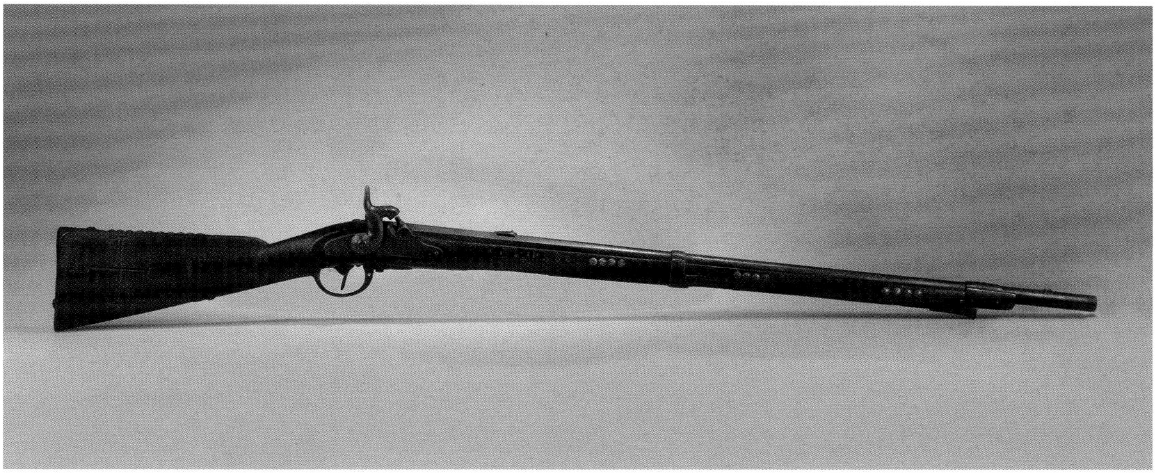

48141

INDIAN MUSKET WITH CARVED AND TACKED STOCK

Circa 1862
Length 48⅜ in.

This .50 caliber Austrian musket was imported to the Confederacy during the Civil War, circumventing the Union blockade, and used to arm Confederate troops in Texas and the West. The original spring, hammer, and nipple are present while the ramrod is missing. The lockplate is stamped "862". The stock has a fine patina and is uncleaned. This gun subsequently found its way into Indian hands. The stock is carved on each side with a four directions symbol and decorated with brass tacks.

Provenance
Tommy Haas, Riverton, Utah.

Estimate: $2,000-$3,000

48142

CHEYENNE PICTOGRAPHIC DANCE SHIELD DEPICTING WARRIORS ON HORSEBACK

Circa 1890
Diameter 16 in.

This late 19th century shield is composed of a thin rawhide base and a native tanned hide cover. The cover is painted with two mounted warriors, each wearing eagle feather bonnets with trailers, set against a yellow background. Below the central black horizon band is the image of a buffalo, painted in black against the blue green background. A red and navy blue wool cloth banner is tied to the rim in classic Plains fashion. The thin rawhide base together with the pictographic subjects clearly indicate that this is a dance shield from the reservation period.

Provenance
Collected by Charles Edward Mendenhall (1849-1937).
Skinners Auctioneers, Sale 2237, Lot 150, May 22, 2004.

Estimate: $4,000-$6,000

48143

APACHE BOW CASE AND QUIVER

Circa 1870
Length 39 in. bow case; Length 29 in. quiver

This utilitarian set is made of native tanned hide rubbed overall with kaolin, stitched with sinew, and bound together with hide lacing. There are two five-point stars painted in indigo on the bow case. In addition, there is a plain wood bow and five arrows, two with metal points; the remaining three are missing their tips.

Estimate: $3,000-$5,000

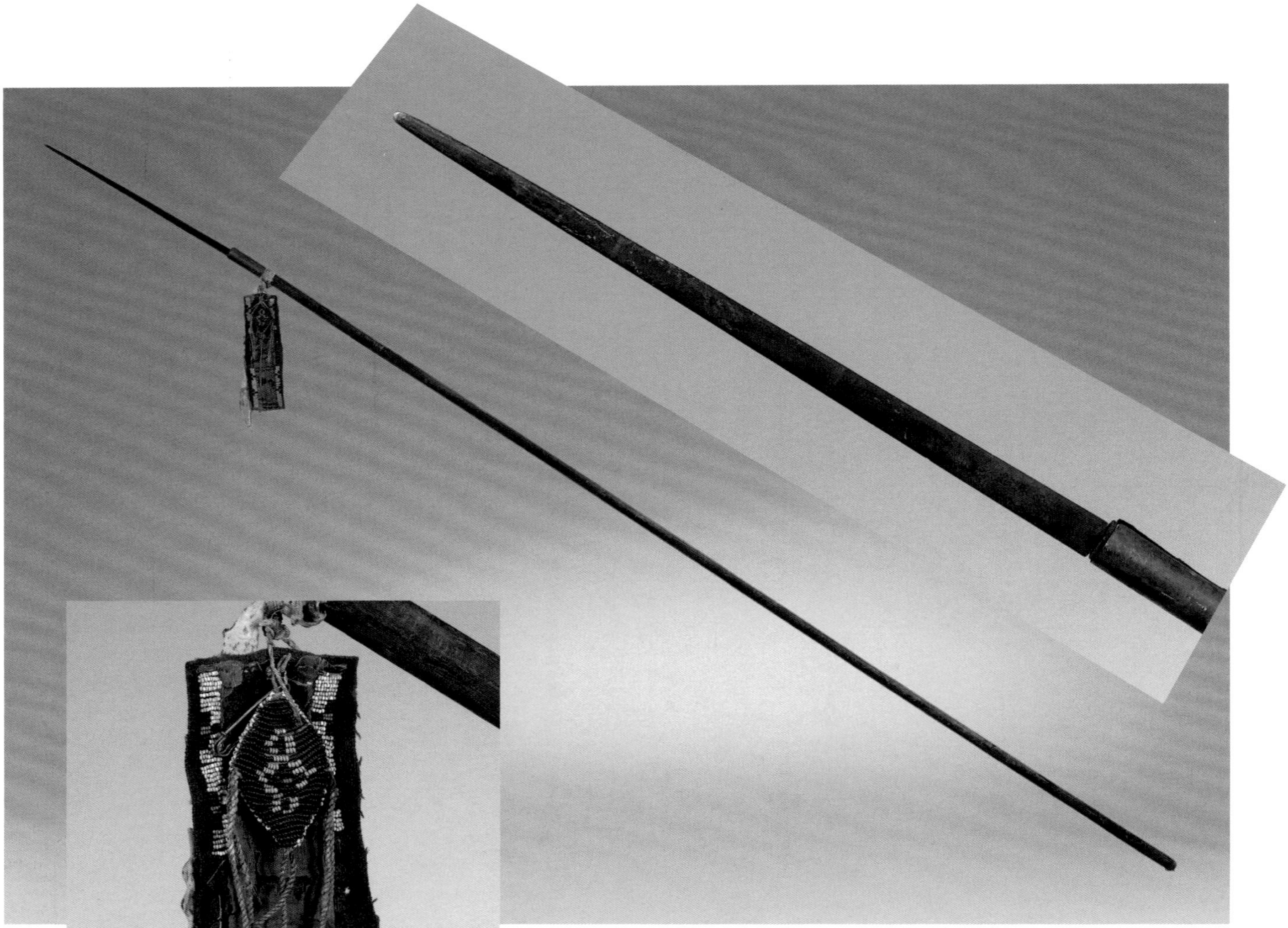

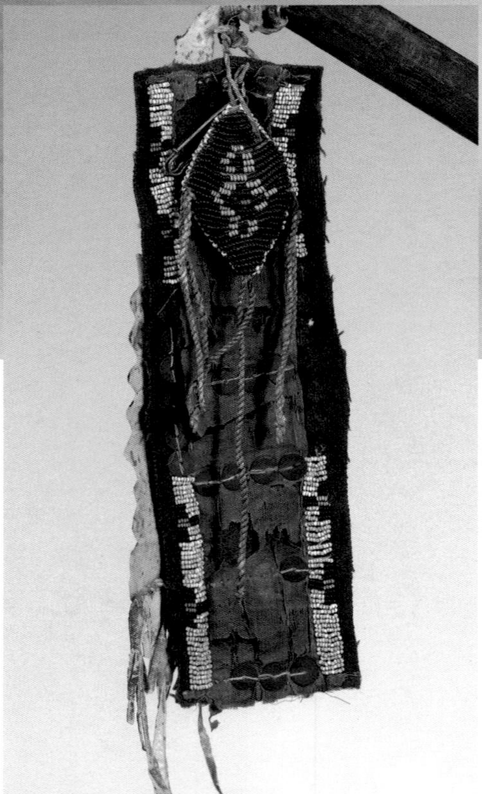

48144

KIOWA WARRIOR'S LANCE COLLECTED BY JAMES MOONEY

Circa 1860
Length 101 in.

This lance is characterized by a long (16") double edged blade, which may have been adapted from a sword or bayonet. It is fixed to the 7-foot long wood handle with a sheet metal collar. The lance is decorated with a small beaded amulet, a plain tanned hide pendant with scalloped sides and bottom fringe, and a red wool stroud pendant partially beaded with one lane along each side, cotton cloth, and metal sequins. (The red cloth has been tested by David Wenger, Ph.D. and is pure cochineal-dyed.)
Authentic lances have always been scarce and are perhaps the rarest form of the Indian weaponry. It is very unusual to find an intact, unrestored example with such impeccable documentation.

Provenance
Collected in Oklahoma from the Kiowa by James Mooney, senior anthropologist for the Smithsonian Institution's Bureau of Ethnology. Descended in the family with an accompanying letter from Mooney's grandson, Anton Levandowsky, dated April 16, 2000. Trotta-Bono, Shrub Oak, New York. (James Mooney is best known for his monumental study of the Ghost Dance religion, "The Ghost Dance Religion and the Sioux Outbreak of 1890", published in the *14th Annual Report of the Bureau of American Ethnology*, 1896. James Mooney was a prolific scholar and produced notable studies based upon his fieldwork with the Cherokee and Kiowa. In 1891, while doing research on the Kiowa-Comanche Reservation he photographed a Kiowa named Adalpepti mounted on horseback wearing an eagle feather bonnet with trailer, holding his shield, and carrying a lance. The lance pictured bears a strong resemblance to the Hendershott example and may be the same. See: Merrill, Hansson,Greene,and Reuss, *A Guide to the Kiowa Collections at the Smithsonian Institution*, Smithsonian Institution Press, Washington, D.C., 1997, p. 308.)

Estimate: $10,000-$20,000

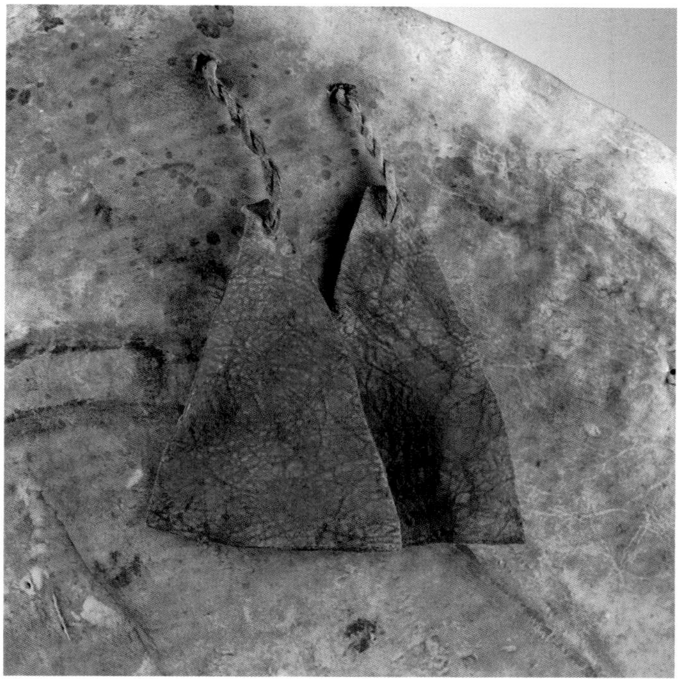

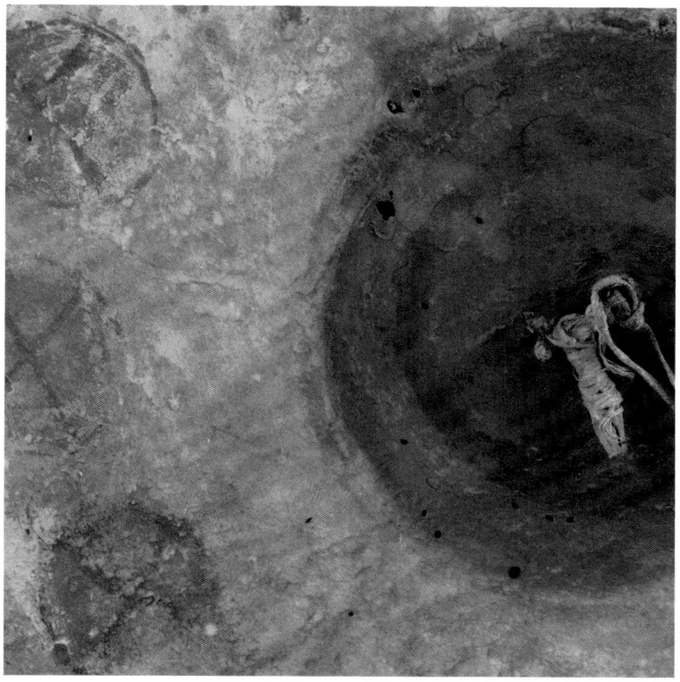

48145

KIOWA PAINTED HIDE WAR SHIELD

Circa 1850
Diameter 18 in.

This shield is composed of a native tanned hide cover and a buffalo rawhide base with the buffalo hair attached. The soft tanned cover is painted with a central sun symbol in red, green, and blue, an elongated crescent moon above, flanked by six red spheres, and a dragonfly at the bottom, center. A pair of tanned hide "ears" painted red and blue orient the shield. A brass hawk bell is fastened to the outer cover and traces of other attachments remain. The cover is gathered and laced in, on the reverse, in typical Plains fashion.

Provenance
Collected by Father William Thomson of the Benedictine Monastery in Canon City, Colorado.

Estimate: $10,000-$15,000

48146

MIMBRES WOOD BOW AND ARROW

Circa 1000-1200 AD
Length 53¾ in. the bow; Length 35 in. the arrow

This ancient wooden bow is wrapped with sinew at various points along its length. Pitch residue is also present. The bow is accompanied by a single reed arrow with a foreshaft with a flint point.

Cached in caves, bows and arrows from the prehistoric Southwest have survived the ravages of time and weather. A group of three, nearly identical to this example, is illustrated in Forrest Fenn's collection. "The bow and arrow made their appearance in America about two thousand years ago...The three Southwest bows shown here could have been made as long ago as 1150. All are wrapped with sinew bands around the shafts, which are nearly circular in cross section. Such wrappings are designed to increase the force of the bow as well as to prevent the wood from shivering from the vibrations of firing...These bows have no nocks to hold the bowstring in place. They rely upon the strings end nooses and the wrappings, as well as the tapering tips, to keep the strings in place."

Provenance
Richard Corrow Collection, Santa Fe, New Mexico.

Reference
Hanson, James A. *Spirits in the Art*. Kansas City: The Lowell Press, 1994, pp. 180 and 181.

Estimate: $2,000-$4,000

48147

TAOS PUEBLO DANCE SHIELD

Circa 1890
Diameter 16½ in.

This late 19th century shield is made of thin buffalo rawhide (as evidenced by the brown epidermis and traces of fur on the reverse). The front is painted with a sunburst in the center, a black crescent above, and a series of black dots around the perimeter. A red trade wool banner is attached to the rim in typical fashion.

Estimate: $1,000-$2,000

48148

SIOUX MINIATURE BOW CASE AND QUIVER

Circa 1865
Length of bow case 12 in.; Length of quiver 9 in.;
Length of bow 16 in.; Length of arrows 11½ in.

This rare example is made of native tanned buffalo hide and decorated with fine porcupine quillwork. The top and bottom of both the bow case and quiver are decorated with quilled panels. The intervening space is filled with narrow, single lines of quillwork. The set is complete with a miniature wood bow with sinew bowstring and five miniature arrows. The set is a faithful recreation of a full scale ensemble. It was likely made for a warrior's favored son.

Provenance
Gallery West, Tucson, Arizona.

Estimate: $8,000-$12,000

48149

COMANCHE WOOD BOW AND ARROW, CAPTURED AT FORT BROWN, TEXAS, 1846

Length 51¾ in. bow; Length 27 in. arrow.

The carved wood bow shows traces of red and dark blue paint in a geometric design overall. It is complete with its sinew bowstring and a single iron tipped arrow. An inscription on the arrow states: "captured on May 8, 1846 at Fort Brown, Texas".

Estimate: $1,200-$1,800

48150

SOUTHERN PLAINS BOW AND ARROWS

Circa 1860
Length 45 in. bow; Length 27 in. longest arrow

This wood bow is sinew backed and complete with its sinew bowstring. The sinew backing and the sides of the bow are painted green. Two iron tipped arrows accompany the bow. (The bow is cracked in one spot.)

Estimate: $500-$1,000

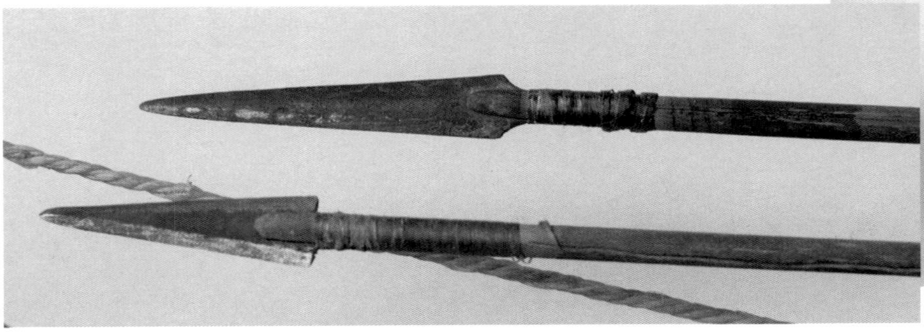

48151

KIOWA MODEL SHIELD

Circa 1890
Diameter 14 in.

The model shield is made with a rawhide base and a native tanned hide cover. The shield cover is painted with a highly stylized bear paw outlined in red paint. A cow tail and two bead wrapped fringes with tin cones and dyed red horsehair are tied to the shield. On the reverse, the tanned cover is fitted and laced over the rawhide base in typical Plains fashion. Portions of the rawhide base have been rubbed with white and green paint. (For further information and related examples see: McCoy, Ron, "Miniature Shields: James Mooney's Fieldwork Among the Kiowa and Kiowa-Apache," *American Indian Art Magazine*, Volume 20, Number 3, Summer, 1995, pp. 64-71).

Provenance
Sotheby's: American Indian Art, Andy Warhol Collection, Lot 2537, April 28, 1998.

Estimate: $2,000-$4,000

48152

KIOWA WARRIOR'S BOW CASE AND QUIVER

Circa 1870
Length 54 in.

This classic set is fashioned from native tanned buffalo hide. There is minimal beading at the top of both bow case and quiver. Traces of red and yellow ochre paint remain. A plain wood bow (missing the bowstring) and three iron tipped arrows complete the set. A strike-a-light case is tied to the quiver. It is beaded on saddle leather with a central stepped diamond in red and blue, outlined in white, against a navy blue background. Tin cones further decorate the case and the fringe is wrapped with bands of German silver. A brass concho is fastened to the cover flap. The strike-a-light case holds a firesteel and a carved bone vent pick used to clean a percussion rifle. An awl case, also beaded on saddle leather, is decorated with diagonal stripes in white against a navy blue background and suspended from the set.

Provenance
Tom Haas, Riverton, Utah

Reference
Identical to the set illustrated on page 179 in Steve Alley and Jim Hamm, *Encyclopedia of Native American Bows, Arrows, and Quivers, Volume 2, Plains and Southwest*. Goldthwaite, Texas: Bois d'Arc Press, 2002.

Estimate: $15,000-$25,000

48153

PLAINS INDIAN BUFFALO HIDE BOW CASE AND HORSE HIDE QUIVER

Circa 1860
Length 46 in. overall with bow;
Length 39 in. bow case
Length 27 in. quiver

This rare set consists of a buffalo hide bow case, a horse hide quiver, and a buffalo hide carrying strap. Traces of red wool cloth remain. A plain wood bow with a sinew bowstring and three arrows, two with metal points, accompanies the ensemble. This Civil War-era set shows good age and heavy use. An old collection tag reads, "Central Plains Horse Hide Quiver 1860".

Estimate: $8,000-$12,000

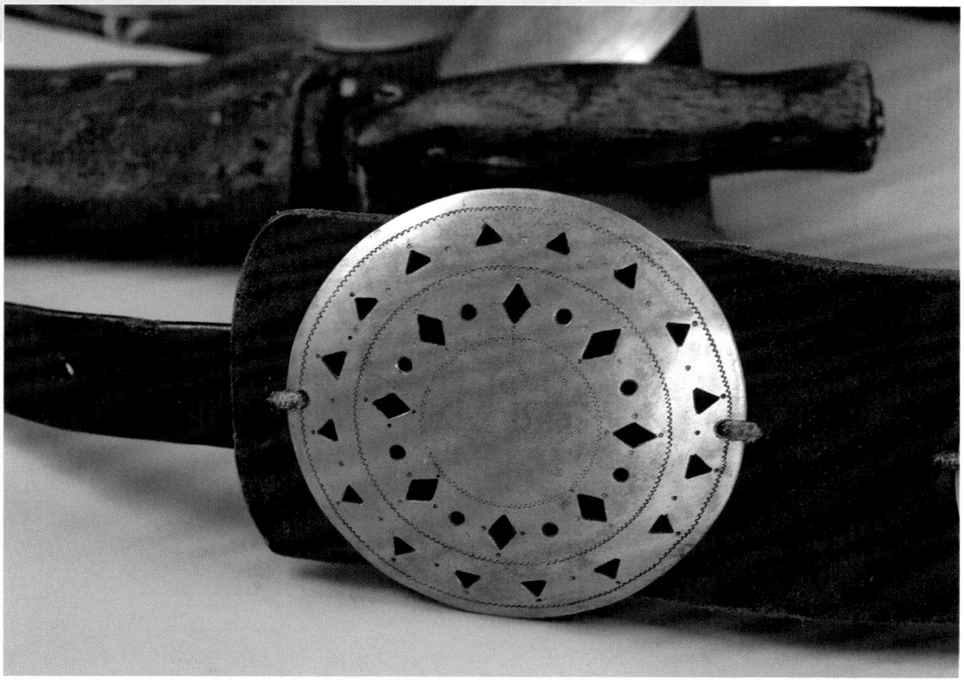

48154

SOUTHERN PLAINS BELT WITH KNIFE CASE

Circa 1875
Length of belt 46 in.
Length of belt drop 26½ in.

This commercially tanned leather belt is decorated with nine German silver conchos, together with an attached belt drop decorated with twelve German silver conchos in graduated sizes. The belt drop indicates that this was a woman's ensemble. A buffalo rawhide knife case, complete with knife, is attached to the belt. Some of the conchos have rocker engraving and one has cutout designs.

Provenance
Sherwoods Spirit of America, Santa Fe, New Mexico.

Estimate: $3,000-$4,000

48155

PLAINS INDIAN ANTLER HANDLE KNIFE

Circa 1850
Length 14¼ in.

The single edge steel blade is fitted to an antler handle. The grip is fastened to the blade with a single rivet and a lead collar.

Estimate: $400-$600

48156

LOT OF THREE TRADE KNIVES

Circa 1875
Lengths 10½ in. 15 in. 10¾ in.

All have single edge steel blades and are fitted with wood grips. Two knives are stamped on the left face with the maker's name. These knives are typical examples of those used to butcher buffalo in the field.

Estimate: $200-$300

48157

SIOUX PAINTED WOOD BOW

Circa 1875
Length 38¼ in.

The bow is painted with a yellow wash on the front surface while the back is finely carved with a series of small triangles connected by an engraved line, grouped in pairs, and painted either red or green along the length. The bow is complete with the original sinew bowstring.

Publications

Allely, Steve and Hamm, Jim, *Encyclopedia of Native American Bows, Arrows, and Quivers, Volume 2, Plains and Southwest*. Goldthwaite, Texas: Bois d'Arc Press, 2002, p. 156.

Estimate: $1,200-$1,800

48158

MATCHING SET OF FIVE SOUTHERN PLAINS ARROWS

Circa 1880
Length 27½ in. the longest

Each arrow is delicately engraved, then painted in red. Two are engraved with lightning bands, two with designs suggesting arrow points, and one with two lances—one on each side of the long, narrow point.

These rare arrows can be favorably compared with several examples in the literature. A single arrow pictured as figure 3, plate XLIV in *North American Bows, Arrows, and Quivers* is identified as a "Gambling arrow of the Apache Indians". After a brief description, the author states "Used in divination and gambling". A similar group of five carved and engraved arrows is in the Brooklyn Museum collections. They are pictured in *Objects of Myth and Memory*, p. 19, and described as "Kiowa arrows made by F.H. Cushing". Frank Hamilton Cushing (1857-1900) was a pioneer ethnologist who lived with the Zuni from 1879-1884. Cushing and Stewart Culin, curator of the Brooklyn Museum, were great friends and "From Washington, Cushing provided inspiration, encouragement, and most important, examples of games and arrows, many made with his own hands". A third reference can be found in *Bows, Arrows, and Quivers of the American Frontier*, p. 40. This single engraved arrow is identified as Cheyenne. (Note: The Apache example from *North American Bows, Arrows, and Quivers* is illustrated on page 34 of this book.)

Provenance

Richard Corrow Collection, Santa Fe, New Mexico.

References

Mason, Otis Tufton. *North American Bows, Arrows, and Quivers.* Washington: Smithsonian Report for 1893. Government Printing Office, 1894. Plate XLIV.

Fane, Diane, Jacknis, Ira, and Breen, Lise. *Objects of Myth and Memory.* The Brooklyn Museum, 1991, pp. 16-19.

Baldwin, John. *Bows, Arrows, and Quivers of the American Frontier*, West Olive, Michigan: Early American Artistry Trading Company, 1999, pp. 34 and 40.

Estimate: $3,000-$5,000

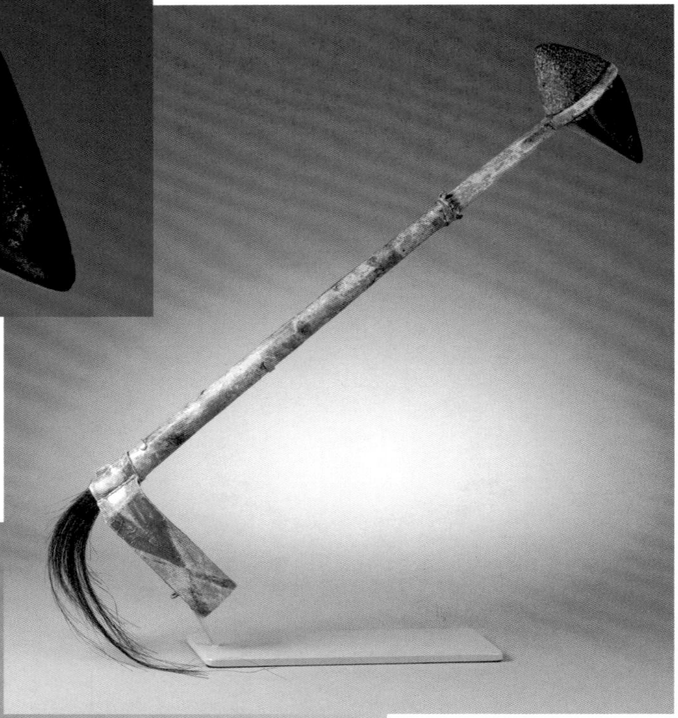

48159

MDEWANKTON SIOUX GRANITE HEAD WAR CLUB DESCENDED IN CHIEF CLOUDMAN'S FAMILY

Circa 1875
Length 22 in.

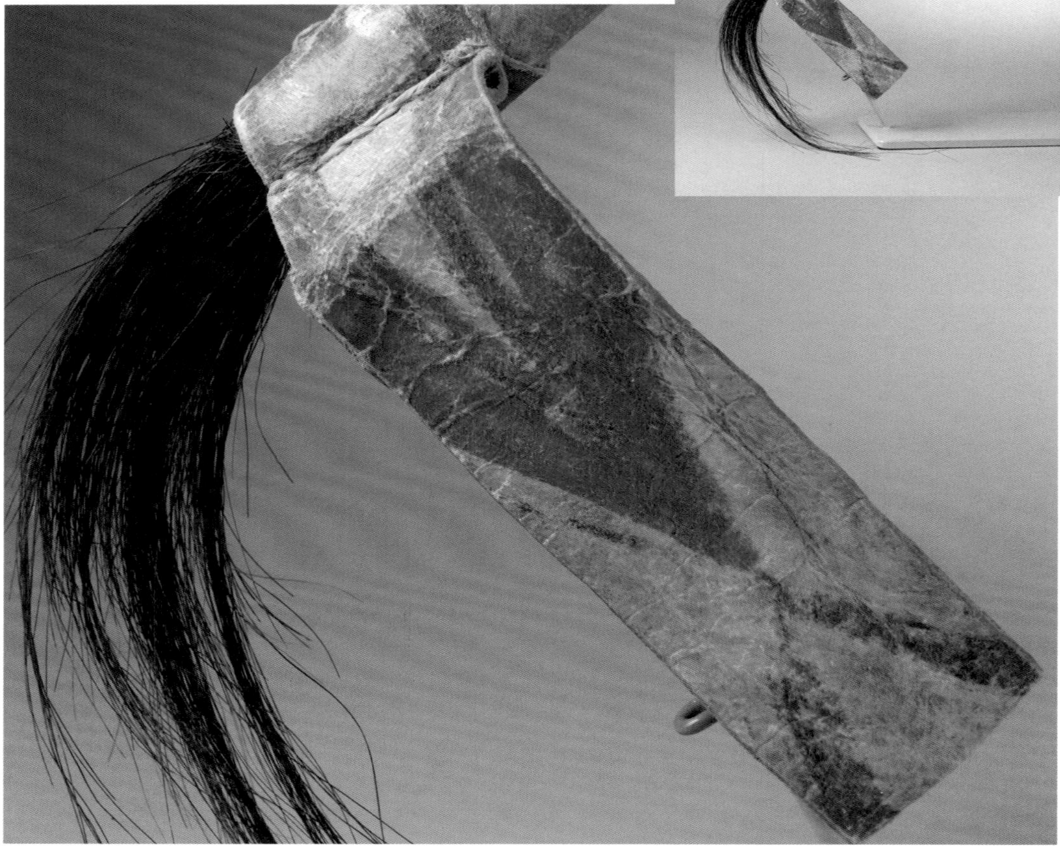

This unusual club is made with a granite head, half of which has been polished, fitted to a wood handle. The handle is wrapped with painted rawhide salvaged from a parfleche case and laced with sinew. There is a tuft of black horsehair at the end of the haft and a wrist strip also fashioned from the parfleche.

Provenance
This is one of three war clubs given to Sheriff Thomas Card Johnson of Knox County Nebraska. His mother, Mary Taliaferro, was the daughter of Chief Cloudman, whose village was at Lake Calhoun in present day Minneapolis. Her autobiography is on micro-film at the Minnesota Historical Society. Jay Mackley, Airville, Pennsylvania.

Estimate: $800-$1,200

48160

SIOUX STONE HEAD WAR CLUB

Circa 1875
Length 26 in.

The stone head is fitted to a wood handle wrapped with rawhide. Half of the stone club head is wrapped in a beaded buffalo hide "hood" with tin cones. The end of the handle is wrapped with fine bands of plaited quillwork in red and white quills, then finished with a tuft of brightly dyed red horsehair.

Estimate: $1,000-$2,000

48161

SIOUX WAR CLUB

Circa 1875
Length 28 in.

The club head is made from two buffalo horns, anchored to a wood handle which has been wrapped with glass seed beads and black and dyed red horsehair. A length of horsehair is attached to the end of the handle.

Provenance
Skinner Auctioneers, Sale 2209, Lot 220, September 20, 2003.

Estimate: $750-$1,250

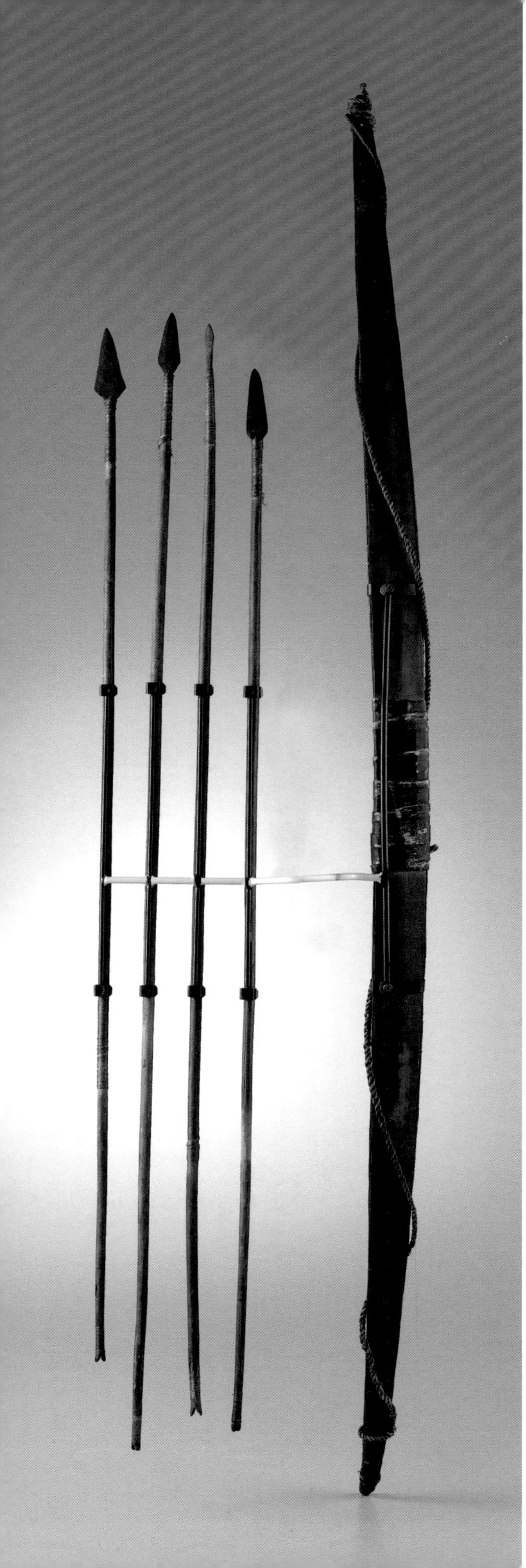

48162

SHOSHONI CHIEF EAGLE EYE'S BOW AND ARROWS CAPTURED FROM HIM IN IDAHO TERRITORY, 1868

Circa 1868
Length 34 in. the bow; Length 26¾ in. the longest arrow

"This important bow and arrow set of historical significance is a masterpiece of American Indian archery. It is a composite bow of wood, sinew backed and sealed with pitch and/or animal tallow, with rawhide wrappings at its grip area concealing bird quills and exhibiting good age and manufacture. This perfectly tillered bow, the relationship and balance of each bow limb to pull uniformly, is a perfect example of the type used in the northwestern Plains and eastern Plateau. Its pull weight would be estimated to be about 40 pounds. Only a few similar examples exist, some made from elk antler are even more rare...The bow retains its original multi-strand, twisted sinew string, again demonstrating a high degree of skill in its making.

"Of the thousands of arrows this author has seen, these arrows represent the finest example of a 'Plains' type self-arrow, that is, of one-piece construction. They average 25 inches in length and the ¼ inches diameter midsection tapers gracefully to both the distal and proximal end, which finishes in a perfectly expanding nock. Two straight shallow grooves representing 'spirit lines' are evident on each arrow. These arrows are carefully hand-hewn to be of the correct spine, meaning, matched to the bow's weight for perfect cast. Few aboriginal arrows exhibit such care in manufacture. The well-fitted points are of native manufacture, and the short cropped fletching would give uniform and speedy flight. There is no doubt this matched set represents one of the best examples of the American Indian bowyer's craft and would be a very formidable weapon in the hands of a warrior on horseback."[1]

The words "Eagle Eye Chief of WeiserSnake Indians, August, 1868" and "Presented to Col. Sinclair" are painted on the face of the bow. Eagle Eye was chief of the Weiser River band of Shoshoni. He is mentioned in numerous accounts during the later 19th century as government officials sought to move all the independent bands onto the Fort Hall Reservation (Idaho). "News also came of a 'band of thieving Snakes' on the headwaters of Weiser River. The commander of Fort Boise immediately sent out a scouting party, and on August 19, 1868, Captain James B. Sinclair reported back to Chief Eagle Eye and his band of forty-one Indians of which thirteen were men. In addition the Captain brought in twenty-one horses and a large quantity of dried roots and salmon, part of which was used as rations by the eighteen soldiers for the last twenty days of the trip. The Indians probably did not appreciate this assault on their winter food supply by their captors, especially a few days later when, in a council with Eagle Eye, Governor Ballard and the army officers satisfied themselves that these Shoshoni were not really hostile and allowed them to return to Weiser Valley. A short while later the governor learned to his chagrin that apparently the same group of Indians had begun committing depredations along the Weiser. He decided it was necessary to dispatch Agent Hough to bring them back if they could be found. Eagle Eye's band continued to cause slight excitement in the area for a number of years before they were finally persuaded to move to a reservation after the turn of the century."[2]

Provenance
Richard Corrow Collection, Santa Fe, New Mexico. This lot is accompanied by Colonel Sinclair's military records from the National Archives. It includes copies of letters from the governor of Idaho territory congratulating Sinclair on capturing Chief Eagle Eye.

Reference
[1]Corrow, Richard personal correspondence, June 9, 2006.
[2]Madsen, Brigham *The Northern Shoshoni*. The Caxton Printers, Caldwell, 1980, p. 54.

Estimate: $5,000-$7,500

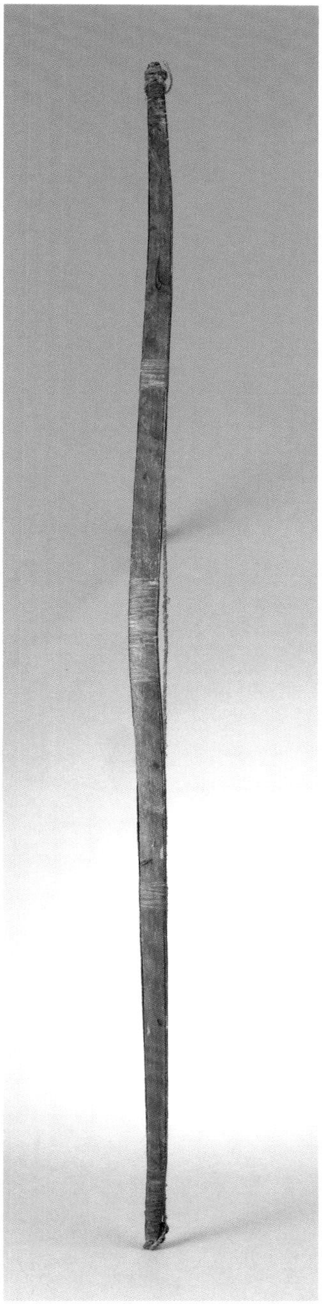

48163

UTE WOOD BOW

Circa 1860
Length 43 in.

This wood bow is backed with sinew and then further strengthened with bands of sinew wrapped horizontally around the bow in five places. This fine utilitarian example is complete with its sinew bowstring.

Provenance
Richard Corrow, Santa Fe, New Mexico.

Estimate: $500-$1,000

48164

SOUTHERN PLAINS WOOD BOW

Circa 1870
Length 43 in.

This ash wood bow is painted red on both the outer and inner surfaces and green along the sides. The bow comes with its original sinew bowstring.

Provenance
Robert Jerich, Countryside, Illinois.

Estimate: $300-$500

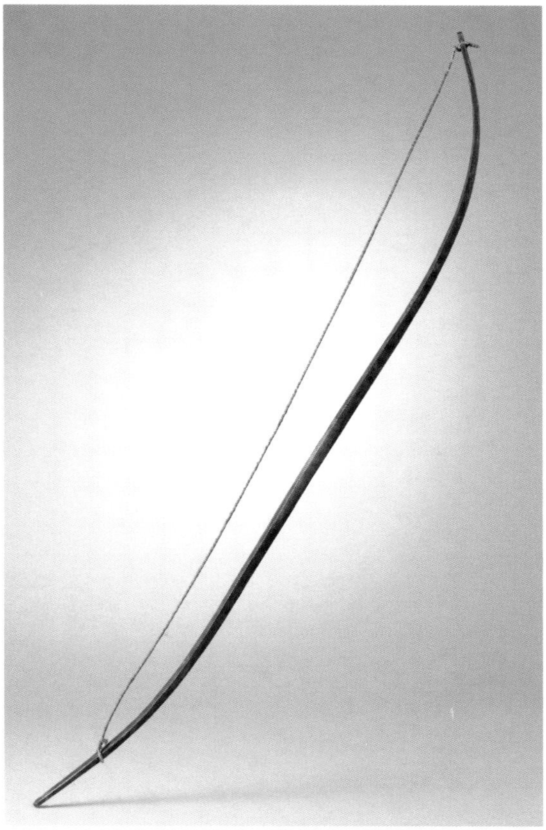

48165

MOJAVE BOW AND ARROW

Circa 1880
Length 54½ in.

This wood bow from the California desert region has curved tips and is painted with a bold pattern of triangles in red and black on the front and a series of dotted crosses in black framed by red diamonds on the inner surface. The ends are wrapped with cotton cord and blue wool yarn. The original vegetal fiber bowstring is intact. A single wood arrow with iron point was collected with the bow.

Provenance
Richard Corrow, Santa Fe, New Mexico.

Estimate: $750-$1,000

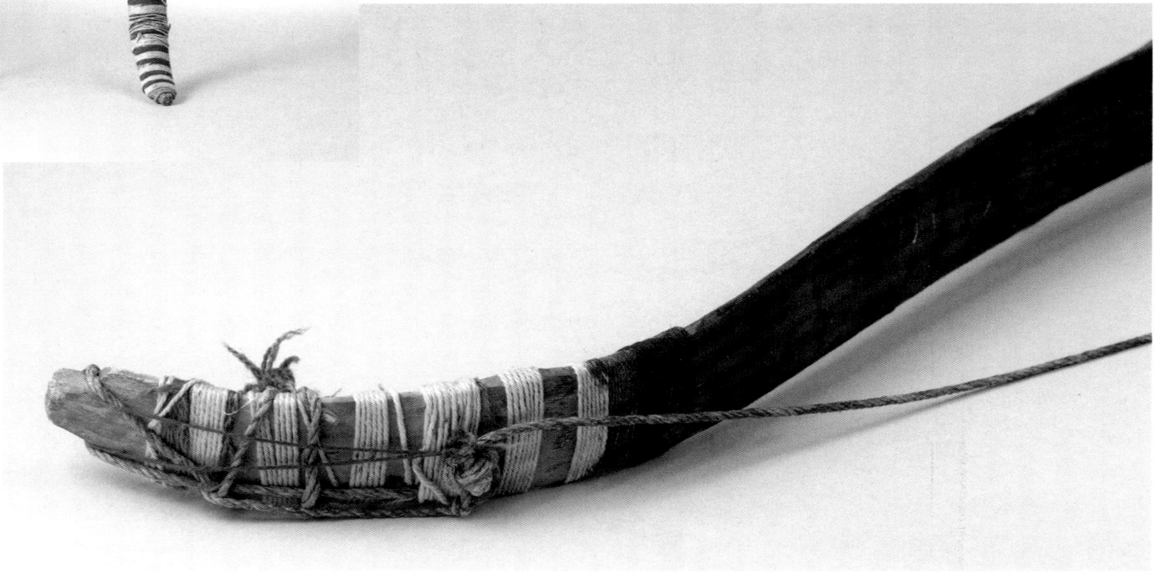

48166

HUPA OTTER FUR QUIVER WITH ARROWS

Circa 1880
Length 27 in. quiver; Length 31¼ in. the longest arrow

This rare quiver is made from a whole tanned otter skin. The lower body and tail have been folded over and back to create a decorative pendant. This area is decorated with abalone shell along its border and down the center. A tab of loom woven beadwork with bead fringe and shell pendants finishes the tail decoration. In addition, diamond and star motifs are painted on the inner surface of the hide. The quiver comes with four equally rare Hupa arrows, three with finely crafted iron points, and one with a chipped flint point.

Two northern California quivers are noted in Mason's landmark study and should be reviewed and compared. One is a quiver made of deerskin from the McCloud River area and the second is made of coyote fur and attributed to the Hupa. (See: Mason, Otis Tufton, *North American Bows, Arrows, and Quivers*, Smithsonian Report for 1893, Washington, D.C., 1894, Plates 91 and 92.) An albumen print in the collections of The Peabody Museum of Natural History, Yale University depicts a Hupa couple in a studio setting. The man is holding an otter fur quiver very similar to this example. (See: Bush, Alfred L. and Mitchell, Lee Clark, *The Photograph and the American Indian*, Princeton, New Jersey, 1994, p. 168.) Another quiver, also made of otter fur, is attributed to the Karuk. (See: Baldwin, John, *Bows, Arrows, and Quivers of the American Frontier*, Early American Artistry Trading Company, West Olive, Michigan, 1999, p. 92, figure 132.)

Provenance
Richard Corrow Collection, Santa Fe, New Mexico.

Estimate: $4,000-$6,000

48167

MODOC WOOD BOW PAINTED WITH MALTESE CROSSES

Circa 1880
Length 53½ in.

This classic example is carved of yew wood and finely painted with a pattern of Maltese crosses in black against a green background and lightning bands in black and red over the natural wood background. The bow is complete with a sinew bowstring.

Estimate: $1,000-$2,000

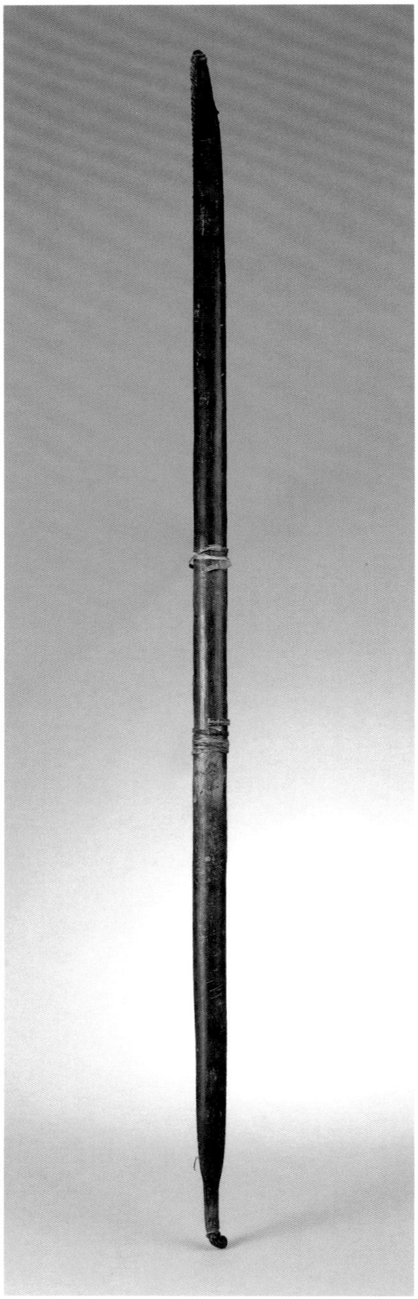

48168

MIWOK SINEW WOOD BOW (YOSEMITE REGION)

Circa 1860
Length 44¼ in.

This plain yew wood bow is fully sinew backed and has its original sinew bowstring. The bow exhibits a fine, warm patina consistent with its age.

Estimate: $500-$1,000

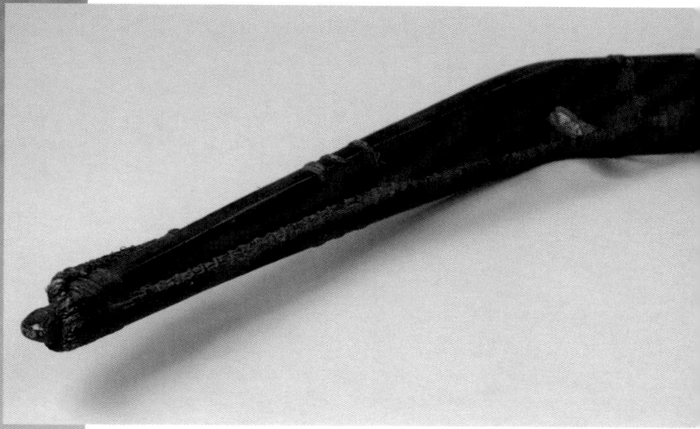

48169

MODOC PAINTED WOOD BOW WITH FOUR ARROWS

Circa 1880
Length 36 in. bow; Length of arrows 30½ in. the longest

This carved yew wood bow is painted on the inner surface with a patter of triangular arrow point motifs in black against a white background and framed along the sides with a series of right triangles painted in red. The bow is complete with a sinew bowstring and is accompanied by four stone tipped arrows.

Provenance
Richard Corrow Collection, Santa Fe, New Mexico.

Estimate: $1,000-$2,000

48170

ESKIMO SINEW BACKED WOOD BOW

Circa 1880
Length 55½ in.

The bow has elaborate sinew cable backing and two bone standoffs, all adding strength and elasticity, making it many times more powerful than an unreinforced wood bow. The bow is painted with an overall pattern of black circles framed by red and black horizontal bands against a lightly painted green background.

Estimate: $2,000-$3,000

48171

ESKIMO ARROW STRAIGHTENER

Circa 1880
Length 9 in. Width 1¾ in.

"The arrowshaft straightener is a vital implement in a hunter's tool kit, and is used to straighten the wooden shafts of arrows used to hunt caribou, birds, and fish. Arrowshaft straighteners are usually made out of tough fossil ivory which is found eroding out of thawing permafrost banks." This carved bone example depicts a swimming polar bear. (For related examples see: Hoffman, Walter, "The Graphic Art of the Eskimos," *Smithsonian Institution Annual Report for 1895*, Washington, D.C., 1897, Plates 7 and 8.)

Provenance
Merrill Domas, Old Chatham, New York.

Reference
Fitzhugh, William and Kaplan, Susan, *Inua: Spirit World of the Bering Sea Eskimo*, Smithsonian Institution Press, Washington, D.C., 1982, p. 56.

Estimate: $1,500-$2,500

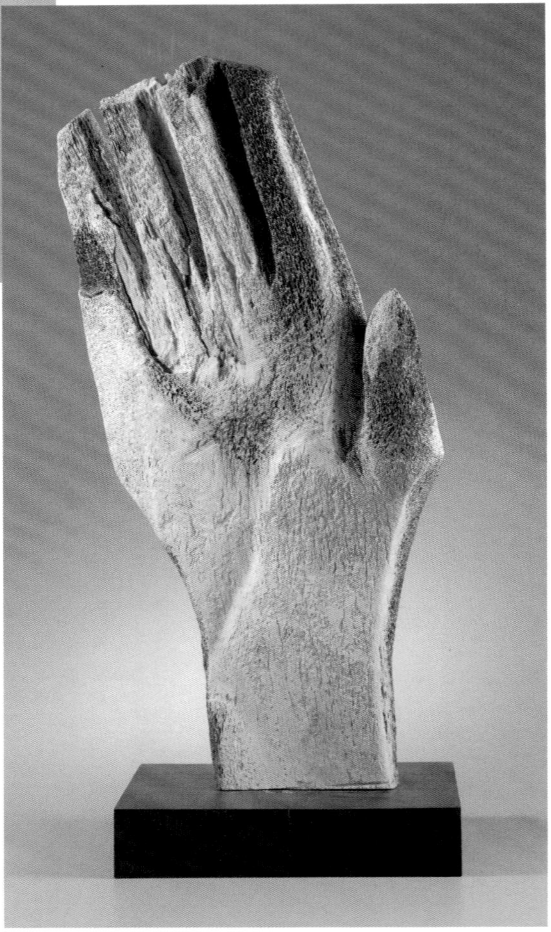

48172

WHALEBONE CARVING OF A HAND

Circa 1972
Length 24¾ in.

The barren landscape of the far north provided scant resources for the Inuit. Everything in the environment was evaluated for practical applications. Whalebone was used in the making of kayaks, umiaks, sleds, and a host of tools and weapons. Its use by contemporary artists was a natural extension for this familiar material. This sculpture is by the Inuit artist, Isaacie.

Provenance
Canadian Arctic Producers, Ltd., Ottawa, Canada, 1972.
Amon Carter Museum, Fort Worth, Texas.

Estimate: $400-$600

48173

WHALEBONE CARVING – HEAD OF AN INUIT MAN

Circa 1968
Height 10 in.

Beginning in the 1960s the Canadian government assisted with programs to benefit the native peoples of the Northwest Territories and Arctic. They helped in the establishment of artist cooperatives in the north and the marketing of prints, soapstone sculptures, and whalebone carvings in the larger cities of the southern provinces. The success of these endeavors continues to the present. This untitled sculpture is carved from weathered whalebone by Cedric, an Inuit artist.

Provenance
Eskimo Fine Arts, Ottawa, Canada, 1968.
Amon Carter Museum, Fort Worth, Texas.

Estimate: $300-$400

48174

WHALEBONE CARVING OF AN INUIT HUNTER

Circa 1973
Length 15 in.

The flat triangular area on the stomach suggests the artist meant for this figure to be seen lying flat. The concept is likely that of a hunter, lying on the ice and stalking a seal. The sculpture is carved by Tassonyut.

Provenance
Lippel Gallery, 1973. Mr. and Mrs. Stanley Marcus until 1981.
Amon Carter Museum, Fort Worth, Texas.

Estimate: $300-$400

48175

KWAKIUTL SHAMAN'S MASK

Circa 1970
Height 10 in. Width 8¼ in.

This carved and painted cedar wood humanoid mask illustrates the characteristic formality of Kwakiutl carving: "Strong orbs in sharply defined sockets, lips protruding from angled forecheek planes, and rounded flaring nostrils are all in the classic Kwakiutl tradition." This mask is attributed to Lelooska (1933-1996).

Reference
Holm, Bill. *Spirit and Ancestor.* Seattle: University of Washington Press, 1987, p. 112.

Estimate: $1,500-$2,500

48176

TLINGIT SHAMAN'S MASK

Circa 1970
Height 13 in. Width 8⅛ in.

This carved and painted cedar wood mask is a faithful copy of a well-known example in the collections of the National Museum of the American Indian, inventory #9/8302. (See: Feder, Norman. *Two Hundred Years of North American Indian Art.* New York: Praeger Publishers, 1971, item 36, p. 48.) It was collected by George Emmons from a shaman at Point Lena, Alaska in 1919. It probably represents "The Woman Who Married a Frog", a well-known Tlingit myth. This mask is attributed to Lelooska (1933-1996).

Estimate: $2,000-$4,000

48177

KWAKIUTL SHAMANS MASK

Circa 1970
Height 10¾ in. Width 6¾ in.

This carved and painted cedar wood mask has human features but its significance is not known. "Of all Northwest Coast artistic creations, masks have the greatest sculptural variety. They were worn at such social ceremonies as feasts and potlatches, at winter initiation ceremonies, and during magic and curing rituals performed by shamans. Often the exact significance of a mask has been lost because such information was only known by those who owned and used them." This mask is attributed to Lelooska. Lelooska, aka Don Smith (1933-1996), was well known in the Pacific Northwest. He was of mixed-blood Cherokee heritage and adopted as an adult by the prestigious Kwakiutl Sewid clan. He emerged in the late 1950s as one of a handful of artists who proved critical in the renaissance of Northwest Coast Indian art.

Reference
Wardwell, Allen. *Objects of Bright Pride*. Seattle: University of Washington Press, 1988, p. 38.

Estimate: $2,000-$3,000

48178

KWAKIUTL DZOONOKWA MASK

Circa 1970
Height 13¼ in. Width 9 in.

This carved and black painted cedar wood mask represents Dzoonokwa. "Sunken, hollow eyes under a heavy brow, bony face with strong, hooked nose and hollow cheeks, lips pushed forward–these are the marks of the Dzoonokwa, the fearsome giant, usually female, of Kwakiutl mythology. All Northwest Coast people have traditions of giant, often malevolent, human-like creatures who dwell in the dark wilderness and occasionally interact with humans. The Dzoonokwa is the archetypical monster-giant of the Northwest Coast." This mask is attributed to Lelooska (1933-1996).

Reference
Holm, Bill. *Spirit and Ancestor*. Seattle: University of Washington Press, 1987, pp. 106-107.

Estimate: $2,000-$3,000

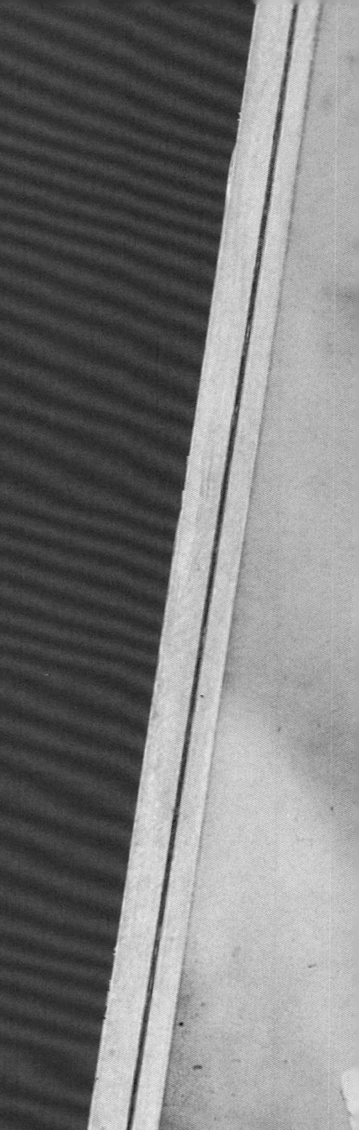
Geo. E.
PHOTOGRA

PHOTOGRAPHS

48179

CARTE DE VISITE – UTE INDIANS AND AN ENGLISHMAN POSED WITH AN ARAPAHO SCALP

Circa 1865-1870
Length 3¾ in. Width 2⅜ in.

The photo is a studio portrait of two Ute warriors posed with their revolvers, an Englishman holding a scalplock tied to a pole, and a woman seated in front. The man standing in the center is Chief Douglass, a prominent figure in the events surrounding the killing of Agent Nathan Meeker at White River Agency on September 30, 1879. A note in period script on the reverse reads "Ute Indians (Squaw and Englishman) with Arapahoes scalp." Photograph by W. G. Chamberlin, Denver, Colorado. Note: This photo has been pasted over another photo, edges of card trimmed, otherwise fine.

Estimate: $1,000-$1,500

48180

CARTE DE VISITE – A STUDIO PORTRAIT OF LITTLE CROW

Circa 1858
Length 3⅝ in. Width 2⅜ in.

The Mdewakanton Sioux chief was the recognized leader of the Minnesota massacre of 1862. Dissatisfied with previous treaty agreements, the Minnesota Sioux bands rose suddenly on August 18, 1862, spreading themselves for more than 200 miles along the frontier and attacking white settlers. The fighting lasted six weeks and took the lives of nearly five hundred whites, mostly civilians, and an unknown but substantial number of Indians. Little Crow and some 200 to 300 tribesmen eventually fled westward. Little Crow was shot and killed by a white settler on July 3, 1863. Photograph by Joel E. Whitney, St. Paul, Minnesota with his studio imprint and titles. Reverse side is blank. Minor foxing in printed area, otherwise good.

Estimate: $500-$750

48181

CARTE DE VISITE – STUDIO PORTRAIT OF UTE CHIEF PIAH HOLDING A COLT PISTOL

Circa 1865
Length 4 in. Width 2½ in.

Piah is posed wearing a feather bonnet with trailer and a wool cloth shirt decorated with beaded shoulder and sleeve strips. A wide beaded strap crosses his chest bandolier fashion to secure a powder horn visible under his right arm. He is also wearing a German silver pectoral ornament, hide leggings, a wool breechcloth, moccasins, and holding a colt revolver. Photograph by W.G. Chamberlin, Denver, Colorado with his studio imprint on the reverse.

Estimate: $600-$900

48182

CARTE DE VISITE – STUDIO PORTRAIT OF UTE CHIEF CURECANTI AND TWO WOMEN

Circa 1865
Length 4 in. Width 2½ in.

The seated man is wearing a bandolier bag decorated with floral designs of a style commonly associated with Cree and Metis people. His leggings and moccasins are typically Ute. The woman on the left is wearing a cloth dress with a beaded tab bag tied to her belt. The woman on the right is wearing a hide dress and a leather belt decorated with large metal studs. Photograph by W.G. Chamberlin, Denver, Colorado with his studio imprint on the reverse.

Estimate: $500-$750

48183

CARTE DE VISITE – STUDIO PORTRAIT OF THE DAUGHTER OF BLACK TEETH

Circa 1880
Length 4¼ in. Width 2½ in.

This Sioux girl is wearing an elk tooth dress, a bone hairpipe breastplate, dentalium shell earrings, a choker necklace, beaded leggings, and moccasins. Breastplates of the type pictured here were men's accessories. It is likely this was a studio prop inserted by the photographer. Photograph by W. R. Cross, Niobara, Nebraska (New Spotted Tail Agency) with his studio imprint on the reverse. Very good condition.

Estimate: $300-$500

48184

CARTE DE VISITE – A STUDIO PORTRAIT OF THREE UTE CHIEFS WEARING CIVIL WAR UNIFORMS

Circa 1865
Length 4 in. Width 2⁷⁄₁₆ in.

In this group photo the standing man is wearing a Confederate coat and vest while the man seated to his right is wearing a Union coat with shoulder insignia. The photographer is unidentified. Written in period script on the reverse "Ute chiefs...(the three names difficult to decipher)."

Estimate: $300-$500

48185

CARTE DE VISITE – STUDIO PORTRAIT OF UNIDENTIFIED INDIAN

Circa 1868
Length 4 in. Width 2 3/8 in.

The subject is dressed in a wool capote with a cartridge belt slung across his chest. He has a choker necklace made of large glass beads and two brass earrings in each ear. Photograph by G.B. and J.L. Collins, Leavenworth, Kansas with their studio imprint on the reverse.

Estimate: $300-$500

48186

CARTE DE VISITE – PORTRAIT OF TONCON, A KIOWA CHIEF, WEARING A CIVIL WAR UNIFORM, TAKEN AT FORT SILL, INDIAN TERRITORY

Circa 1865
Length 4 1/4 in. Width 2 1/2 in.

Toncon is wearing a military officer's frock coat with epaulets, a hairpipe breastplate, and earrings with hairpipe pendants. Photographer unknown. Written in period script on the reverse, "Toncon, Kiowa Chief" and "W. F. Hope, Ft. Sill, I. T."

Estimate: $200-$400

48187

CABINET CARD – STUDIO PORTRAIT OF UTE CHIEF JOHNSON

Circa 1870
Length 6½ in. Width 4¼ in.

He is holding a pipestem and tobacco bag in his left had and a large scalplock is fixed to a staff in his right hand. Note that the butt of a holstered pistol is visible in the folds of his blanket. The chief has otter fur braid wraps and a bead necklace. Chief Johnson participated in the Meeker Massacre on September 30, 1879. Photograph by W. G. Chamberlin, Denver, Colorado. Reverse side is blank. Excellent condition.

Estimate: $1,000-$1,500

48188

CARTE DE VISITE – COL. EDWIN PERRIN WITH A GROUP OF SOUTHERN PLAINS WARRIORS

Circa 1865
Length 2⅜ in. Width 4¾ in.

This interesting image shows eleven warriors posed with Edwin Perrin. Three of the warriors are on horseback, one is holding a rifle and the other appears to be holding a lance. Three shields are visible, a bow case and quiver, a set of hair plates, Saltillo serape, and a Navajo chief's blanket. Col. Edwin Perrin was sent by Edwin Stanton, Lincoln's Secretary of War, to New Mexico in 1862 to help organize and train local volunteers under Kit Carson against the confederate forces that occupied New Mexico. Photograph published by E. & H.T. Anthony, New York with their studio imprint on the reverse.

Provenance
Cowan's Historic Americana Auction, Lot 564, May 10, 2002.

Estimate: $600-$900

48189

CABINET CARD – STUDIO PORTRAIT OF SNAKE AND BIG BELLY, CROW INDIANS

Circa 1885
Length 6½ in. Width 4¼ in.

Both men are wearing loop necklaces and brass armbands. Photograph by D. F. Barry with his studio imprint and title on the front. Reverse side is blank. Very good condition and tone.

Estimate: $600-$800

48190

ALBUMEN PHOTOGRAPH OF LITTLE BIG MOUTH

Circa 1870
Length 7¼ in. Width 5½ in.; as framed Length 13¾ in. Width 11¾ in.

The subject is seated next to his tipi and wearing an eagle feather headdress. A large double bar cross hangs around his neck. Little Big Mouth is holding a pipe and stem and tobacco bag in his left hand. Photograph by Will Soule and signed "Soule" in ink, lower right. Soule operated a photo studio at Fort Sill, Indian Territory between 1870 and 1874. His superb portraits of Kiowa, Comanche, Cheyenne, Arapaho, Caddo, and Witchita Indians are well known to photo historians and collectors. (Photo unexamined out of frame.)

Reference
Belous, Russell and Weinstein, Robert, *Will Soule: Indian Photographer at Fort Sill, Oklahoma, 1869-1874*, The Ward Ritchie Press, 1969, pp. 17-19.

Estimate: $800-$1,200

48191

CABINET CARD – A STUDIO PORTRAIT OF TWO MANDAN WARRIORS AND A WOMAN, "BISMARCK MARY"

Circa 1880
Length 6½ in. Width 4¼ in.

The man on the left is holding a Missouri war ax and the woman has a beaded knife case wedged in her belt. The so-called "Missouri war ax" is first described in the journals of Lewis and Clark. It can be inferred from the diary entry of Merriwether Lewis for February 5, 1805 that the expedition blacksmith was forging these blades to meet Indian demand. Local Indians would bring corn into Fort Mandan to exchange for weapons and other goods during the harsh winter of 1804-05.
Photographer is unidentified. The seated woman is identified in script on the reverse as "Bismarck Mary". Very good condition and tone.

Reference
Moulton, Gary E. (Ed.) *The Journals of the Lewis & Clark Expedition, Volume 3*; University of Nebraska Press, Lincoln, 1987, p. 280 and pp. 286-287.

Estimate: $700-$1,000

48192

CABINET CARD – STUDIO PORTRAIT OF "RED SHIRT AND SQUAW"

Length 6½ in. Width 4¼ in.

Red Shirt is wearing a beaded vest, a bone hairpipe breastplate and a bandolier of carved buffalo horn. He is holding a pipe and stem and a tobacco bag. His wife is wearing a hide dress with a large, fully beaded yoke. She is wearing a necklace made of bone hairpipes and brass beads. Her belt has a pendant decorated with German silver conchos. Photograph by J. S. Meddaugh, Rushville, Nebraska with his studio imprint on the front. Written in period script on the reverse "Red Shirt & Squaw in 1885, Sioux". Very good condition and tone.

Estimate: $500-$750

48193

CABINET CARD – STUDIO PORTRAIT OF CURLEY, THE FAMOUS CROW INDIAN SCOUT WHO SERVED WITH CUSTER'S 7TH CAVALRY

Circa 1885
Length 6½ in. Width 4¼ in.

Curley joined his fellow Crow warriors White Swan, Goes Ahead, White Man Runs Him, Hairy Moccasin, and No Milk as a scout for the Seventh Cavalry on the Little Bighorn expedition. The Crow scouts were not required to engage the enemy and all survived. Curley witnessed parts of the Battle of the Little Bighorn and his translated account appeared in newspapers, leading to the belief that he was the only surviving witness under Custer's immediate command. Photograph by D. F. Barry with his studio imprint and caption on the front of the card. The reverse side is blank. Very good condition.

Estimate: $800-$1,200

48194

CABINET CARD – BLACK BUFFALO BULL, ARIKARA SCOUT WITH CUSTER'S 7TH CAVALRY

Length 6½ in. Width 4¼ in.

In this studio portrait, the Arikara Indian is posed wearing a buffalo fur turban and dentalium shell earrings with abalone shell pendants. Wrapped around his waist is a wool blanket with a wide beaded strip and a U.S. Cavalry sword is cradled in his arms. Photograph by O.S. Goff. Circa 1878. (Note: Incorrectly identified in pencil on both front and back as Little Thunder.)

Estimate: $1,000-$1,500

48195

CABINET CARD – STUDIO PORTRAIT OF PAUL ELK (SIOUX)

Circa 1885
Length 6½ in. Width 4¼ in.

He is wearing a loop necklace, a shell disc choker, and an engraved elk tooth earring is visible. Photograph by George W. Scott at Fort Yates and bearing his studio imprint on the front of the card. The reverse side is blank. Fair condition, some fading and foxing of card stock.

Provenance
Skinners Auctioneers, Sale 2265, Lot 446, January 29, 2005.

Estimate: $200-$300

48196

CABINET CARD – PORTRAIT OF THE LONG DOG (SIOUX) TAKEN AT FORT YATES

Circa 1885
Length 6½ in. Width 4¼ in.

Long Dog is wearing a calico shirt, shell earrings, a Christian cross around his neck, and wool leggings with wide beaded strips. Cradled in his left arm is a club fitted with three knife blades. This formidable weapon probably evolved from the classic gunstock war club. Clubs fitted with two or three knife blades were most popular with the Western Sioux (Teton) bands. These clubs are relatively rare in museum collections and seldom seen in historic photographs. Some years prior, Long Dog posed for D.F. Barry with this club in hand and wearing the same distinctive leggings (see Denver Public Library, Western History Collections, photographs B-382, B-383, and B-384, available online).
Photograph by George W. Scott with his studio imprint on the front. Reverse side is blank. George Scott (1854-1910) was active at Fort Yates during the 1880's. Fort Yates is located on the banks of the Missouri on the Standing Rock Reservation in North Dakota. Fair condition with some stains and fading.

Provenance
Skinners Auctioneers, Sale 2265, Lot 440, January 29, 2005. (Note: This photo is labeled incorrectly in pencil "Low Dog." There was a Hunkpapa Sioux chief by this name photographed by D. F. Barry.)

Estimate: $400-$600

48197

CABINET CARD – A STUDIO PORTRAIT OF THE FAMOUS HUNKPAPA SIOUX CHIEF SITTING BULL

Circa 1885
Length 6½ in. Width 4¼ in.

The traumatic upheavals of recent years are evident in this poignant photo. Sitting Bull appears aged and worn, yet fiercely proud. Within a few short years, on December 15, 1890, Indian police surrounded Sitting Bull's cabin on Grand River to arrest him. A fight ensued between his followers and the Indian police and Sitting Bull was killed, thus closing a dramatic chapter in the American story. Photograph by George W. Scott at Fort Yates and bearing his studio imprint on the front of the card. The reverse side is blank. Fair condition, fading and stains.

Estimate: $500-$750

48198

CABINET CARD – STUDIO PORTRAIT OF BIG HEAD, UPPER YANKTONAI SIOUX CHIEF

Circa 1885
Length 6½ in. Width 4¼ in.

Photograph taken by George W. Scott at Fort Yates and bearing his imprint on the front of the card. The reverse side is blank. Fair condition with fading and light foxing.

Provenance
Skinners Auctioneers, Sale 2265, Lot 446, January 29, 2005.

Estimate: $300-$500

48199

CABINET CARDS (2) – STUDIO PORTRAITS OF MAD BEAR (SIOUX) AND MAD BEAR'S FAMILY

Circa 1885
Length 6½ in. Width 4¼ in. each

Both photographs taken by George W. Scott at Fort Yates and bearing his imprint on the front of the cards. Fair condition with fading, light foxing, one tear.

Provenance
Skinners Auctioneers, Sale 2265, Lot 444, January 29, 2005.

Estimate: $300-$500

48200

CABINET CARD – STUDIO PORTRAIT OF YELLOW HORN AND WOLF (SIOUX INDIANS)

Circa 1885
Length 6½ in. Width 4¼ in.

Yellow Horn is wearing a loop necklace and Wolf is holding the photo of a relative. Photograph taken by George W. Scott at Fort Yates with his studio imprint on the front of the card. Fair condition with fading and foxing.

Provenance
Skinners Auctioneers, Sale 2265, Lot 447, January 29, 2005.

Estimate: $100-$200

48201

CABINET CARD – STUDIO PORTRAIT OF THE HUNKPAPA CHIEF RAIN IN THE FACE

Circa 1885
Length 6½ in. Width 4¼ in.

Rain In the Face is wearing a split horn bonnet decorated with ermine skin and having an eagle feather trailer. He has a fringed hide jacket and is holding a stone head war club. The headdress and club were studio props. Barry posed Sitting Bull wearing these same objects (Lot 48202). It was alleged that Rain In the Face killed Thomas Custer during the Battle of the Little Bighorn and mutilated his body. This myth was then popularized by the poet Henry Wadsworth Longfellow in "The Revenge of Rain In the Face". However, in an interview with the noted Santee Sioux physician and writer, Dr. Charles Eastman, Rain In the Face stated: "Many lies have been told of me. Some say that I killed the Chief (George Armstrong Custer), and others that I cut out the heart of his brother (Tom Custer) because he had caused me to be imprisoned. Why, in that fight the excitement was so great that we scarcely recognized our nearest friends! Everything was done like lightning. After the battle we young men were chasing horses all over the prairie, while the old men and women plundered the bodies." Photograph by D. F. Barry with his studio imprint on the front of the card. Reverse side is blank. Excellent condition and tone.

Reference

Eastman, Charles A., *Indian Heroes and Great Chieftains*. Lincoln: University of Nebraska Press, 1991, p. 150.

Estimate: $1,000-$1,500

48202

CABINET CARD – STUDIO PORTRAIT OF THE FAMOUS HUNKPAPA SIOUX CHIEF SITTING BULL

Circa 1885
Length 6½ in. Width 4¼ in.

In this well known pose, Sitting Bull is wearing a split horn bonnet decorated with ermine skins and having an eagle feather trailer. A beaded knife case is tied to his waist and he is holding a stone head war club. This photo was taken nine years after his stunning victory over Custer's 7th Cavalry on the Little Bighorn, June 25, 1876. Pursued by the United States military, Sitting Bull led his followers into exile in Canada in 1877. He returned to the United States in 1881 with the promise that he could join his people at Standing Rock. However, he was held as a military prisoner for two years at Fort Randall. Released in May, 1883, Sitting Bull continued the struggle to protect his people, their land, and way of life. Photograph by D. F. Barry with his studio imprint on the front of the card. The reverse side is blank. Excellent tone and condition.

Estimate: $1,000-$1,500

48203

CABINET CARD – STUDIO PORTRAIT OF SIOUX CHIEF JOHN GRASS

Circa 1890
Length 6½ in. Width 4¼ in.

James McLaughlin, the Indian Agent at Standing Rock (1881-1895) considered John Grass a "distinguished orator and influential man". McLaughlin sought his assistance in furthering government programs and countering the influence of Sitting Bull during the 1880s. John Grass led the Blackfeet Sioux at the Battle of the Little Big Horn.

Photograph by D. F. Barry with his studio imprint on the front of the card. The reverse side is blank. Excellent condition and tone.

Reference
McLaughlin, James, *My Friend the Indian*. University of Nebraska Press, Lincoln; 1989, p. 100.

Estimate: $600-$800

48204

CABINET CARD – STUDIO PORTRAIT OF THE HUNKPAPA SIOUX CHIEF GALL

Circa 1885
Length 6½ in. Width 4¼ in.

Gall is wearing a large German silver cross and is dressed in a hide jacket, leggings, moccasins, and otter fur braid wraps.

Gall was an esteemed warrior and a fierce opponent of white aggressors prior to his settlement on the Standing Rock Reservation. A large part of his fame centers around his heroics at the Battle of the Little Bighorn on June 25, 1876. Gall admirably led and rallied his fellow warriors throughout the battle, first repulsing Reno's column and then attacking and annihilating Custer and his troops.

D.F. Barry took a number of well known portriats of Gall. In later years, Elizabeth Custer would write the photographer, "Mr. Barry, Painful as it is for me to look upon a pictured face of an Indian, I never dreamed in all my life, there could be so fine a specimen of a warrior, in all the tribes as Chief Gall.–Mrs. Elizabeth B. Custer".

Photograph by D.F. Barry with his studio imprint on the front. The reverse side is blank.

Reference
Heski, Thomas. *The Little Shadow Catcher*. Seattle: Superior Publishing Co., 1978, p.111.

Estimate: $800-$1,200

48205

CABINET CARDS (2) – A SET OF STAGED STUDIO PHOTOGRAPHS OF A FIGHT BETWEEN A SIOUX WARRIOR AND A CAVALRY TROOPER

Circa 1885
Length 6½ in. Width 4¼ in. each

The photos depict hand to hand combat between a Sioux Indian and a United States soldier in the first and the taking of the soldier's scalp in the second. Photographs taken by George W. Scott at Fort Yates with his studio imprint on the front of each card. Fair condition with fading and foxing.

Provenance
Skinners Auctioneers, Sale 2265, Lot 445, January 29, 2005.

Estimate: $200-$400

48206

CABINET CARD – FIELD PHOTOGRAPH ENTITLED "WAR PARTY"

Circa 1890
Length 6½ in. Width 4¼ in.

The photo depicts five Hunkpapa Sioux dancers posed in front of a log cabin at Standing Rock Agency. The dancers are wearing breechcloths, leather belts studded with brass tacks, dance bells around their calves, etc. Photograph by D. F. Barry with his imprint on the front. Printed on the reverse is his advertisement for "Photos of All Noted Indians". Very good condition.

Estimate: $600-$800

48207

CABINET CARD – A STUDIO PORTRAIT OF THE HUNKPAPA SIOUX CHIEF RAIN IN THE FACE

Circa 1893
Length 6½ in. Width 4¼ in.

He is posed seated wearing an eagle feather bonnet, a hide coat with porcupine quill decoration, and a wool blanket wrapped around his waist. He is holding a single eagle feather, a pipe and stem and a tobacco bag. Photograph by George E. Spencer and bearing his studio imprint on the front of the card. The reverse side is blank. Very good condition.

Estimate: $800-$1,200

48208

CABINET CARD – STUDIO PORTRAIT OF CHIEF LAST HORSE HOLDING A HORSE EFFIGY STICK

Circa 1893
Length 6½ in. Width 4¼ in.

He is wearing an eagle feather bonnet and an otter fur necklace decorated with trade mirrors. He is holding a wood horse effigy stick. Although quite rare, horse sticks have been noted from a number of northern Plains tribes. These dramatic objects were made to honor and commemorate a favorite steed. They were proudly carried at dances during the early reservation years and used for the recounting of war exploits. (For a discussion of horse effigy sticks and a similar photograph of Last Horse, posed standing, in the same studio setting, see: West, Ian "Plains Indian Horse Sticks" in *American Indian Art Magazine*, Volume 3, Number 2, Spring, 1978, pp. 58-67).
Photograph by George E. Spencer, Fort Sheridan (Illinois) bearing his studio imprint on the front of the card.
The reverse side is blank. Very good condition, minor abrasion, great tone, tack hole at top.

Estimate: $2,000-$3,000

48209

CABINET CARD – STUDIO PORTRAIT OF THE HUNKPAPA SIOUX CHIEF RAIN IN THE FACE

Circa 1893
Length 6½ in. Width 4¼ in.

He is posed wearing a hide coat with porcupine quill decoration. Photograph by George E. Spencer and bearing his studio imprint on the front of the card. The reverse side is blank. Very good condition.

Estimate: $800-$1,200

48210

CABINET CARD – STUDIO PORTRAIT OF LONE BEAR

Circa 1890
Length 6½ in. Width 4¼ in.

He is posed seated, wearing an eagle feather bonnet, a bone hairpipe breastplate, brass armbands, and holding a pipe and stem. Photograph by D. H. Spencer and bearing his studio imprint on the front of the card. The reverse side is blank. Good condition, note two tack holes at bottom.

Estimate: $600-$800

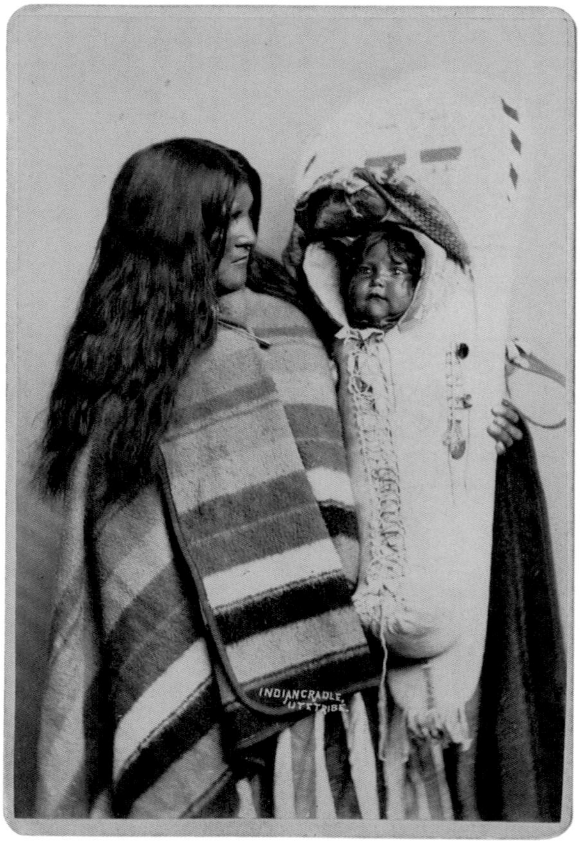

48211

CABINET CARD – STUDIO PORTRAIT OF UTE CHIEF WOOLY HEAD AND HIS FAMILY

Circa 1888
Length 6½ in. Width 4¼ in.

A fine Ute cradleboard is central to the composition. For reasons unknown, a dead pelican has been included on the left side of the photo. The reverse bears the studio imprint of the photographer, C.R. Savage, Salt Lake City. Fine condition and great tone.

Estimate: $400-$600

48212

CABINET CARD – STUDIO PORTRAIT OF CHIEF WOOLY HEAD'S WIFE AND CHILD

Circa 1888
Length 6½ in. Width 4¼ in.

The infant is laced into her finely beaded cradleboard. Note the blanket pin (a huge safety pin) near the mother's shoulder. The reverse bears the studio imprint of the photographer, C.R. Savage, Salt Lake City. "Chief Wooly Heads wife & child" is written on the reverse in period script. Excellent condition and great tone.

Estimate: $300-$500

48213

CABINET CARD – FIELD PHOTOGRAPH OF CHEYENNE SCOUTS

Circa 1884
Length 4¼ in. Width 6 in.

This photo depicts eleven men, nine of whom are holding Springfield trapdoor carbines. There is one sergeant, one corporal, and the remaining men are privates. The Indian scouts are wearing United States Army issue cavalry boots, jackets, pants, cartridge belts, and slouch hats. Photograph by William S. Prettyman with portions of his studio logo printed on the reverse. Written in ink, in period script, is the identification "Indian scouts of the U.S. Army, Cheyenne tribe."

Estimate: $500-$750

48214

CABINET CARD – STUDIO PORTRAIT OF CHIEF NO NECK HOLDING AN EFFIGY PIPE

Circa 1893
Length 6½ in. Width 4¼ in.

He is seated, wearing an eagle feather bonnet with trailer, a bone hairpipe breastplate, a U.S. Grant peace medal and holding a pipe and stem. The pipe stem is finely carved with the heads of a big horn ram, an elk, a buffalo, and a turtle. The pictured stem is nearly identical to an example offered in this sale (Lot 48089). Photograph by George E. Spencer bearing his studio imprint on the front of the card. Reverse side is blank. Very good condition and tone. Note tack hole on right side.

Estimate: $800-$1,200

48215

CABINET CARD – STUDIO PORTRAIT OF CHIEF NO NECK HOLDING AN EFFIGY PIPE

Circa 1893
Length 6½ in. Width 4¼ in.

He is standing, wearing an eagle feather bonnet with trailer, a bone hairpipe breastplate, leggings with beaded strips, moccasins, and a wool blanket with a beaded strip. He is holding a pipe and stem and a fully beaded tobacco bag. Note the word "WILD" and the two American flags visible on the beaded blanket strip. No Neck traveled for many seasons with Buffalo Bill Cody's Wild West Show. He appeared in "The Indian Wars" filmed by Buffalo Bill on the Pine Ridge Reservation in 1913. Photograph by George E. Spencer, Fort Sheridan (Illinois) bearing his studio imprint on the front of the card. Very good condition and great tone, note small tack holes at top and bottom. Reverse side is blank.

Fort Sheridan is located on the far north side of Chicago overlooking Lake Michigan. It was established in 1887 in response to the famous Haymarket Square Riot of 1886. Concern over the need for a military garrison led the Commercial Club of Chicago to donate land to the federal government for this purpose.
Following the Ghost Dance "Outbreak" and the Wounded Knee Massacre (December 19, 1890) on the Pine Ridge Reservation, General Nelson Miles took 30 Sioux Indians identified as "ringleaders" back to his headquarters at Fort Sheridan where they were imprisoned. Preeminent in this group were Short Bull and Kicking Bear. A little more than a year previous, Short Bull had traveled to Nevada to meet Wovoka, the Paiute prophet, and learn about his vision. Kicking Bear was part of a subsequent Sioux delegation that traveled to the western agencies to better understand the new messiah and his Ghost Dance movement. Strange as it seems, Buffalo Bill Cody was allowed to recruit from this group for his upcoming show season. Twenty-three of the prisoners, joined by an additional seventy-five Sioux, sailed for Europe on April 1, 1891 where they performed successfully through the summer and fall.

Reference

Moses, L.G., *Wild West Shows and the Images of American Indians, 1883-1933*. University of New Mexico Press, Albuquerque, 1996, pp. 99, 106-128, 232.

Estimate: $800-$1,200

48216

CABINET CARDS (3) – A GROUP OF THREE STUDIO PORTRAITS OF SIOUX INDIANS

Circa 1885
Length 6½ in. Width 4¼ in. each

The set includes Mrs. Two Bear posed with her child and wearing dentalium shell earrings; Pretty Bird wearing a choker necklace, a necklace made of multiple loops of brass beads and bone hairpipes, and two elaborate pair of dentalium shell earrings; and Crawler posed seated holding an eagle wing fan. Photographs taken by George W. Scott at Fort Yates and bearing his imprint on the front of the cards. The reverse sides are blank. Fair condition with fading and foxing.

Provenance
Skinners Auctioneers, Sale 2265, Lot 447, January 29, 2005.

Estimate: $300-$500

48217

CABINET CARD – STUDIO PORTRAIT OF SIOUX "CHIEF WHITE DEER, U.S.S."

Circa 1893
Length 6⅛ in. Width 4¼ in.

U.S. Indian Scout White Deer is holding an 1873 Springfield trapdoor carbine, wearing an eagle feather bonnet with trailer, a U.S. Grant peace medal and cartridge belt. Information written on the reverse states that White Horse enlisted as a scout on November 27, 1890 at Pine Ridge Agency and was discharged with the rank of sergeant on May 26, 1891. Photo by Fitzsimmons and Bauman, Crawford, Nebraska. Very good condition with minor scuffing.

Estimate: $600-$900

48218

BOUDOIR CARD – STUDIO PORTRAIT OF CHIRICAHUA APACHE MAN AND WOMAN

Length 8½ in. Width 5¼ in.

The woman is wearing a classic Apache hide dress, heavily ornamented with tin cones and hide fring, and boot moccasins with cactus guards. She is holding a hair bow in her right hand. The man is wearing a painted hide jacket decorated with brass studs and heavy fringing and boot moccasins with cactus guards. He is holding a Springfield trapdoor carbine. An Apache burden basket rests on the ground to his left.

Beginning in the mid-1870s and continuing up until his final surrender in 1886, Geronimo was the senior Chiricahua war leader. Constantly pursued by U.S. troops, his efforts to evade capture and remain free are legendary. Frank Randall was able to photograph a number of Geronimo's warriors in the spring of 1884 following their surrender to General George Crook and their return to the San Carlos Reservation. Geronimo and other Chiricahua remained at large in southern Arizona and Mexico at this time. Photograph taken by A. Frank Randall, Wilcox, Arizona Territory. On the reverse, glued over the photographer's studio imprint, is a strip of paper stating "Copyrighted May 16th, 1884, by A.F. Randall, in the Library of Congress, Washington, D.C."

Estimate: $1,000-$1,500

48219

BOUDOIR CARD – STUDIO PORTRAIT OF A CHIRICAHUA APACHE WOMAN

Spring 1884
Length 8 in. Width 5¼ in.

The Apache woman is posed with a Mexican Saltillo serape held above her shoulders. She is wearing a cloth blouse, a hide skirt elaborately decorated with rows of tin cones and fringe, and a knife case is fastened to her belt. Photograph by A. Frank Randall, Wilcox, Arizona Territory with his studio imprint stamped in purple ink on the reverse.

Estimate: $500-$750

48220

CABINET CARD – STUDIO PORTRAIT OF FOUR YUMA GIRLS

Circa 1870
Length 6½ in. Width 4¼ in.

The two girls on the right are holding pottery effigy vessels. These ceramics were likely made for sale to traders and tourists. Stamped in ink on the reverse "From Gold's Free Museum. Dealer in Indian & Mexican Potteries, Curiosities, & C., J. Gold, Manager, Santa Fe, N.M." Printed on the front "152. Yuma Indians of Arizona. Continent Stereoscopic Co., New York." Very good condition and tone.

Estimate: $400-$600

48221

BOUDOIR CARD – STUDIO PORTRAIT OF NACHEZ (SON OF COCHISE) AND HIS WIFE

Spring 1884
Length 8½ in. Width 5¼ in.

The words "Nachez...Nai-chi-ti, son of Cochise and wife, Chief of Chiricahua Apache" are printed in the negative. Also known as Naiche, Nachez is posed wearing a headband, dressed in a cloth shirt, vest, and pants but wearing traditional boot moccasins with cactus guards. His wife is dressed in a cotton blouse, dress, and head scarf. Her boot moccasins, also with cactus guards, are visible in the photo.

"Nachez was the son of Cochise and nominally head chief of the Chiricahuas, but like Mangus he was not warlike enough to satisfy his people and had been pushed aside – first by Juh, then by Geronimo, who arose as war leader after Juh had drowned in the autumn of 1883." Nachez participated in the uprising of 1885-1886 and remained with Geronimo and other "hostile" Chiricahua hiding out in Mexico. They were intensively tracked by United States Army troops, aided by Apache scouts. Geronimo and Nachez finally surrendered to General Nelson Miles in September, 1886. Photo by A. Frank Randall, Wilcox, Arizona Territory with his studio imprint stamped in purple ink on the reverse. A separate typed note is posted on the reverse stating "Entered according to act of Congress in the year 1884, by A.F. Randall in the office of the Librarian of Congress, at Washington."

Reference

Worcester, Donald E., *The Apaches*. Norman: University of Oklahoma Press, 1979, p. 277.

Estimate: $1,000-$1,500

48222

BOUDOIR CARD – STUDIO PORTRAIT OF CHIRICAHUA APACHE CHIEF BONITO

Spring, 1884
Length 8½ in. Width 5¼ in.

Bonito is posed wearing a United States Army cartridge belt, boot moccasins with cactus guards, and holding a rifle across his lap. An Apache *tus* (water jar) is on the ground to his left. Photograph by A. Frank Randall, Wilcox, Arizona Territory with his studio imprint stamped in purple ink on the reverse. A separate paper glued to the reverse states "Entered according to act of Congress in the year 1884, by A.F. Randall, in the office of the Librarian of Congress at Washington." Also written on the reverse, in period script, is "Bonita, Chiricahua Apache Chief, Killed Judge McComas." In March of 1883, Bonito (also spelled Benito) and Chatto led twenty-six warriors on a series of raids into southern Arizona and New Mexico. Near Silver City, New Mexico the raiders came upon a buckboard carrying federal judge H.C. McComas, his wife, and their six year old son, Charlie. The two adults were killed and the child taken hostage. Bonito and the other warriors surrendered to General George Crook in May, 1883 and were taken to the San Carlos Reservation (Arizona). The fate of Charlie McComas became one of the enduring mysteries of the time.

Reference
Debo, Angie, *Geronimo*. University of Oklahoma Press, Norman, 1976, pp. 165-168.

Estimate: $1,000-$2,000

48223

CABINET CARD – STUDIO PORTRAIT OF NANAKE WEARING A CLASSIC NAVAJO SERAPE

Circa 1885
Length 6½ in. Width 4¼ in.

He is posed with a Navajo blanket draped over his shoulder. The reverse reads "Nanake, Member of the little fire. Moqui by birth and Zuni by adoption" in period script. The reverse also bears the studio imprint of J. W. Block & Co., Photographic Artists, 333 Washington St., Boston. Very good condition, light foxing.

Estimate: $400-$600

48224

BOUDOIR CARD – STUDIO PORTRAIT OF CHATTO, CHIRICAHUA APACHE

Spring, 1884
Length 8½ in. Width 5¼ in.

Chatto is posed with a wool blanket wrapped around his waist and holding a rifle. In March, 1883 Chatto and Bonito led twenty-six Chiricahua warriors on a series of lightning raids in southern Arizona and New Mexico. Pursued by General George Crook and the United States Army, they fled over the border into the Sierra Madre mountains of Mexico. Eventually, negotiations were conducted and arrangements made for their surrender. In February, 1884 Chatto and his band crossed back into Arizona where, under military escort, they were returned to the San Carlos Reservation. Frank Randall took this photograph shortly thereafter. Chatto later became a sergeant in General Crook's regiment of Apache scouts.

Photo by Frank Randall, Wilcox, Arizona Territory, with his studio imprint stamped in purple ink on the reverse. A separate typed note is pasted on the reverse stating "Entered according to act of Congress in the year 1884, by A.F. Randall in the office of the Librarian of Congress, at Washington." Also, written in period script "Chatto Chiricahua Apache Chief".

Estimate: $1,000-$1,500

48225

CABINET SIZE PHOTO MOUNTED ON GRAY CARD STOCK – QUANAH PARKER AND WIVES

Circa 1892
Length 8 in. Width 5¾ in.

The famous Comanche Chief Quanah Parker is posed with his wives To-pay and Cho-ny. Quanah Parker was the son of Peta Nocona, a prominent Comanche war chief, and Cynthia Ann Parker, a noted white captive who had been living with the Comanche since her capture at the age of nine on May 19, 1836. Their Comanche camp was attacked by Texas Rangers in 1861 and Cynthia Ann and her young daughter fled on horseback. She was captured by the Rangers and reunited with her white relations. However, she was never reconciled to the loss of her Comanche family and died unhappily in 1870.

Quanah Parker participated in significant historic events such as the Battle of Adobe Walls in June, 1874, but he is best known for the leadership of his people following their settlement on the Comanche-Kiowa Reservation in Oklahoma in 1875. He died on February 25, 1911. Photograph by Irwin, Chickasha, Indian Territory. Reverse side is blank. Good condition, dark tones, tack holes on corners

Reference
Hagan, William T., *Quanah Parker, Comanche Chief.* Norman: University of Oklahoma Press, 1973.

Estimate: $500-$750

48226

CABINET CARD – STUDIO PORTRAIT OF TWO KIOWA GIRLS DRESSED IN TRADITIONAL ATTIRE

W.P. Bliss worked at Fort Sill between 1873 and 1875
Length 6½ in. Width 4¼ in.

The girl on the left is seated on a chair draped with a buffalo robe. She is wearing a painted hide dress with several rows of elk teeth decoration. The standing girl is wearing a wool cloth dress heavily embellished with elk teeth. Both children are wearing leather belts decorated with German silver conchos, the belt pendants visible with each. The reverse side bears the studio imprint of "W.P. Bliss, Photographer, Fort Sill, Indian Territory". Very good condition and tone.

Provenance
Skinners Auctioneers, Sale 2265, Lot 441, January 29, 2005.

Estimate: $400-$600

48227

CABINET CARD – A STUDIO PORTRAIT OF TWO YOUNG KIOWA GIRLS

Circa 1885
Length 6½ in. Width 4¼ in.

Both girls are wearing elk teeth dresses and boot moccasins. A strike-a-light case is visible next to the right hand of the seated child. The photographer is unidentified. The reverse side of the card is blank. Very good condition and tone.

Estimate: $300-$500

48228

CABINET CARD – A STUDIO PORTRAIT OF TWO KIOWA GIRLS

Circa: 1890
Length 6½ in. Width 4¼ in.

Both girls are wearing hide dresses decorated with cowrie shells and traditional boot moccasins. Written on the reverse, "Josie, Mexican & Indian". The reverse also bears the ink stamp "C. C. Stotz, Photographer, El Reno, O.T.". The front bears the imprint of "Shuck, Ground Floor Studio, Columbus, Neb.".

Estimate: $300-$500

48229

CABINET CARD – PHOTOGRAPH OF COMANCHE TRIBAL POLICE HOLDING THEIR WINCHESTER RIFLES

Circa 1890
Length 6½ in. Width 4¼ in.

This photo was taken at Anadarko Agency on the Kiowa-Comanche Reservation, Indian Territory (Oklahoma). Each man is dressed in traditional Comanche shirt, leggings, and moccasins and each is holding a Winchester rifle. Photograph by Irwin, Chickasha, Indian Territory with his studio imprint on the front. Written on reverse "Indian Scouts of Anadarko". Very good condition, light tone.

Estimate: $700-$1,000

48230

CABINET SIZE PHOTO MOUNTED ON CARD STOCK – QUANAH PARKER AND WIVES

Circa 1892
Length 7⅜ in. Width 5¼ in.

In this well known image, the famous Comanche Chief Quanah Parker is posed on the front porch of his house with his wives To-pay and Cho-ny. Quanah is wearing hide leggings and moccasins, his hair braids wrapped with otter fur. Photograph by Irwin, Chickasha, Indian Territory with his studio imprint on the front of the card. Reverse side is blank. Very good condition with nice tone.

Working out of Chickasha, Indian Territory, Irwin traveled to Fort Sill and Anadarko to photograph the local Indian people. He compiled a fine body of work, including field photographs and studio portraits. Many of these images were reproduced for sale as cabinet cards. His subjects include Kiowa, Comanche, Wichita, and Caddo Indians. Irwin also photographed Geronimo while he was imprisoned at Fort Sill.

Estimate: $1,000-$1,500

48231

CABINET CARD – STUDIO PORTRAIT OF AR-KO, COMANCHE, AND CAPTAIN OF THE TRIBAL POLICE

Circa 1889-1891
Length 6½ in. Width 4¼ in.

Ar-ko is wearing traditional hide leggings and moccasins and a beaded strap is worn across his chest. The small circular beaded pouch worn as a necklace served as a container for a peyote button, indicating membership in the Native American Church. He is also wearing fancy German silver earrings and holding an eagle feather fan. Photograph by William Lenny between 1889 and 1891. The cabinet card bears the studio imprint "Sawyers and Connolley, Purcell, Ind. Ter." The reverse side is blank. Excellent condition and tone.

Estimate: $700-$1,000

48232

CABINET CARD – STUDIO PORTRAIT OF TWO KIOWA-APACHE CHIEFS, DA-VA-KO AND DOR-CON-EACH-LA

Circa 1889-1891
Length 6½ in. Width 4¼ in.

The seated man is wearing a traditional Southern Plains hide shirt and a bone hairpipe breastplate. Both men have their hair braids wrapped with otter fur and each holds an eagle feather fan. Photograph by William Lenny between 1889 and 1891. Working out of Purcell, Indian Territory, William Lenny traveled to Anadarko to record life on the Kiowa-Comanche Reservation and the Wichita-Caddo Reservation. He compiled an important record of life on the reservation, taking a number of impressive field photographs and studio portraits. Subjects included Kiowa, Comanche, Kiowa-Apache, Caddo, Wichita, Delaware and Oto Indians. In late 1890, William Sawyers purchased Lenny's interest in their business. John Connolley then worked for the studio in 1891 and 1892. This print was made from Lenny's glass plate negative.

Printed on the front of the card, "Apache Chiefs" and "Sawyers and Connolley, Purcell, Ind. Ter.". The reverse side is blank. Excellent condition and tone.

Reference
Miller, David and Hays, Joe, *In Citizen's Garb: The Lenny and Sawyers Images of Native Americans on the Southern Plains 1889-1891*. Museum of the Great Plains, Lawton, Oklahoma, 2005.

Estimate: $700-$1,000

48233

CABINET CARD – STUDIO PORTRAIT OF A CHEYENNE COUPLE

Circa 1890
Length 6½ in. Width 4¼ in.

The man is wearing a classic Southern Plains shirt, hide leggings, and his hair braids are wrapped in otter fur. Note the horse figures on the border of his moccasins, a popular Cheyenne design motif. The woman is wearing a cloth dress and shawl. Her leather belt with German silver conchos and her bead necklace were typical fashions of the time. Photo by C.C. Stotz, El Reno, Oklahoma with his studio imprint on the front. The reverse side is blank.

Estimate: $400-$600

48234

PHOTOGRAPHS (15) OF SOUTHERN PLAINS INDIANS

This varied group of cabinet sized photographs are mostly studio portraits. The condition ranges from good to poor.

Provenance
Skinners Auctioneers, Sale 2265, Lot 451, January 29, 2005.

Estimate: $400-$600

End of Native American Art Session

Bibliography

Allely, Steve, and Jim Hamm. *Encyclopedia of Native American Bows, Arrows, and Quivers, Volume 2, Plains and Southwest*. Goldthwaite, Texas: Bois d'Arc Press, 2002.

Baldwin, John. *Bows, Arrows, and Quivers of the American Frontier*. West Olive, Michigan: Early American Artistry Trading Company, 1999.

Baldwin, John. *Tomahawks and Pipe Axes of the American Frontier*. West Olive, Michigan: Early American Artistry Trading Company, 1995.

Barrett, Samuel. *Pomo Indian Basketry*. Berkeley: University of California, Phoebe Hearst Museum of Anthropology, 1996.

Bates, Craig, and Martha J. Lee. *Tradition and Innovation*. Yosemite Association, Yosemite National Park, California, 1990.

Belous, Russell, and Robert Weinstein. *Will Soule: Indian Photographer at Fort Sill, Oklahoma, 1869–1874*. The Ward Ritchie Press, 1969.

Bernstein, Bruce, and J.J Brody. *Voices in Clay*. Oxford, Ohio: Miami University Art Museum, 2001.

Bernstein, Bruce. *Native American Basketry: The Hartman Collection*. St. Joseph, Missouri: The Albrecht–Kemper Museum of Art, 1996.

Berthrong, Daniel J. *The Southern Cheyennes*. Norman: University of Oklahoma Press, 1963.

Bibby, Brian. *The Fine Art of California Indian Basketry*. Sacramento: Crocker Art Museum, 1996.

Blackard, David. *Patchwork and Palmettos*. Fort Lauderdale Historical Society, 1990.

Blish, Helen H. *A Pictographic History of the Oglala Sioux*. Lincoln: University of Nebraska Press, 1967.

Blomberg, Nancy. *Navajo Textiles: The William Randolph Hearst Collection*. Tucson: University of Arizona Press, 1988.

Bunzel, Ruth. *The Pueblo Potter*. New York: Dover Publications, Inc., 1972.

Bush, Alfred L., and Lee Clark Mitchell. *The Photograph and the American Indian*. Princeton: Princeton University Press, 1994.

Coe, Ralph T. *The Responsive Eye*. New Haven: Yale University Press, 2003.

Conn, Richard. *Circles of the World*. Denver Art Museum, 1982.

Conn, Richard. *Native American Art in the Denver Art Museum*. Denver Art Museum, 1979.

Debo, Angie. *Geronimo*. Norman: University of Oklahoma Press, 1976.

Dorsey, James O. *A Study of Siouan Cults. Eleventh Annual Report of the Bureau of Ethnology*. Washington, D.C.: Smithsonian Institution, 1894.

Eastman, Charles A. *Indian Heroes and Great Chieftains*. Lincoln: University of Nebraska Press, 1991.

Ewers, John C. *Plains Indian Painting*. Stanford: Stanford University Press, 1939.

Ewers, John C. *Plains Indian Sculpture*. Washington, D.C.: Smithsonian Institution Press, 1986.

Fane, Diane, Ira Jacknis, and Lise Breen. *Objects of Myth and Memory*. The Brooklyn Museum, 1991.

Ferg, Alan, ed. *Western Apache Material Culture*. Tucson: University of Arizona Press, 1987.

Fitzhugh, William, and Susan Kaplan. *Inua: Spirit World of the Bering Sea Eskimo*. Washington, D.C.: Smithsonian Institution Press, 1982.

Furst, Jill Leslie. *Mojave Pottery, Mojave People*. Santa Fe: School of American Research Press, 2001.

Hagan, William T. *Quanah Parker, Comanche Chief*. Norman: University of Oklahoma Press, 1973.

Hail, Barbara. *Hau, Kóla*. Providence: Brown University, Haffenreffer Museum of Anthropology, 1980.

Hanson, James A. *Little Chief's Gatherings*. Crawford, Nebraska: The Fur Press, 1996.

Hanson, James A. *Metal Weapons, Tools, and Ornaments of the Teton Dakota Indians*. Lincoln: University of Nebraska Press, 1975.

Hanson, James. *Spirits in the Art*. Kansas City: The Lowell Press, 1994.

Herbst, Toby, and Joel Kopp. *The Flag in American Indian Art*. Cooperstown: New York State Historical Association, 1993.

Heski, Thomas. *The Little Shadow Catcher.* Seattle: Superior Publishing Co., 1978.

Hoffman, Walter. *The Graphic Art of the Eskimos.* Washington, D.C.: Smithsonian Annual Report for 1895, 1897.

Holm, Bill. *Spirit and Ancestor.* Seattle: University of Washington Press and Thomas Burke Memorial Washington State Museum, 1987.

Howard, James. "The Tree Dweller Cults of the Dakota". *Journal of American Folklore, Volume 68, Number 268.* Richmond, Virginia, 1955.

Kaufman, Alice, and Chris Selser. *The Navajo Weaving Tradition: 1650 to the Present.* New York, E.P. Dutton, Inc., 1985.

Kramer, Barbara. *Nampeyo and Her Pottery.* Albuquerque: University of New Mexico Press, 1996.

Latta, Frank. *Handbook of Yokuts Indians.* Santa Cruz, California: Bear State Books, 1977.

Lessard, Rosemary. "Lakota Cradles". *American Indian Art Magazine, Volume 16, Number 1.* Scottsdale, Arizona, Winter, 1990.

Madsen, Brigham. *The Northern Shoshoni.* Caldwell, Idaho: The Caxton Printers, 1980.

Mason, Otis Tufton. *North American Bows, Arrows, and Quivers.* Washington, D.C.: Smithsonian Report for 1893, 1894.

McCoy, Ron. "Miniature Shields: James Mooney's Fieldwork Among the Kiowa and Kiowa–Apache." *American Indian Art Magazine, Volume 20, Number 3.* Scottsdale, Arizona, Summer, 1995.

McLaughlin. *My Friend the Indian.* Lincoln: University of Nebraska Press, 1989.

Merrill, William, Marian Hansson, Candace Greene, and Frederick Reuss. *A Guide to the Kiowa Collections at the Smithsonian Institution.* Washington, D.C.: Smithsonian Institution Press, 1997.

Miller, David, and Joe Hays. *In Citizen's Garb: The Lenny and Sawyers Images of Native Americans on the Southern Plains, 1889–1891.* Lawton, Oklahoma: Museum of the Great Plains, 2005.

Moses, L.G. *Wild West Shows and the Images of American Indians, 1883–1933.* Albuquerque: University of New Mexico Press, 1996.

Moulton, Gary E., ed. *The Journals of the Lewis and Clark Expedition, Volume 3.* Lincoln: University of Nebraska Press, 1987.

O'Connor, Nancy. *Fred E. Miller: Photographer of the Crows.* University of Montana, Missoula and Carnan VidFilm, Malibu, 1985.

Peterson, Harold. *American Indian Tomahawks.* New York: Museum of the American Indian, Heye Foundation, 1971.

Pohrt, Richard. *The American Indian/The American Flag.* Flint Institute of Arts, 1975.

Slater, Eva. *Panamint Shoshone Basketry.* Morongo Valley, California: Sagebrush Press, 2000.

Spivey, Richard. *Maria.* Flagstaff: Northland Publishing, 1994.

Thompson, Judy. *The North American Indian Collection: A Catalogue.* Berne Historical Museum, Switzerland, 1977.

Vestal, Stanley. *Sitting Bull: Champion of the Sioux.* Norman: University of Oklahoma Press, 1957.

Vincent, Gilbert, Sherry Brydon, and Ralph T. Coe, eds. *Art of the North American Indians: The Thaw Collection.* Cooperstown: New York State Historical Association, Fenimore Art Museum, 2000.

Wardwell, Allen. *Objects of Bright Pride.* Seattle: University of Washington Press, 1988.

West, Ian. "Plains Indian Horse Sticks." *American Indian Art Magazine, Volume 3, Number 2.* Scottsdale, Arizona, Spring, 1978.

Wheat, Joe Ben, and Ann Lane Hedlund, ed. *Blanket Weaving in the Southwest.* Tucson: University of Arizona Press, 2003.

Whitaker, Kathleen. *Southwest Textiles: Weavings of the Navajo and Pueblo.* Seattle: University of Washington Press, 2002.

Wissler, Clark. "Societies and Ceremonial Associations of the Oglala Division of the Teton–Dakota." *Anthropological Papers of the American Museum of Natural History, Volume XI, Part 1.* New York, 1912.

Wright, Barton. *Pueblo Shields.* Flagstaff: Northland Press, 1976.

Wroth, William, ed. *Ute Indian Arts and Culture.* Colorado Springs: Taylor Museum of the Colorado Springs Fine Arts Center, 2000.

HERITAGE
IMPORTANT FINE ART AUCTION
November 9–10, 2006 • Dallas, Texas • Live and Online
Maxfield Parrish (American 1870–1966)
Poet's Dream, 1901
Oil on panel
Private Collection
Photo from the archives of Alma Gilbert; used with permission.
To receive a complimentary catalogue or book of your choice, simply register online at HA.com/Join. Enter Reference #5116.
Annual Sales Exceeding $500 Million • Over 250,000 Registered Online Bidder-Members
3500 Maple Ave, 17th Floor • Dallas, Texas 75219 • 214-443-8444 • 800-872-6467 ext. 444 • HA.com/FineArt
THE INTELLIGENT ALTERNATIVE
HERITAGE
Auction Galleries

HERITAGE
Important Fine Art Auction

November 9-10, 2006 • Dallas, Texas • Live and Online

Peter Paul Rubens (Flemish 1577-1640)
Allegory of the Spanish Monarchy (Fortitude), ca. 1630
Oil on panel
Private Collection

To receive a complimentary catalogue or book of your choice, simply register online at HA.com/Join. Enter Reference #5116.

Annual Sales Exceeding $500 Million • Over 250,000 Registered Online Bidder-Members

3500 Maple Ave, 17th Floor • Dallas, Texas 75219 • 214-443-8444 • 800-872-6467 ext. 444 • HA.com/FineArt

Auctioneer John Petty. TX License #00013740 • This auction is subject to a 19.5% Buyer's Premium

The Intelligent Alternative
HERITAGE
Auction Galleries

5116

NEW YORK STATE AUCTIONS ONLY
These Terms and Conditions of Sale are designed to conform to the applicable sections of the New York City Department of Consumer Affairs Rules and Regulations as Amended. This sale is a Public Auction Sale conducted by Auctioneer. The New York City licensed auctioneers are: Kathleen Guzman, No. 0762165-Day, and Samuel W. Foose, No. 0952360-Day, No. 0952361-Night, who will conduct the Sale on behalf of Heritage Auctions, Inc. ("Auctioneer"). All lots are subject to: the consignor's rights to bid thereon in accord with these Terms and Conditions of Sale, consignor's option to receive advances on their consignments, and Auctioneer, in its sole discretion, may offer limited extended financing to registered bidders, in accord with Auctioneer's internal credit standards. A registered bidder may inquire whether a lot is subject to an advance or a reserve. Auctioneer has made advances to various consignors in this sale.

AUCTIONEER AND AUCTION:

1. This Auction is presented by Heritage Numismatic Auctions, Inc.; or its subsidiary Currency Auctions of America, Inc.; or their affiliate, Heritage Auctions, Inc. d/b/a Heritage Auction Galleries, Heritage Art Auctions, Heritage Fine & Decorative Arts Auctions, Heritage Comics Auctions, Heritage-Slater Americana, Heritage Vintage Movie Posters, or Heritage Sports Collectibles Auctions, as identified with the applicable licensing information on the title page of the catalog or on the Internet site (the "Auctioneer"). The Auction is conducted under these Terms and Conditions of Auction and applicable state and local law.

BUYER'S PREMIUM:

2. On bids placed through Heritage, a Buyer's Premium of fifteen percent (15%) for Heritage Numismatic Auctions Inc, Heritage-CAA, and Heritage Movie Posters or nineteen and one-half percent (19.5%) for Heritage Sports Collectibles, Heritage Comics Auctions, Heritage Music & Entertainment Memorabilia, Heritage Art Auctions and Heritage Americana of the hammer price will be added to the successful bid. If the bid is placed through eBay Live a Buyer's Premium equal to the normal Buyer's Premium plus an additional five percent (5%) of the hammer price will be added to the successful bid up to a maximum Buyer's Premium of Twenty Two and one-half percent (22.5%). There is a minimum Buyer's Premium of $9.00 per lot.

AUCTION VENUES:

3. Exclusively Internet, Continuous Internet, Internet Currency, Amazing Comics Auctions, Amazing Sports Auctions, and Online Session are Auctions conducted on the Internet. Signature Auctions accept bids on the Internet first, followed by a floor bidding session; bids may be placed prior to the floor bidding session by Internet, telephone, fax, or mail.

BIDDERS:

4. Any person participating or registering for the Auction agrees to be bound by and accepts these Terms and Conditions of Auction ("Bidder(s)").
5. All Bidders must meet Auctioneer's qualifications to bid. Any Bidder who is not a customer in good standing of the Auctioneer may be disqualified at Auctioneer's sole option and will not be awarded lots. Such a determination may be made by Auctioneer in its sole and unlimited discretion, at any time prior to, during, or even after the close of the Auction.
6. If an entity places a bid, then the person executing the bid on behalf of the entity agrees to personally guarantee payment for any successful bid.
7. Auctioneer reserves the right to exclude any person it deems in its sole opinion is disruptive to the Auction or is otherwise commercially unsuitable.
8. CREDIT REFERENCES: Bidders who do not have established credit with the Auctioneer must either furnish satisfactory credit information (including two collectibles-related business references) well in advance of the Auction or supply valid credit card information. Bids placed through our Interactive Internet program will only be accepted from pre-registered Bidders; Bidders who are not members of HeritageAuctions.com or affiliates should pre-register at least two business days before the first session to allow adequate time to contact references.

BIDDING OPTIONS:

9. Bids may be placed for a Signature Auction as set forth in the printed catalog section entitled "Choose your bidding method." For Exclusively Internet, Continuous Internet, Internet Currency, Amazing Comics Auctions, Amazing Sports Auctions, and Online Session auctions, see the alternatives shown on each website. Review at HeritageAuctions.com/common/howtobid.php.
10. Presentment of Bids: Non-Internet bids (including but not limited to podium, fax, phone and mail bids) are treated similar to floor bids in that they must be on-increment or at a half increment (called a cut bid). Any podium, fax, phone, or mail bids that do not conform to a full or half increment will be rounded up or down to the nearest full or half increment and will be considered your high bid.
11. Auctioneer's Execution of Certain Bids. Auctioneer cannot be responsible for your errors in bidding, so carefully check that each bid is entered correctly. When identical mail or FAX bids are submitted, preference is given to the first received. To ensure the greatest accuracy, your written bids should be entered on the standard printed bid sheet and be received at Auctioneer's place of business at least two business days before the Auction start. Auctioneer is not responsible for executing mail bids or FAX bids received on or after the day the first lot is sold, nor Internet bids submitted after the published closing time; nor is Auctioneer responsible for proper execution of bids submitted by telephone, mail, FAX, e-mail, Internet, or in person once the Auction begins. Internet bids may not be withdrawn until your written request is received and acknowledged by Auctioneer (FAX: 214-443-8425); such requests must state the reason, and may constitute grounds for withdrawal of bidding privileges. Lots won by mail Bidders will not be delivered at the Auction unless prearranged in advance. The decision of the Auctioneer and declaration of the winning Bidder is final.
12. Caveat as to Bids. Bid increments (over the current bid level) determine the lowest amount you may bid on a particular lot. Bids greater than one increment over the current bid can be any whole dollar amount. It is possible under several circumstances for winning bids to be between increments, sometimes only $1 above the previous increment. Please see: *"How can I lose by less than an increment?"* on our website.
13. Bidding Increments: The following chart governs current bidding increments.

Current Bid	Bid Increment	Current Bid	Bid Increment
< $10	$1	$3,000 - $4,999	$250
$10 - $29	$2	$5,000 - $9,999	$500
$30 - $59	$3	$10,000 - $19,999	$1,000
$60 - $99	$5	$20,000 - $29,999	$2,000
$100 - $199	$10	$30,000 - $49,999	$2,500
$200 - $299	$20	$50,000 - $99,999	$5,000
$300 - $499	$25	$100,000 - $249,999	$10,000
$500 - $999	$50	$250,000 - $499,999	$25,000
$1,000 - $1,999	$100	$500,000 - $1,499,999	$50,000
$2,000 - $2,999	$200	> $1,500,000	$100,000

CONDUCTING THE AUCTION:

14. Notice of the consignor's liberty to place reserve bids on his lots in the Auction is hereby made in accordance with Article 2 of the Texas Uniform Commercial Code. A reserve is an amount below which the lot will not sell. THE CONSIGNOR OF PROPERTY MAY PLACE WRITTEN RESERVE BIDS ON HIS LOTS IN ADVANCE OF THE AUCTION; ON SUCH LOTS, IF THE HAMMER PRICE DOES NOT MEET THE RESERVE, THE CONSIGNOR MAY PAY A REDUCED COMMISSION ON THOSE LOTS. Reserves are generally posted online about 3 days prior to the Auction closing on Internet-Only Auctions, and 7 days prior to the Auction on Signature Auctions. Any successful bid placed by a consignor on his consigned lot on the Auction floor or by telephone during the live session, or after the reserves for an Auction have been posted, will be considered an unqualified bid, and in such instances the consignor agrees to pay full Buyer's Premium and Seller's Commissions on any lot so repurchased.
15. The highest qualified Bidder shall be the buyer. In the event of any dispute between floor Bidders at a Signature Auction, Auctioneer may at his sole discretion reoffer the lot. Auctioneer's decision shall be final and binding upon all Bidders.
16. Auctioneer reserves the right to refuse to honor any bid or to limit the amount of any bid which, in his sole discretion, is not submitted in "Good Faith," or is not supported by satisfactory credit, numismatic references, or otherwise. A bid is considered not made in "Good Faith" when an insolvent or irresponsible person, or a person under the age of eighteen makes it. Regardless of the disclosure of his identity, any bid by a consignor or his agent on a lot consigned by him is deemed to be made in "Good Faith". NOMINAL BIDS - The Auctioneer may at its sole discretion reject nominal bids, small opening bids or very nominal advances. If a lot fails to open for 40% to 60% of the low estimate, the Auctioneer may pass the item from the block to be re-offered at a subsequent auction, or may place a protective bid on behalf of the consignor.
17. All items are to be purchased per lot as numerically indicated and no lots will be broken. Auctioneer reserves the right to withdraw, prior to the close, any lots from the Auction.
18. Bids will be accepted in whole dollar amounts only. No "buy" or "unlimited" bids will be accepted. Bidders will be awarded lots at approximately the increment of the next highest bid. No additional commission is charged for executing bids. Off-increment bids may be accepted by the Auctioneer at Signature Auctions.
19. Auctioneer reserves the right to rescind the sale in the event of nonpayment, breach of a warranty, disputed ownership, auctioneer's clerical error or omission in exercising bids and reserves, or otherwise.
20. Outage Policy: Auctioneer occasionally experiences Internet and/or Server outages during which Bidders cannot participate or place bids. If such outage occurs, we may at our discretion extend bidding for the auction up to 24 hours. At our discretion, Auctioneer may consider two outages that occur very closely to one another to be one outage when extending such Auction. This policy applies only to widespread outages and not to isolated problems that occur in various parts of the country from time to time.
21. Scheduled Downtime: Auctioneer periodically schedules system downtime for maintenance and other purposes; this scheduled downtime is not covered by the Outage Policy.
22. The Auctioneer or its affiliates may consign items to be sold in the Auction, and may bid on those lots or any other lots. Auctioneer or affiliates expressly reserve the right to modify any such reserve bids on these items or any others at any time prior to the live auction or the online closing based upon data made known to the Auctioneer or its affiliates. The Auctioneer may extend advances, guarantees, or loans to certain consignors, and may extend financing or other credits at varying rates to certain Bidders in the auction.
23. The Auctioneer has the right to sell certain items after the close of the sale. Items sold by Auctioneer post sale shall be considered sold during the auction and all these Terms and Conditions shall apply to such sales including but not limited to the payment of the buyer's fee, return rights and disclaimers.

PAYMENT:

24. All sales are strictly for cash in United States dollars. Cash includes: U.S. currency, bank wire, cashier checks, travelers checks, and bank money orders, all subject to reporting requirements. Credit Card (Visa or Master Card only) and PayPal payments may be accepted up to $10,000 from non-dealers at the sole discretion of the auctioneer, subject to the following limitations: a) sales are only to the cardholder, b) purchases are shipped to the cardholder's registered and verified address, c) Auctioneer may pre-approve the cardholder's credit line, d) a credit card transaction may not be used in conjunction with any other financing or extended terms offered by the Auctioneer, and must transact immediately upon invoice presentation, e) rights of return are governed by these Terms and Conditions, which supersede those conditions promulgated by the card issuer, f) floor Bidders must present their card. Personal or corporate checks may be subject to clearing before delivery of the purchases.
25. Payment is due upon closing of the Auction session, or upon presentment of an invoice. Auctioneer reserves the right to void an invoice if payment in full of the invoice is not received within 7 days after the close of the Auction.
26. Lots delivered in the States of Texas, California, or other states where the Auction may be held, are subject to all applicable state and local taxes, unless appropriate permits are on file with us. Bidder agrees to pay Auctioneer the actual amount of tax due in the event that sales tax is not properly collected due to: 1) an expired, inaccurate, inappropriate tax certificate or declaration, 2) an incorrect interpretation of the applicable statute, 3) or any other reason.. Lots from different Auctions may not be aggregated for sales tax purposes.
27. In the event that a Bidder's payment is dishonored upon presentment(s), Bidder shall pay the maximum statutory processing fee set by applicable state law.
28. If the Auction invoice(s) submitted by Auctioneer is not paid in full when due, the unpaid balance will bear interest at the highest rate permitted by law from the date of invoice until paid. If the Auctioneer refers the invoice(s) to an attorney for collection, the buyer agrees to pay attorney's fees, court costs, and other collection costs incurred by Auctioneer. If Auctioneer assigns collection to its in-house legal staff, such attorney's time expended on the matter shall be compensated at a rate comparable to the hourly rate of independent attorneys.
29. In the event a successful Bidder fails to pay all amounts due, Auctioneer reserves the right to resell the merchandise, and such Bidder agrees to pay for the reasonable costs of resale, including a 10% seller's commission, and also to pay any difference between the resale price and the price of the previously successful bid.
30. Auctioneer reserves the right to require payment in full in good funds before delivery of the merchandise to the buyer.
31. Auctioneer shall have a lien against the merchandise purchased by the buyer to secure payment of the Auction invoice. Auctioneer is further granted a lien and the right to retain possession of any other property of the buyer then held by the Auctioneer or its affiliates to secure payment of any Auction invoice or any other amounts due the Auctioneer from the buyer. With respect to these lien rights, Auctioneer shall have all the rights of a secured creditor under Article 9 of the Texas Uniform Commercial Code. In addition, with respect to payment of the Auction invoice(s), the buyer waives any and all rights of offset he might otherwise have against the Auctioneer and the consignor of the merchandise included on the invoice.
32. If a Bidder owes Auctioneer or its affiliates on any account, Auctioneer and its affiliates shall have the right to offset such unpaid account by any credit balance due Bidder, and it may secure by possessory lien any unpaid amount by any of the Bidder's property in their possession.
33. Title shall not pass to the successful Bidder until all invoices are paid in full. It is the responsibility of the buyer to provide adequate insurance coverage for the items once they have been delivered.

RETURN POLICIES:

34. A FINE ARTS, DECORATIVE ARTS OR MEMORABILIA lot (Autographs, Sports Collectibles, or Music, Entertainment, Political, Americana and/or Pop Culture memorabilia): The Auction is not on approval. When the lot is accompanied by a Certificate of Authenticity (or its equivalent) from an independent third party authentication provider, buyer has no right of return. Uncertified lots or under extremely limited circumstances not including authenticity (e.g. gross cataloging error), a purchaser who did not bid from the floor may request Auctioneer to evaluate voiding a sale; such request must be made in

writing detailing the alleged gross error, and submission of the lot to Auctioneer must be pre-approved by Auctioneer. A bidder must notify the appropriate department head (check the inside front cover of the catalog or our website for a listing of department heads) in writing of the purchaser's request and such notice must be mailed within three (3) days of the mail bidder's receipt of the lot. Any lot that is to be evaluated for return must be received in our offices within 30 days after Auction. AFTER THAT 30 DAY PERIOD, NO LOT MAY BE RETURNED FOR ANY REASONS. Lots returned must be in the same condition as when sold and must include the Certificate of Authenticity, if any. No lots purchased by floor bidders may be returned (including those bidders acting as agents for others). Late remittance for purchases may be considered just cause to revoke all return privileges.

35. COINS, CURRENCY, COMICS AND SPORTSCARDS Signature Auctions: The Auction is not on approval. No certified material may be returned because of possible differences of opinion with respect to the grade offered by any third-party organization, dealer, or service. No guarantee of grade is offered for uncertified Property sold and subsequently submitted to a third-party grading service. There are absolutely no exceptions to this policy. Under extremely limited circumstances, (e.g. gross cataloging error) a purchaser, who did not bid from the floor, may request Auctioneer to evaluate voiding a sale; such request must be made in writing detailing the alleged gross error, and submission of the lot to the Auctioneer must be pre-approved by the Auctioneer; bidder must notify Ron Brackemyre, (ext. 312) in writing of the such request and such notice must be mailed within three (3) days of the mail bidder's receipt of the lot. Any lot that is to be evaluated must be in our offices within 30 days after Auction. Grading or method of manufacture do not qualify for this evaluation process nor do such complaints constitute a basis to challenge the authenticity of a lot. AFTER THAT 30-DAY PERIOD, NO LOTS MAY BE RETURNED FOR REASONS OTHER THAN AUTHENTICITY. Lots returned must be housed intact in the original holder. No lots purchased by floor Bidders may be returned (including those Bidders acting as agents for others). Late remittance for purchases may be considered just cause to revoke all return privileges.

36. Exclusively Internet, Internet Currency, Amazing Comics Auctions, Amazing Sports Auctions, and Online Session auctions: THREE (3) DAY RETURN POLICY. All lots (Exception: Third party graded notes are not returnable for any reason whatsoever) paid for within seven days of the Auction closing are sold with a three (3) day return privilege. You may return lots under the following conditions: Within three days of receipt of the lot, you must first notify Auctioneer by contacting Customer Service by phone (1-800-872-6467) or e-mail (Bid@HeritageAuctions.com), and immediately mail the lot(s) fully insured to the attention of Returns, Heritage, 3500 Maple Avenue, 17th Floor, Dallas TX 75219-3941. Lots must be housed intact in their original holder and condition. You are responsible for the insured, safe delivery of any lots. A non-negotiable return fee of 5% of the purchase price ($10 per lot minimum) will be deducted from the refund for each returned lot or billed directly. Postage and handling fees are not refunded. After the three-day period (from receipt), no items may be returned for any reason. Late remittance for purchases revokes all Return-Restock privileges.

37. All Bidders who have inspected the lots prior to the auction will not be granted any return privileges, except for reasons of authenticity.

DELIVERY; SHIPPING AND HANDLING CHARGES:

38. Postage, handling and insurance charges will be added to invoices. Please either refer to Auctioneer's website HeritageAuctions.com/common/shipping.php for the latest charges or call Auctioneer.

39. Auctioneer is unable to combine purchases from other auctions or Heritage Rare Coin Galleries into one package for shipping purposes. Successful overseas Bidders shall provide written shipping instructions, including specified customs declarations, to the Auctioneer for any lots to be delivered outside of the United States. NOTE: Declaration value shall be the item(s) hammer price together with its buyer's premium.

40. All shipping charges will be borne by the successful Bidder. Due to the nature of some items sold, it shall be the responsibility for the successful bidder to arrange pick-up and shipping through third parties, as to such items Auctioneer shall have no liability. Any risk of loss during shipment will be borne by the buyer following Auctioneer's delivery to the designated common carrier, regardless of domestic or foreign shipment. Any request for shipping verification for undelivered packages must be made within 30 days of shipment by Auctioneer.

41. In the event an item is damaged either through handling or in transit, Auctioneer's maximum liability shall be the amount of the successful bid including the Buyer's Premium. On the fall of Auctioneer's hammer, Buyers of Fine Arts and Decorative Arts lots assumes full risk and responsibility for lot, including shipment by common carrier, and must provide their own insurance coverage for shipments.

CATALOGING, WARRANTIES AND DISCLAIMERS:

42. NO WARRANTY, WHETHER EXPRESSED OR IMPLIED, IS MADE WITH RESPECT TO ANY DESCRIPTION CONTAINED IN THIS AUCTION OR ANY SECOND OPINE. Any description of the items or second opine contained in this auction is for the sole purpose of identifying the items for those Bidders who do not have the opportunity to view the lots prior to bidding, and no description of items has been made part of the basis of the bargain or has created any express warranty that the goods would conform to any description made by Auctioneer.

43. Auctioneer is selling only such right or title to the items being sold as Auctioneer may have by virtue of consignment agreements on the date of auction and disclaims any warranty of title to the Property.

44. Translations of foreign language documents are provided as a convenience to interested parties. Heritage makes no representation as to the accuracy of those translations and will not be held responsible for errors in bidding arising from inaccuracies in translation.

45. In the event of an attribution error, Auctioneer may at its sole discretion, correct the error on the Internet, or, if discovered at a later date, to refund the buyer's money without further obligation. Under no circumstances shall the obligation of the Auctioneer to any Bidder be in excess of the purchase price for any lot in dispute.

46. Auctioneer disclaims any warranty of merchantability or fitness for any particular purposes.

47. Auctioneer disclaims all liability for damages, consequential or otherwise, arising out of or in connection with the sale of any property by Auctioneer to Bidder. No third party may rely on any benefit of these Terms and Conditions and any rights, if any, established hereunder are personal to the Bidder and may not be assigned. Any statement made by the Auctioneer is an opinion and does not constitute a warranty or representation. No employee of Auctioneer may alter these Terms and Conditions, and, unless signed by a principal of Auctioneer, any such alteration is null and void.

48F. FINE AND DECORATIVE ARTS – Auctioneer warrants bold-faced items in the descriptions, which are otherwise provided for identification purposes only. Bidders who intend to challenge the bold-faced items in the descriptions of a lot must notify Auctioneer in writing within thirty (30) days of the Auction's conclusion. Auctioneer's maximum liability shall not exceed the high bid on that lot, which bid shall be deemed for all purposes the value of the lot. In the event Auctioneer cannot deliver the lot or subsequently it is established that the lot lacks title, provenance, authenticity, or other transfer or condition issue is claimed, Auctioneer's liability shall be limited to recission of sale and refund of purchase price. After one year has elapsed, Auctioneer's maximum liability shall be limited to any commissions and fees Auctioneer earned on that lot. Nothwitstanding any other provision, while title to an item is warranted, authenticity or provenance is a matter of opinion and is not warranted or part of Auctioneer's representations.

49. All non-certified coins, currency, and comics are guaranteed genuine, but are not guaranteed as to grade, since grading is a matter of opinion, an art and not a science, and therefore the opinion rendered by the Auctioneer or any third party grading service may not agree with the opinion of others (including trained experts), and the same expert may not grade the same item with the same grade at two different times. Auctioneer has graded the non-certified numismatic items, in the Auctioneer's opinion, to their current interpretation of the American Numismatic Association's standards as of the date the catalog was prepared. There is no guarantee or warranty implied or expressed that the grading standards utilized by the Auctioneer will meet the standards of ANACS, NGC, PCGS, ICG, CGC, CGA or any other grading service at any time in the future.

50. Since we cannot examine encapsulated notes or comics, they are sold "as is" without our grading opinion, and may not be returned for any reason. Auctioneer shall not be liable for any patent or latent defect or controversy pertaining to or arising from any encapsulated collectible. In any such instance, purchaser's remedy, if any, shall be solely against the service certifying the collectible.

51. Due to changing grading standards over time, differing interpretations, and to possible mishandling of items by subsequent owners, Auctioneer reserves the right to grade items differently than shown on certificates from any grading service that accompany the items. Auctioneer also reserves the right to grade items differently than the grades shown in the catalog should such items be reconsigned to any future auction.

52. Although consensus grading is employed by most grading services, it should be noted as aforesaid that grading is not an exact science. In fact, it is entirely possible that if a lot is broken out of a plastic holder and resubmitted to another grading service or even to the same service, the lot could come back with a different grade assigned.

53. Certification does not guarantee protection against the normal risks associated with potentially volatile markets. The degree of liquidity for certified coins and collectibles will vary according to general market conditions and the particular lot involved. For some lots there may be no active market at all at certain points in time.

RELEASE:

54. In consideration of participation in the auction and the placing of a bid, a Bidder expressly releases Auctioneer, its officers, directors and employees, its affiliates, and its outside experts that provide second opines from any and all claims, cause of action, chose of action, whether at law or equity or any arbitration or mediation rights existing under the rules of any professional society or affiliation based upon the assigned grade or a derivative theory, breach of warranty express or implied, representation or other matter set forth within these Terms and Conditions of Auction or otherwise, except as specifically declared herein; e.g., authenticity, typographical error, etc., and as to those matters, the rights and privileges conferred therein are strictly construed and is the exclusive remedy. Purchaser, by non-compliance to its express terms of a granted remedy, shall waive any claim against Auctioneer.

DISPUTE RESOLUTION AND ARBITRATION PROVISION:

55. By placing a bid or otherwise participating in the auction, such person or entity accepts these Terms and Conditions of Auction, and specifically agrees to the alternative dispute resolution provided herein. Arbitration replaces the right to go to court, including the right to a jury trial.

56. Auctioneer in no event shall be responsible for consequential damages, incidental damages, compensatory damages, or other damages arising from the auction of any lot. Auctioneer's maximum liability shall not exceed the high bid on that lot, which bid shall be deemed for all purposes the value of the lot. In the event that Auctioneer cannot deliver the lot or subsequently it is established that the lot lacks title, provenance, authenticity, or other transfer or condition issue is claimed, Auctioneer's liability shall be limited to recission of sale and refund of purchase price. After one year has elapsed, Auctioneer's maximum liability shall be limited to any commissions and fees Auctioneer earned on that lot.

57. Any claim as to provenance or authenticity must be first transmitted to Auctioneer by credible and definitive evidence and there is no assurance after such presentment that Auctioneer will validate the claim. Authentication is not an exact science and contrary opinions may not be recognized by Auctioneer. Even if Auctioneer agrees with the contrary opinion of such authentication, our liability for reimbursement for such service shall not exceed $500.

58. Provenance and authenticity are not guaranteed by the Auctioneer, but rather are guaranteed by the consignor. Any action or claim shall include the consignor with Auctioneer acting as interpleador or nominal party. While every effort is made to determine provenance and authenticity, it is up to the Bidder to arrive at that conclusion prior to bidding.

59. If any dispute arises regarding payment, authenticity, grading, description, provenance, or any other matter pertaining to the Auction, the Bidder or a participant in the Auction and/or the Auctioneer agree that the dispute shall be submitted, if otherwise mutually unresolved, to binding arbitration in accordance with the commercial rules of the American Arbitration Association (A.A.A.). A.A.A. arbitration shall be conducted under the provisions of the Federal Arbitration Act with locale in Dallas, Texas. Any claim made by a Bidder has to be presented within one (1) year or it is barred. The prevailing party may be awarded his reasonable attorney's fees and costs. An award granted in arbitration is enforceable in any court of competent jurisdiction. No claims of any kind (except for reasons of authenticity) can be considered after the settlements have been made with the consignors. Any dispute after the settlement date is strictly between the Bidder and consignor without involvement or responsibility of the Auctioneer. NOTE: Purchasers of rare coins or currency through Heritage have available the option of arbitration by the Professional Numismatists Guild (PNG); if an election is not made within ten (10) days of an unresolved dispute, Auctioneer may elect either PNG or A.A.A. Arbitration.

60. In consideration of his participation in or application for the auction, a person or entity (whether the successful Bidder, a Bidder, a purchaser and/or other Auction participant or registrant) agrees that all disputes in any way relating to, arising under, connected with, or incidental to these Terms and Conditions and purchases or default in payment thereof shall be arbitrated pursuant to the arbitration provision. In the event that any matter including actions to compel arbitration, construe the agreement, actions in aid or arbitration or otherwise needs to be litigated, such litigation shall be exclusively in the Courts of the State of Texas, in Dallas County, Texas, and if necessary the corresponding appellate courts. The successful Bidder, purchaser, or Auction participant also expressly submits himself to the personal jurisdiction of the State of Texas.

MISCELLANEOUS:

61. Agreements between Bidders and consignors to effectuate a non-sale of an item at Auction, inhibit bidding on a consigned item to enter into a private sale agreement for said item, or to utilize the Auctioneer's Auction to obtain sales for non-selling consigned items subsequent to the auction, are strictly prohibited. If a subsequent sale of a previously consigned item occurs in violation of this provision, Auctioneer reserves the right to charge Bidder the applicable Buyer's Premium and consignor a Seller's Commission as determined for each auction venue and by the terms of the seller's agreement.

62. Acceptance of these terms and conditions qualifies Bidder as a Heritage customer who has consented to be contacted by Heritage in the future. In conformity with "do-not-call" regulations promulgated by the Federal or State regulatory agencies, participation by the Bidder is affirmative consent to being contacted at the phone number shown in his application and this consent shall remain in effect until it is revoked in writing. Heritage may from time to time contact Bidder concerning sale, purchase and auction opportunities available through Heritage and its affiliates and subsidiaries.

63. Storage of purchased coins and currency: Purchasers are advised that certain types of plastic may react with a coin's metal or transfer plasticizer to notes and may cause damage. Caution should be used to avoid storage in materials that are not inert.

STATE NOTICES:

64. Notice as to an Auction Sale in California. Auctioneer has in compliance with Title 2.95 of the California Civil Code as amended October 11, 1993 Sec. 1812.600, posted with the California Secretary of State its bonds for it and its employees and the auction is being conducted in compliance with Sec. 2338 of the Commercial Code and Sec. 535 of the Penal Code.

Rev. 7_20_06

Choose Your Bidding Method

Mail Bidding at Auction

Mail bidding at auction is fun and easy and only requires a few simple steps.

1. Look through the catalog, and determine the lots of interest.
2. Research their market value by checking price lists and other price guidelines.
3. Fill out your bid sheet, entering your maximum bid on each lot.
4. Verify your bids!
5. Mail Early. Preference is given to the first bids received in case of a tie. When bidding by mail, you frequently purchase items at less than your maximum bid.

Bidding is opened at the published increment above the second highest mail or Internet bid; we act on your behalf as the highest mail bidder. If bidding proceeds, we act as your agent, bidding in increments over the previous bid. This process is continued until you are awarded the lot or you are outbid.

An example of this procedure: You submit a bid of $100, and the second highest mail bid is at $50. Bidding starts at $51 on your behalf. If no other bids are placed, you purchase the lot for $51. If other bids are placed, we bid for you in the posted increments until we reach your maximum bid of $100. If bidding passes your maximum: if you are bidding through the Internet, we will contact you by e-mail; if you bid by mail, we take no other action. Bidding continues until the final bidder wins.

Telephone Bidding

To participate by telephone, please make arrangements at least one week before the sale date with Customer Service, 1-800-872-6467, Ext. 150.

We strongly recommend that you place preliminary bids by mail, fax, or Internet, even if you intend to participate by telephone. On many occasions this dual approach has helped reduce disappointments due to telephone problems, unexpected travel, late night sessions and time zone differences, etc. We will make sure that you do not bid against yourself.

Mail Bidding Instructions

1. **Name, Address, City, State, Zip**
   Your address is needed to mail your purchases. We need your telephone number to communicate any problems or changes that may affect your bids.

2. **References**
   If you have not established credit with us from previous auctions, you must send a 25% deposit, or list dealers with whom you have credit established.

3. **Lot Numbers and Bids**
   List all lots you desire to purchase. On the reverse are additional columns; you may also use another sheet. Under "Amount" enter the maximum you would pay for that lot (whole dollar amounts only). We will purchase the lot(s) for you as much below your bids as possible.

4. **Total Bid Sheet**
   Add up all bids and list that total in the appropriate box.

5. **Sign Your Bid Sheet**
   By signing the bid sheet, you have agreed to abide by the Terms of Auction listed in the auction catalog.

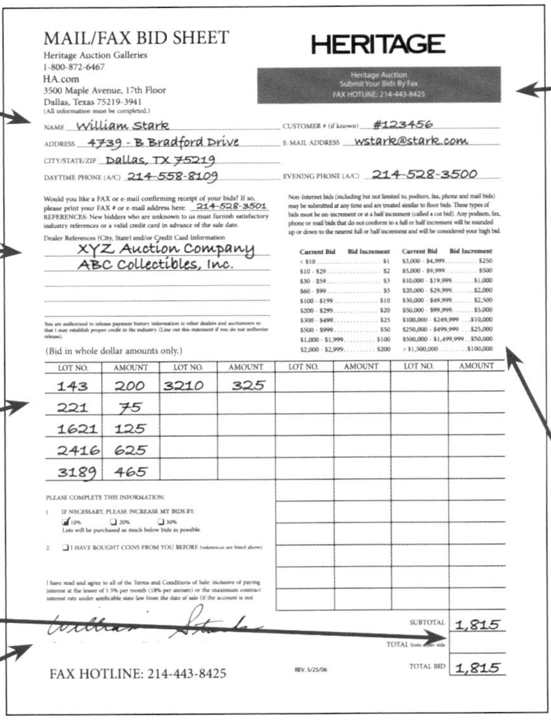

MAIL/FAX BID SHEET

HERITAGE

Heritage Auction Galleries
1-800-872-6467
HA.com
3500 Maple Avenue, 17th Floor
Dallas, Texas 75219-3941
(All information must be completed.)

Heritage Auction
Submit Your Bids By Fax
FAX HOTLINE: 214-443-8425

NAME William Stark — CUSTOMER # (if known) #123456
ADDRESS 4739 - B Bradford Drive — E-MAIL ADDRESS wstark@stark.com
CITY/STATE/ZIP Dallas, TX 75219
DAYTIME PHONE (A/C) 214-558-8109 — EVENING PHONE (A/C) 214-528-3500

Would you like a FAX or e-mail confirming receipt of your bids? If so, please print your FAX # or e-mail address here: 214-528-3501
REFERENCES: New bidders who are unknown to us must furnish satisfactory industry references or a valid credit card in advance of the sale date.
Dealer References (City, State) and/or Credit Card Information:
XYZ Auction Company
ABC Collectibles, Inc.

You are authorized to release payment history information to other dealers and auctioneers so that I may establish proper credit in the industry. (Line out this statement if you do not authorize release).

Non-Internet bids (including but not limited to, podium, fax, phone and mail bids) may be submitted at any time and are treated similar to floor bids. These types of bids must be on-increment or at a half increment (called a cut bid). Any podium, fax, phone or mail bids that do not conform to a full or half increment will be rounded up or down to the nearest full or half increment and will be considered your high bid.

Current Bid	Bid Increment	Current Bid	Bid Increment
< $10	$1	$3,000 - $4,999	$250
$10 - $29	$2	$5,000 - $9,999	$500
$30 - $59	$3	$10,000 - $19,999	$1,000
$60 - $99	$5	$20,000 - $29,999	$2,000
$100 - $199	$10	$30,000 - $49,999	$2,500
$200 - $299	$20	$50,000 - $99,999	$5,000
$300 - $499	$25	$100,000 - $249,999	$10,000
$500 - $999	$50	$250,000 - $499,999	$25,000
$1,000 - $1,999	$100	$500,000 - $1,499,999	$50,000
$2,000 - $2,999	$200	> $1,500,000	$100,000

(Bid in whole dollar amounts only.)

LOT NO.	AMOUNT	LOT NO.	AMOUNT	LOT NO.	AMOUNT	LOT NO.	AMOUNT
143	200	3210	325				
221	75						
1621	125						
2416	625						
3189	465						

PLEASE COMPLETE THIS INFORMATION:
1. IF NECESSARY, PLEASE INCREASE MY BIDS BY: ☑ 10% ☐ 20% ☐ 30%
Lots will be purchased as much below bids as possible.
2. ☐ I HAVE BOUGHT COINS FROM YOU BEFORE (references are listed above)

I have read and agree to all of the Terms and Conditions of Sale: inclusive of paying interest at the lesser of 1.5% per month (18% per annum) or the maximum contract interest rate under applicable state law from the date of sale (if the account is not

SUBTOTAL 1,815
TOTAL from other side
TOTAL BID 1,815

FAX HOTLINE: 214-443-8425

REV. 5/25/06

The official prices realized list that accompanies our auction catalogs is reserved for bidders and consignors only. We are happy to mail one to others upon receipt of $1.00. Written requests should be directed to Customer Service.

6. **Fax Your Bid Sheet**
   When time is short submit a Mail Bid Sheet on our exclusive Fax Hotline. There's no faster method to get your bids to us *instantly*. Simply use the **Heritage Fax Hotline number: 214-443-8425**.

When you send us your original after faxing, mark it "Confirmation of Fax" (preferably in red!)

7. **Bidding Increments**
   To facilitate bidding, please consult the following chart. Bids will be accepted on the increments or on the half increments.

7_18_06

Interactive Internet™ Bidding

You can now bid with Heritage's exclusive *Interactive Internet*™ program, available only at our web site: HA.com. It's fun, and it's easy!

1. Register online at: **HA.com**
2. View the full-color photography of every single lot in the online catalog!
3. Construct your own personal catalog for preview.
4. View the current opening bids on lots you want; review the prices realized archive.
5. Bid and receive immediate notification if you are the top bidder; later, if someone else bids higher, you will be notified automatically by e-mail.
6. The *Interactive Internet*™ program opens the lot on the floor at one increment over the second highest bid. As the high bidder, your secret maximum bid will compete for you during the floor auction, and it is possible that you may be outbid on the floor after Internet bidding closes. Bid early, as the earliest bird wins in the event of a tie bid.
7. After the sale, you will be notified of your success. It's that easy!

Interactive Internet™ Bidding Instructions

1. Log Onto Website

Log onto **HA.com** and chose the portal you're interested in (i.e., coins, comics, movie posters, fine arts, etc.).

2. Search for Lots

Search or browse for the lot you are interested in. You can do this from the home page, from the Auctions home page, or from the home page for the particular auction in which you wish to participate.

3. Select Lots

Click on the link or the photo icon for the lot you want to bid on.

4. Enter Bid

At the top of the page, next to a small picture of the item, is a box outlining the current bid. Enter the amount of your secret maximum bid in the textbox next to "Secret Maximum Bid." The secret maximum bid is the maximum amount you are willing to pay for the item you are bidding on (for more information about bidding and bid increments, please see the section labeled "Bidding Increments" elsewhere in this catalog). Click on the button marked "Place Absentee Bid." A new area on the same page will open up for you to enter your username (or e-mail address) and password. Enter these, then click "Place Absentee Bid" again.

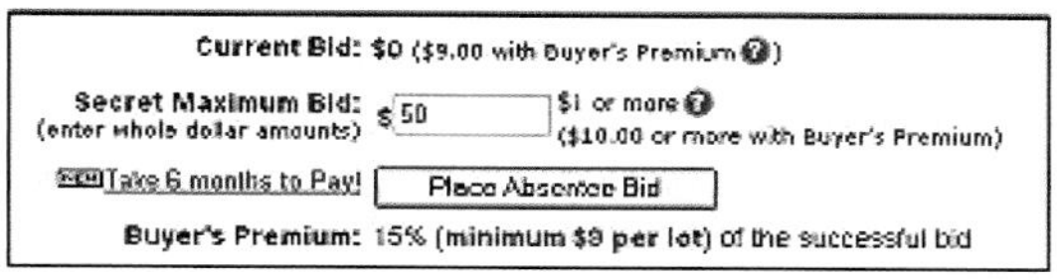

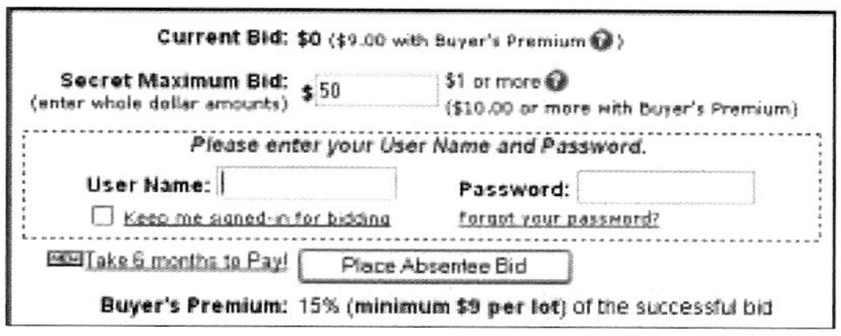

5. Confirm Absentee Bid

You are taken to a page labeled, "Please Confirm Your Bid." This page shows you the name of the item you're bidding on, the current bid, and the maximum bid. When you are satisfied that all the information shown is correct, click on the button labeled, "Confirm Bid."

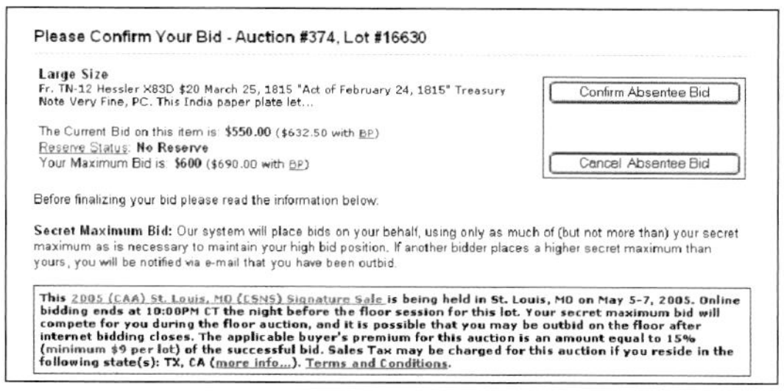

6. Bidding Status Notification

One of two pages is now displayed.

a. If your bid is the current high bid, you will be notified and given additional information as to what might happen to affect your high bidder status over the course of the remainder of the auction. You will also receive a Bid Confirmation notice via email.

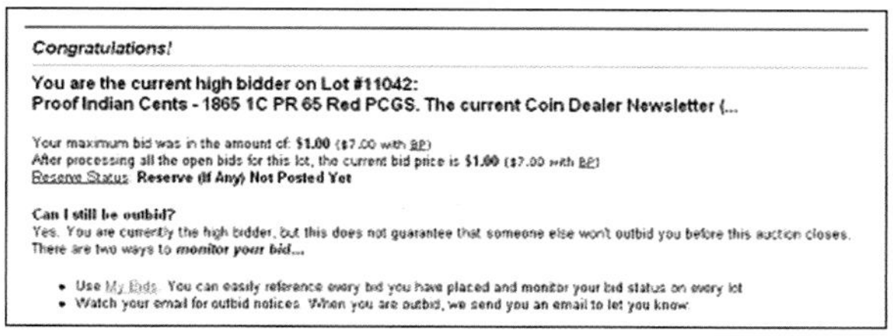

b. If your bid is not the current high bid, you will be notified of that fact and given the opportunity to increase your bid.

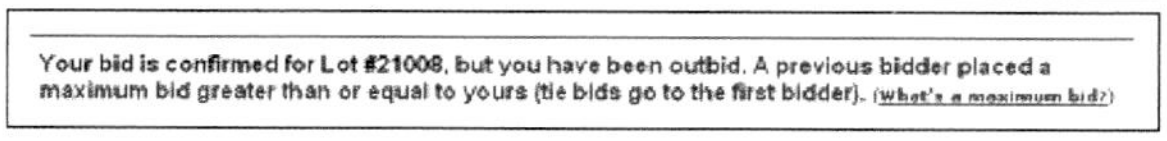

7_18_06